REGIONAL STUDIES OF
THE UNITED STATES
AND CANADA

REGIONAL STUDIES OF THE UNITED STATES AND CANADA

KENNETH R. SEALY, M.Sc.(Econ.), Ph.D.
Reader in Geography at the London School of Economics and Political Science

and

HENRY REES, M.Sc.(Econ.), Ph.D.
Principal Lecturer in Geography
St Paul's College of Education, Rugby

GEORGE G. HARRAP & CO. LTD
London Toronto Wellington Sydney

First published in Great Britain 1968
by George G. Harrap & Co. Ltd
182 High Holborn, London, W.C.1

SBN 245 59118 4

Composed in Lumitype Times type and printed by
Butler & Tanner Ltd, Frome and London
Made in Great Britain

PREFACE

When the publishers invited us to prepare a work on the United States and Canada to form one of their advanced geography text-books we were a little hesitant. When we were students there were virtually only two general text-books on North America: these were the scholarly work by Professors L. Rodwell Jones and P. W. Bryan and the more racy account by Russell Smith (which began, 'Hell is hot. Did you ever wonder why?'). Now there are several excellent texts at the command of the student, and we were not sure that we could improve on them.

However, it will be evident that we have made the attempt. We have tried to produce a regional geography that is not only accurate and up to date, but one that will also interest our reader and stimulate his or her quest for a better understanding of the two great nations that constitute Anglo-America.

We should like to record our appreciation of the many hours spent by Miss Stephanie Hall in converting our rough drafts into the finished maps that now adorn the book.

August 1968

H.R.
K.R.S.

CONTENTS

ILLUSTRATIONS

PLATES

MAPS AND DIAGRAMS

Fig. *page*

INTRODUCTION: THE REGIONAL FRAMEWORK

The concept of the 'region' is one of the basic tools of the geographer. It forms a valuable labour-saving device, for instead of contemplating innumerable unrelated facts we recognize that one set of phenomena, such as the Cretaceous rocks of the prairies or the fiord coasts of British Columbia, extends over a wide area, and imparts to it a distinct character.

Where several such elements are found to be combined over a common area we distinguish a region. Its boundaries may divide it sharply from its neighbours, or they may take the form of indeterminate zones of transitional character: thus the Great Plains possess a clear western border (the first ranges of the Rocky Mountains) but their eastern border is less distinct. Sometimes two adjacent regions possess a common belt in which they overlap: the Tennessee valley falls within both Appalachia and the South, and the Pittsburgh district has links with both Appalachia and the Great Lakes.

Some of our major problems in regional division arise along the United States–Canada frontier. This in some parts forms a significant economic divide, which is well seen in the prairies. Few roads or railways cross the international frontier, yet there are extensive networks of communications on each side, which channel the farm produce eastward. There is, of course, no sudden climatic change at the border; but there are differences in the physiography, for the three 'prairie steps' of Canada reduce to the two long and short grass divisions of the Great Plains. Accordingly, while we recognize certain features that are common to both, we have separated the American Great Plains (Chapter Six) from the Canadian Prairies (Chapter Nine).

In the west, there is much to be said for combining the American north-west with the Canadian British Columbia, for the basin of the Columbia river lies astride the frontier, and forest industries, salmon fisheries, and fruit-growing are common to both. But if we wish to do this we at once meet the problem of defining a southern boundary for this enlarged British Columbia. The boundary of the Columbia river basin would be quite unrealistic, for the Snake river drains extensive lava plateaux and large areas of the semi-arid Great Basin: these have little or nothing in common with the fiord coasts, forested ridges, and deep glaciated valleys of southern British Columbia. Here too, therefore, we adopt the international frontier as our regional boundary, and separate British Columbia (Chapter Ten) from the (American) West (Chapter Seven).

This results in a very long chapter on the West. It would be possible to examine this immense area on a strictly regional basis, and the student is invited to make the attempt for himself, beginning with, say, the Coast Ranges of Washington and Oregon and ending with the Southern Rockies. We have preferred, however, a more systematic approach, which draws attention to the common elements that bind the region together; accordingly we examine its physiographic character, its climate, its historical geography, and its present economic activities, making appropriate reference to the harnessing of its two major river systems.

In the eastern half of the continent the frontier passes through the middle of four of the Great Lakes, and it would be clearly unthinkable to attempt to use it as a regional boundary. The Great Lakes and their borders form a clear physical and economic unit whose significance in recent years has been enhanced by the construction of the St Lawrence Seaway jointly by the two nations. This region we examine in Chapter Three.

There is one other human phenomenon that suffers from our regional division: this is Megalopolis – the vast urban sprawl that extends from Boston in the north-east to Washington in the south-west. The suburbs of the many urban centres are virtually indistinguishable one from another. Yet the factors, physical and human, that have aided the development of New York are quite different from those that apply to Boston and Washington, and we are not unduly concerned that in our regional division Megalopolis is split between Chapters One and Three.

We do not provide any systematic discussion of the structure, climate, vegetation, historical and economic geography of the continent as a whole, for these are adequately treated in the standard texts. Instead we plunge into the heart of our subject and choose as our first region New England and New York. It includes the earliest English settlement on the mainland and the largest metropolitan area in the western world.

CHAPTER ONE

NEW ENGLAND AND NEW YORK

The Growth of Manufacture in the North-east

Manufacturing is a complex activity, based as it is on numerous decisions regarding resources, costs, and markets, many elements of which are subject to change. In some areas the story is one not of expansion but of decline. Even when circumstances change unfavourably, the industry may persist in the area because of its large investment in plant, banking, and services covering the needs of its workers.

Industrial areas therefore show much variety: there are 'growth' areas where new industries are rapidly expanding; in contrast there are old-established zones, some decaying, some becoming rejuvenated, and others subject to deliberate planning. Large agglomerations may show all these faces in different measure, and within an area as large as the north-eastern U.S.A. we may expect complexity, not only because of its size and resources but also on account of its experience of more than a century of factory industry.

In all the pioneer settlements domestic crafts and industries were necessary for survival; but the impetus towards specialization was greatest in New England and the middle Atlantic colonies. These harsher tidewater lands with only limited farming possibilities bred a group of more versatile communities whose members gained their livelihood from the forests and the sea as much as from agriculture. Colder climes meant stout boots and warm clothing; to utilize the produce of the sea one needed ships and fishing-gear. Knives and pots and pans were needed in the home as well as the ship, and the itinerant Yankee pedlar would distribute them farther afield.

In New England, New York, and eastern Pennsylvania the steeply graded streams provided sites for the early forges and mills; these used as raw material either the bog ores of New England or the sedimentary ores of the Appalachians. The abundant forests provided charcoal for the forges, and timber for buildings and for ships. There was a premium on invention, for labour was scarce, and by the end of the eighteenth century the first cotton-mills were operating, metal and leather industries were established, and the timber and shipbuilding industries were growing.

The early manufactures were stimulated by the westward movement of the frontier. Between 1820 and 1860 six million immigrants arrived at the ports of the North-east. Many of them moved west: they needed wagons and boats, clothing, metal goods, arms and ammunition, and the factories of the north-east were busy supplying them. Massachusetts and Connecticut expanded their textile, clothing, leather, and metal industries; and an iron industry flourished in the Lackawanna valley of eastern Pennsylvania from Scranton to Nanticoke, using the local anthracite as fuel in place of the traditional charcoal.

To the west, the growing number of settlers moving down the Ohio were served by Pittsburgh. Its early iron industry was based on Appalachian ore smelted by charcoal, but by the 1830's there was an expanding market for iron: steamboats were now plying on the Ohio, and they needed engines and boilers and fittings. Under the stimulus of a brisk demand the ironmasters began to utilize the abundant local resources of bituminous coal in the form of coke. In the 1840's the Lake Superior ores were discovered (p. 36); but at the time they meant little to Pittsburgh, for its markets were limited, its communications were poor, and the Great Lakes had yet to become a commercial highway.

The steamboat traffic and its promise of expanding trade was viewed with some concern by the communities in New York and Pennsylvania, and as a counter-measure they sought to improve their communications across the Appalachians. Only one venture proved successful at the time: this was the construction of the Erie Canal, which connected Albany with Buffalo by way of the Mohawk gap and so provided a through route by water from Lake Erie to New York. It was opened in 1825 (p. 32); there was an astonishing fall in freight costs, and New York rapidly assumed first place among the seaboard cities.

This success stimulated action in Philadelphia and Baltimore; but physically they were ill-placed to benefit from canals, and waterways such as the Pennsylvania Canal (intended to serve Philadelphia) were short-lived. In the event they were unnecessary, for the period following 1830 saw the development of the railway system. By the beginning of the Civil War its main pattern as far west as the Mississippi was established, with a notable concentration of lines in the northern half of the country.

The stage was thus set for industrial expansion before the outbreak of the Civil War in 1861: indeed, one of the major causes of conflict was the growing contrast between the agricultural South, depending on the export of staple crops, and the industrial capitalism of the North. The war stimulated many northern industries, particularly in munitions, transport, and clothing, and its result was an overwhelming victory for the North. Business-men and financiers now gained considerable control over the political machine, and were able to stimulate further growth of industry.

During the following fifty years there was an enormous growth in industry, and the American civilization was transformed into an urban way of life. At its base were the heavy industries, dominated by the iron and steel of Pittsburgh and forty other neighbouring towns. The local coal-mining industry expanded, and Connellsville erected great coking plants. The raw material was now the Lake Superior ores, and this was the beginning of the vast open-cast workings at Hibbing, on the Mesabi Range. The framework was completed by the opening of the Soo canals and the extension of the railways right across the continent. Around the seemingly endless supplies of ore, coal, timber, and cotton arose the complex industrial structure that stretched from Boston through New York, Philadelphia, and Baltimore to Chicago and St Louis in the west.

In the meantime immigration continued at an increasing pace. Fourteen million entered between 1865 and 1900, and a further 13 million between 1901 and 1914. Former immigrants had been mainly English and German settlers attracted by cheap land for farming; now people were coming from eastern Europe, and many of them were absorbed at low wages in the growing industries.

The phenomenal increase in wealth was concentrated in the hands of a few industrial magnates, beginning with Vanderbilt and Gould after the Civil War. After 1880 railway 'pools' and industrial 'trusts' gained the control of many industries, and so arose the oil empire of John D. Rockefeller and the steel trust of Andrew Carnegie. The peak of 'big business' came when the banker J. Pierpont Morgan was able to acquire Carnegie's interests for about 500 million dollars, and so founded the United States Steel Corporation, controlling 70 per cent. of the nation's steel output.

The dominance of Pittsburgh is due as much to Carnegie and Morgan as to its natural advantages. By the 'Pittsburgh Plus' pricing system all steel shipments, from whatever plant, paid mill price plus the transport costs to the market from Pittsburgh. Even if a customer fetched a load of steel from a mill in his own city he would pay a price equivalent to steel produced in Pittsburgh and shipped from there. Small wonder that the main steel-users – engineering firms and manufacturers of constructional steel and transport equipment – established themselves near Pittsburgh. Birmingham, Alabama, languished under the control of the 'giant of the north', and the steel industries developed slowly on the shore of Lake Erie in spite of their greater locational advantages. Only when the 'Pittsburgh Plus' system was declared illegal in 1924 were other centres able to challenge Pittsburgh.

Expansion and adjustment took place in other industries too. Textile machinery was produced near the cotton-mills of New England, while the manufacture of farm machinery and of transport equipment was attracted to Chicago. The production of machine tools was more widespread, for it served a number of scattered centres in New England, Ohio, Michigan, and Illinois.

After the First World War new industries appeared on the scene: chief among them were the petroleum, aluminium, automobile, and electrical industries. They did not necessarily benefit the North-east. The oil industry played an important part in the development of Oklahoma, Texas, and California, while electrical energy and the automobile loosened the ties between industry and the coalfields. Accessibility to the market remained important, and this favoured some parts of the north-east at the expense of others: in particular the lakeshore and seaboard sites gained over more 'inland' areas like Pittsburgh.

Changes also took place within the older industries. Iron and steel entered its modern phase with improvements in technique that reduced the ratio of coal to ore, and so made the lakeshore sites more attractive. Changes in coke-making had a similar effect: the new by-product ovens made available a range of useful materials such as benzene and tar oils which were marketed more cheaply in the consuming areas: this spelt the decline of Connellsville.

The latest developments in the iron and steel industry include the decline of the Lake Superior ores, the use of the St Lawrence Seaway for the transport of Labrador ores, and the import of ore from overseas: they favour the lake centres at Cleveland, Buffalo, Chicago–Gary, and Detroit, which are well placed at transhipment points for coal and ore. Steel-works have been established in similar sites on the Atlantic seaboard, at Sparrows Point and in the Fairless Hills near Baltimore; they have access both to imported ore and to local and overseas markets. Pittsburgh has not been eclipsed, but has lost its supremacy. Iron- and steel-making capacity is now more widespread and more sensitive to modern requirements for space, water, access to markets, and the utilization of scrap.

The rise of new industries such as plastics, electronics, and aircraft production appears more spectacular when it occurs in areas where formerly little industry existed; but the North-east still acts as a powerful magnet. We may illustrate the process from a single industry, the manufacture of motor-cars.

This activity is associated particularly with Detroit and with Henry Ford. Detroit had at the end of the nineteenth century industries using timber from the forests of northern Michigan. Prominent among them was the building of carriages, and this was followed by the manufacture of bicycles. This was to form the setting of Ford's activities. By the early 1900's the motor-car had appeared; but it was Ford who realized that for success it was necessary to concentrate on a limited number of models, and to use standardized parts, for only the manufacture of parts in large numbers could justify the cost of tooling. It was the beginning of mass-production.

To reap the economies of scale Ford engaged in the manufacture of the iron and steel, and at first left the making of components and the final assembly to the satellite towns of Grand Rapids, Flint, Lansing, Akron, and Fort Wayne. 'Model T' began the venture, and about 10,000 were produced in 1909: this car continued until 1927, and in all more than 15 million models were manufactured. We may therefore summarize the advantages of Detroit as follows: a tradition of carriage-building and the existence of a supply of appropriately skilled labour; the general accessibility of iron and coal; the presence of a market and of available capital for subsequent growth.

Today, then, we see the North-east as a palimpsest of American industry. Founded in the early colonial period, it has weathered many changes. Its resources, accessibility, and great urban market are still dominant. New industries of the twentieth century began here, and most of them still prosper; but not all the region has advanced equally, and within it are a number of separate districts, each with its own story. In general it still remains the greatest area of urban and industrial development in North America.

From this broad survey of the North-east we move to a discussion of its sub-regions, and we begin with New England, noting first its physical character.

NEW ENGLAND

Physical Basis

The name 'New England' is applied to the six states that lie east of the Hudson river – that is, Maine, New Hampshire, Vermont, Massachusetts, Rhode Island, and Connecticut.

Physically there are many similarities between New England and the Canadian Shield. Pre-Cambrian and early Palaeozoic rocks have been metamorphosed into shales, quartzites, gneisses, and similar material – for the most part of little service for farming. As in the Canadian Shield, these rocks have been subjected to the scouring action of thick sheets of ice, so that most of the loose material has been eroded from the hills and deposited in the fringing lowlands. The coastal margins of Connecticut and Rhode Island are composed of glacial drift; the lowland west of Boston bay is strewn with drumlins, and some of them have been partially submerged to form the islands in the bay itself. A belt of terminal moraines marks a temporary halting-place of the ice front, and reveals itself as hummocky tracts of coarse sands strewn with granite boulders. It passes through the south-west of Rhode Island and into the western part of the Cape Cod peninsula, and a second parallel zone farther south occupies most of Long Island and continues in Martha's Vineyard and Nantucket Island.

In Maine and northern New Hampshire the landscape of forest, river, lake, marsh, and waterfall is reminiscent of the Canadian Shield; but farther to the south-west there are significant differences, for here the structure has a distinct north-and-south grain. It is in fact a continuation of certain elements in the Appalachian province. We refer below (p. 87) to the Great Appalachian Valley, which is developed on steeply inclined and relatively soft Silurian or older limestones. In the Appalachians its direction is generally north-east and south-west; but in its most northerly stretch it turns to take up a north-and-south alignment, forming the Hudson and Champlain valleys – a striking trench that stretches in a straight line for 340 miles from New York to the neighbourhood of Montreal.

In the Appalachians the Great Valley is overlooked from the south-east by the Blue Ridge – in reality the raised and faulted edge of the Piedmont Plateau; and in the same way the Hudson and Champlain valleys are bordered to the east by the abrupt edge of the Taconic mountains.

A further link with the lands to the south-west rather than those to the north lies in the Triassic valley of the Connecticut river. This long and straight trench is of course a structural feature rather than a simple river valley, and it corresponds with the similar and parallel feature that overlooks the Hudson river from the west, and with the Triassic lowland of western New Jersey. In all three areas the soft Triassic sediments are interrupted by sheets of lava; and these, being more resistant than the sandstones above and below, stand out to form ridges. In cooling the volcanic masses have contracted to form hexagonal columns, which are well seen in the Palisades of New York and in the cliff-like Holyoke Range of the Connecticut valley. The human importance of the Triassic rocks lies in their potential value for agriculture.

Climate

With mountain summits of 5000 to 6000 feet on the one hand, and deep sheltered valleys on the other, New England offers a wide range of climates from place to place. Yet some elements remain constant throughout the province. A continuous stream of depressions adds variety to the weather, so that frequent storms of rain or snow (about one a fortnight) are separated by a few days of sunshine. This rainfall or snowfall is distributed regularly throughout the year; it is everywhere adequate for farming, and nowhere really excessive. It ranges from about 32 inches per annum in the sheltered Champlain valley in the north-west and in northern Maine to over 45 inches on exposed mountain slopes and in the south-west. New York city experiences 41·6 inches. In general precipitation may be expected one day in every three.

The winters are severe, and each year the snow lies deep. Boston and New York harbours are open throughout the year, and therefore have an important advantage over the St Lawrence ports; but in winter there is a good deal of floating ice. However, the summers are surprisingly warm in the lowlands, and in the interior of Massachusetts the temperature reaches on the average 90°F. on 14 days during the year.

The climate is favourable for the temperate cereals and vegetables. Even in the farms of the north the growing season lasts more than 100 days; in the centre it reaches 150; and along the south-eastern coasts between 175 and 200 days. Yet we cannot avoid being surprised when we contemplate the growing of tobacco in this region of traditionally raw winters.

The Development of Manufactures

This far north-eastern corner of the United States was the first portion of the continent to be settled permanently by Europeans, and in spite of the lapse of more than three centuries it retains a distinctive culture and outlook, which in part stems from the conditions of the early settlers.

In December 1620 the *Mayflower*, sailing from Plymouth in England, brought about a hundred Puritan men, women, and children in search of a new life free from religious persecution. They had intended settling farther south, in Virginia; but they were driven ashore in Massachusetts, and christened their first settlement New Plymouth (it appears to be a coincidence that Captain John Smith had already called the same spot Plymouth six years earlier).

During the first terrible winter nearly half the colonists died; but they were joined by 35 newcomers in 1622, and a further 96 in 1623; about 2000 more landed in 1630, and another 16,000 or so during the following ten years. With the final overthrow of the Stuart kings much of the persecution of the Puritans ceased; there was then little incentive to emigrate, and the New England colony received few additions from abroad for two centuries. The early settlers therefore impressed their traditions very firmly upon the new land.

The migration had been organized on a basis of church communities. Religion pervaded life: work and thrift were moral virtues and idleness a sin. The winter climate was harsh; fertile areas were small and few; and the employment of slaves was inappropriate. Without coal or metals, the colonists were forced to economize in raw materials, and to rely largely on their own skills. They became resourceful handymen and inventors; they would repair clothes and implements until they were beyond repair. The farm was a family affair: it gained little from later mechanization, and remains small. New Englanders educated their children at Harvard (founded in 1636 at Cambridge, Mass.) rather than in England; they became (and to some extent remain) insular, conservative, and provincial.

With only meagre land resources, they turned to the sea, fishing for cod and whale from innumerable small coastal harbours and river ports, and building up a commerce with Europe and the West Indies. Their typical craft became the schooner, which appears to have been developed from English prototypes. In 1713 the first schooner was afloat, conceived, built, and launched at Gloucester, Massachusetts. It was a two-masted vessel, rigged fore and aft – a very fast ship designed partly with the object of economizing in the number of crew.

Gradually a pool of capital was built up; textiles were added to shipbuilding, and later, metal-work and paper-making. New England was the earliest region in the United States to develop manufactures, and for long was the leading industrial district of the nation. Its waterfalls and rapids were adequate for the water-power stage of industry; but other than this the chief local resource was the accumulated skill of the inhabitants. For raw materials the region had to look elsewhere; and, partly as a result, its manufactures are exceptionally varied: they include cotton and woollen goods, clothing, leather goods, rubber manufactures, hardware, paper, textile machinery, and miscellaneous metal manufactures. In most cases these are goods which require little raw material but a great deal of skilled labour; and in many of these spheres New England produces a share of the national output that is out of all proportion to its population.

But the industrial supremacy of New England could not be expected to last indefinitely: it had no coal, iron, or oil, and no major sources of hydro-electricity; and its communications with the centre and west of the United States were difficult. By 1919 it was feeling the competition of other industries, and in particular of industries in the South. A measure of decline was experienced in the woollen industry, in leather, and in some branches of the metal industry such as watch and clock making; but the cotton industry met with disaster.

In 1926 there were 15 major American centres of the cotton industry in New England, each with over 250,000 spindles. They included coastal places such as Providence, Fall River, and New Bedford, and inland sites such as the Merrimack towns of Lowell, Lawrence, and Manchester (Fig. 1). Careful studies have been made of the changing fortunes of the Merrimack towns. These were some of the earliest industrial towns of America: they were established on almost virgin sites amid the farms and forests, where falls or rapids allowed the harnessing of water power.

The major mills of Lowell were built in 1823, and those of Lawrence in 1848. At Manchester, about 1838, the Merrimack was dammed, and the water was led in a canal along the east bank to supply power to a whole row of mills. These, the Amoskeag mills, eventually stretched for a mile between the canal and the river. Elegant and substantial terrace houses three storeys high were built to house the workers, and

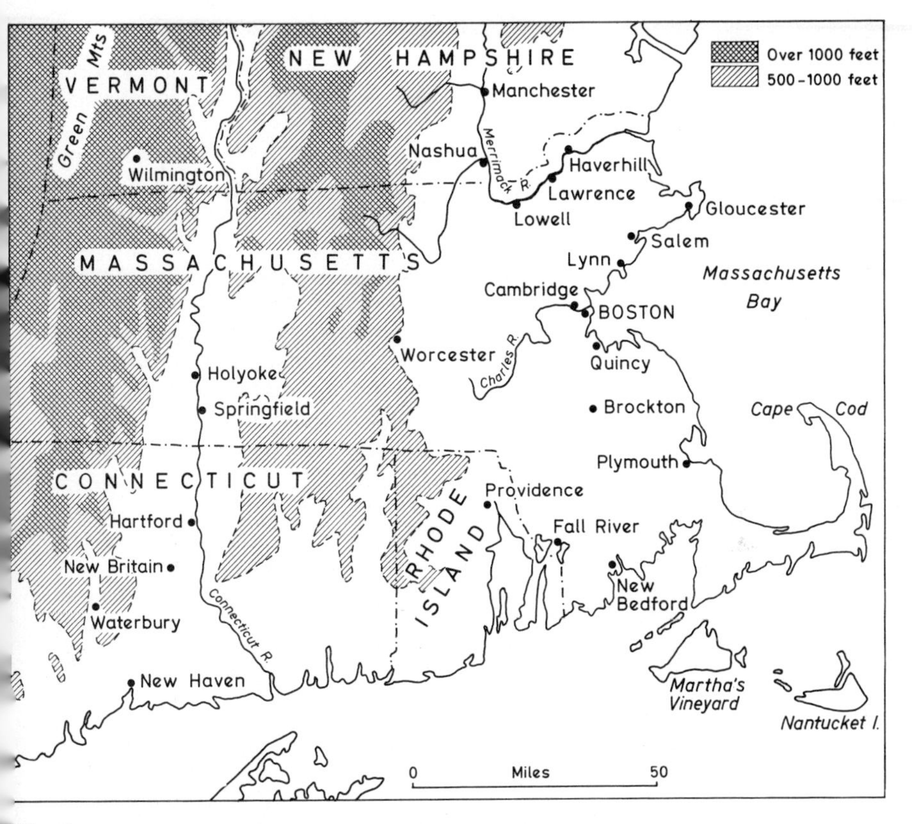

Fig. 1. SOUTH-EASTERN NEW ENGLAND
The map illustrates the towns mentioned in the text.

the town of Manchester was built round the mills and became almost completely dependent on them. Steam-powered mills were later constructed on the opposite bank of the river.

At their peak in 1922 the Amoskeag mills employed 17,500 workers. Then they began to feel the competition of the growing cotton industry of the Piedmont Plateau, where labour was cheaper, power more plentiful, and the raw material close at hand. They weathered the Great Depression by reducing the number of employees; but in 1935 they were forced to close. Eleven thousand textile workers were thrown out of employment, and it has taken many years for the city to recover. The old mill buildings are now occupied by about 120 different firms, mainly engaged in light industries such as the manufacture of clothing, toys, surgical dressings, and electrical apparatus.

In nearby Lawrence three-quarters of the labour force were employed in textiles. The reputation of this centre was based on wool: it was the foremost centre of the worsted industry in the United States, and one of its giant mills – the Wool Worsted mill – was the largest in the world. It covered 68 acres, employed 7000 people, and produced 6000 miles of cloth each year. In the decline of this industry 24,000 people became unemployed in Lawrence.

Textile manufacture remains a significant industry in New England, but it is no longer the dominant activity. Such factories as remain tend to concentrate on high-quality goods, where skill is still at a premium, and where the manufacturer is prepared to study the changes in fashion. The woollen industry has suffered far less than cotton: it depends largely on imported fleeces, and since Boston has for long been a major importer and market for wool, New England can compete successfully with the South in this industry. New England remains the chief woollen district of the nation, and in 1956 operated 47 per cent. of its woollen spindles.

While textiles have declined drastically, the leather industries have remained more stable, though even here some recession has occurred. The manufacture of footwear was in existence by 1800 in Haverhill and other towns of the lower Merrimack, but it did not become a factory industry till after 1860. Today the leather industry remains concentrated largely in Boston and its satellites, including Brockton, Lynn, Haverhill, and Worcester, and it has become associated with the production of rubber goods.

A significant element in the manufacture of shoes is that the machinery is not normally owned by the manufacturer but leased from the maker, so that older centres do not become handicapped through the use of obsolete equipment. In 1956 New England leather workers represented almost 30 per cent. of the nation's total. The district is the largest producer of ladies' shoes in the country, and has a large share in the production of rubber footwear. Boston remains both the chief importer of leather in the United States and its leading leather market.

The decline in textile employment has been offset to a limited extent by a remarkable expansion in the metal trades. These include a varied assortment of activities: the production of radio, telephone, and electronic equipment; aircraft engines and propeller units; scientific and measuring apparatus; office equipment such as typewriters and adding and dictating machines. All use skilled labour but require little raw material, so that New England competes on favourable terms with other centres. Boston engages largely in these activities, and benefits from its research and training facilities in electronics.

As in the English Black Country, some industries have become highly localized. Thus the Hartford district produces more than two-thirds of all the aircraft propellers and parts in the United States! The town began a firearms industry over a hundred years ago, and, to assist it, developed the production of machine tools. Today, in addition to this and aircraft manufactures, it produces precision apparatus such as calculating machines and electrical equipment.

Waterbury and New Haven in Connecticut and Waltham in the Boston district are still noted for clocks and watches, and New England as a whole accounts for more than a quarter of the national employment in this industry. Another highly localized activity is the rolling and drawing of non-ferrous metals – this is concentrated in Waterbury and other towns of the Naugatuk valley of western Connecticut.

In addition to these mainly light industries, New England for long has engaged in paper-making. In part the industry utilizes local timber, but much of the raw material is now imported from Canada, the South, and even Scandinavia.

Paper-making requires enormous quantities of pure water, and of this, at least, New England has ample supplies; an additional asset is the huge market for paper that exists in the north-eastern United States. But, compared with other paper-making districts, fuel and power in New England are relatively expensive. In 1956 the region accounted for 13·2 per cent. of the total employment in the industry. Important centres of the pulp and paper industry are the Springfield–Holyoke district and the upper valley of the Merrimack.

Farming

New England has experienced a long and continuous decline in the number of farms, in the area cultivated, and in the number of people employed on the land. Folk have moved away from the farms to the growing towns, where life is both more comfortable and more exciting; or they have moved westward to richer soils and a more congenial climate. New Englanders have scattered the names of their towns across the United States: there are 14 Concords, 16 Plymouths, 15 Portlands, 23 Salems, and 19 Lexingtons outside New England.

In the landscape the rural exodus reveals itself in the ruined farmhouse and abandoned land, or in the farm that has been bought by the city man for the sake of its hunting and fishing. The census returns show a startling reduction in the number of farms since 1880, and it is

State	*Year*	*Number of Farms*	*Average Size*
Connecticut	1880	30,592	
	1965	8,292	106·7 ac.
Maine	1880	64,309	
	1959	17,360	177·5 ac.
Vermont	1880	35,522	
	1959	12,099	234·4 ac.

NOTE. 1880 figures for the average sizes of farms are not available.

known that during this period the total area of the agricultural land of New England has almost halved.

Nevertheless, farming still plays a vital part in the region's economy, and has its own distinct character. Apart from a few specialist activities, which we notice below, the New England farmer concentrates mainly on dairying, and in particular on the production of fresh milk. No other region of the United States has so large a proportion of its improved land under hay. The famous dairy state of Wisconsin has 37 per cent. of its crop-land in hay; but in New England the corresponding proportion is 75 per cent., and in Vermont it is as high as 88 per cent. This concentration on fresh milk is in part related to the luxuriant growth of grass in this humid atmosphere, with its warm summers, but it also reflects the enormous demand for daily milk from nearby Megalopolis.

Scientific improvements in the dairy herds have increased the milk-yields greatly during recent decades, so that there is a greater output from a smaller number of cattle. Improvements in the pastures have also played an important part, and one far-sighted farmer in Vermont has liberally fertilized his land for 20 years: as a result he has trebled the number in his dairy herd, and doubled the average output of milk per cow.

Second to dairy farming is the raising of poultry, mainly for egg production; here too the nearby market has proved a potent spur. Poultry farming is a recent, growing, and profitable enterprise: it is important in all the urban fringe districts, and in New Hampshire it forms the leading source of farm income.

Four other specialized products add character to the farming in particular localities in New England: there are cranberries, maple sugar, potatoes, and tobacco (Fig. 2). Cranberries of various types grow wild in the eastern United States, from Maine as far south as Georgia; but their cultivation is concentrated in the Cape Cod peninsula and the district to the west of Massachusetts bay. The cranberry is a marsh plant, and cultivation takes place in the peat bogs which occupy glacial hollows. Much careful preparation of the land is needed: the turf is cleared, and the exposed peat is covered with about three inches of sand; the land must be thoroughly drained, and the water-supply controlled so that the surface may be temporarily flooded. The fruit is harvested in the autumn and sold both fresh and canned; it is eaten in pies and tarts, and with turkey as the traditional cranberry sauce. This small district produces two-thirds of all the cranberry sauce in the United States.

The maple sugar industry is carried on along the lower slopes of the

---

Fig. 2. FOUR NEW ENGLAND FARM PRODUCTS

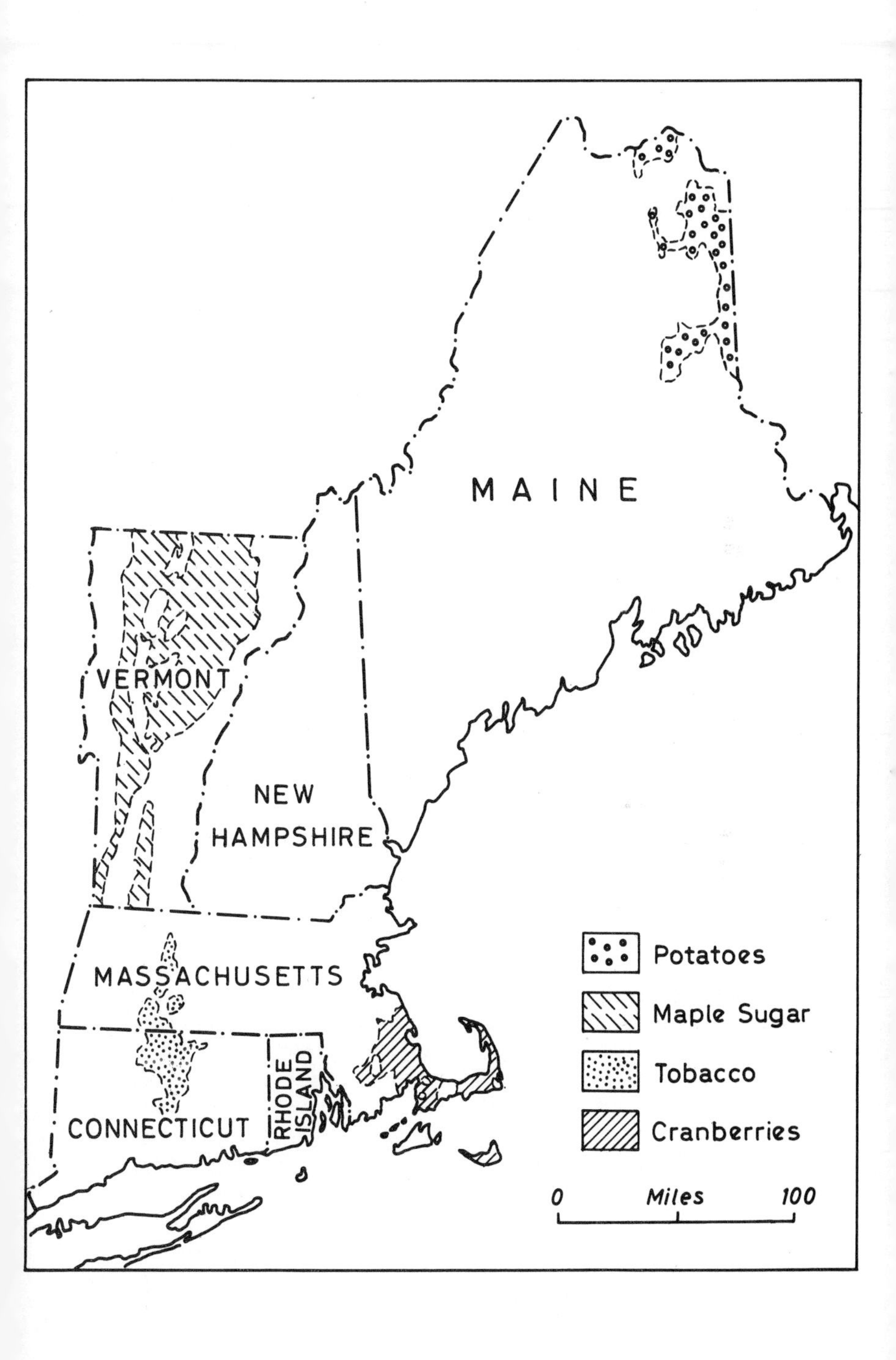
MAINE
VERMONT
NEW
HAMPSHIRE
MASSACHUSETTS
CONNECTICUT
RHODE
ISLAND
Potatoes
Maple Sugar
Tobacco
Cranberries
0
Miles
100

Green mountains in Vermont and Massachusetts and in the foothills of New Hampshire, and it extends into the adjoining districts of Quebec province. Two species – the sugar maple and the black maple – are commercially important for their sweet sap, and between two and three million of them are tapped in Vermont alone.

The sugar season lasts from early March to the middle of April: the snow is still on the ground, and transport of the colourless sap from the tree to the evaporating tank is traditionally by means of a container mounted on a sled and drawn by a horse, though some producers are now using plastic tubes to move the sap. There is a resemblance – but only a superficial one – to rubber-production. Holes about $\frac{3}{8}$ inch in diameter are drilled into the tree to a depth of about $1\frac{1}{2}$ inches; a metal spout is hammered into each hole, and the issuing sap is collected in buckets. An average tree, more than 2 feet in diameter, will support four buckets and yield about 15 gallons of sap each year: this will be boiled down to a little less than $\frac{1}{2}$ gallon of syrup.

Maple groves are described in terms of the number of buckets hung: one speaks, for example, of a 1200-bucket grove, but almost every farmer in the maple districts will hang a couple of buckets; and in Wilmington, in southern Vermont, even the trees lining the road are tapped. Most of the product is marketed in the form of canned or bottled syrup, but a small proportion is converted into fancy-shaped confectionery. In 1964 Vermont produced 505,000 gallons of maple syrup, valued at $2\frac{1}{4}$ million dollars.

In the long, narrow, and sheltered valley of the Connecticut river, etched out of Triassic rocks, is a famous tobacco-growing industry. Tobacco grows best on light soils, in humid atmospheric conditions, and in partial shade; and in the Connecticut valley these are assured by cultivating the crop below great areas of open-mesh cotton cloth – some of them covering scores of acres. From the air these angular patches of dazzling whiteness give the Connecticut valley a unique and strange appearance.

Differences in climate and soil are reflected in the character of the tobacco leaf. In the Connecticut valley the leaf is large and broad but extremely thin, with fine veins and an open texture; this is particularly suitable for cigar wrappers, and the area supplies about two-thirds of all the nation's needs in this respect. About 20,000 pickers are needed in the summer, and local labour is supplemented by some 5000 migrants from the South and the Caribbean. Tobacco is the leading crop by value in Connecticut: its output in 1965 was worth 25·8 million dollars.

The growing of vegetables is widespread in New England; but there is one district which is outstanding for the cultivation of potatoes: this is Aroostook county, in the far north of Maine. The soils are fertile sandy loams of glacial origin – loose, open, and easily cultivated. The cool and moist weather conditions, together with the long summer days, are ideal for this crop; moreover, in this northerly latitude the potato is less liable to disease, and therefore highly valued as seed.

The industry is highly organized: it makes use of mechanical aids, new pesticides, and modern storage depots. Efforts are made to avoid relying on a single product: potatoes are grown in rotation with hay and oats, and the cultivation of peas and the rearing of beef cattle add diversity to the farm enterprises. Aroostook potatoes are large, and the yield per acre is double the average for the United States. Maine is the leading state in the nation in potato production, and in this small area about one-eighth of the entire output is grown.

In 1964 the potato harvest amounted to 35·2 million cwt., and though its value was not officially mentioned, at the average rate of about two dollars per cwt. it must have been worth at least 70 million dollars. Maine potatoes are sold for either seed or the table in all the states east of the Mississippi, and in several farther west. Publicity too is well organized, and the annual gala with its barrel-rolling contest is a gay occasion.

Boston (population, urban area, 1960: 2,413,236)

Boston was founded in 1630, only ten years after the landing of the Pilgrim Fathers, and was so named because several of the leading settlers had been prominent citizens of the Boston in Lincolnshire, England. A hilly peninsula, thrusting into the deep Massachusetts bay, was seen to be an ideal site for both defence and commerce (Fig. 3); it was soon chosen as the capital of the colony of Massachusetts Bay, and it rapidly became populous and wealthy.

Boston built up a flourishing commerce with Europe and the West Indies, and developed fishing and shipbuilding industries, so that by the middle of the eighteenth century it was larger than New York and Philadelphia, and probably the biggest city in America. But Boston could not retain its supremacy. Although the Charles river afforded a limited access to the interior, the city had neither the productive hinterland of Philadelphia nor the unique communications of New York.

In its industries Boston preserves some elements of the colonial period. It is still the major centre of the Atlantic fisheries. It remains the chief leather market of the United States: hides and skins form a staple import, and leather manufactures (particularly footwear) a staple product. The textile industries have declined, but Boston is still second only to New York in the imports of wool. Shipbuilding is represented by the yard of the Bethlehem Steel Corporation at Quincy, on the southern outskirts of the city; this is one of the world's major shipyards, and is equipped to build tankers of over 100,000 tons d.w.

Other industries of Boston include the manufacture of electrical

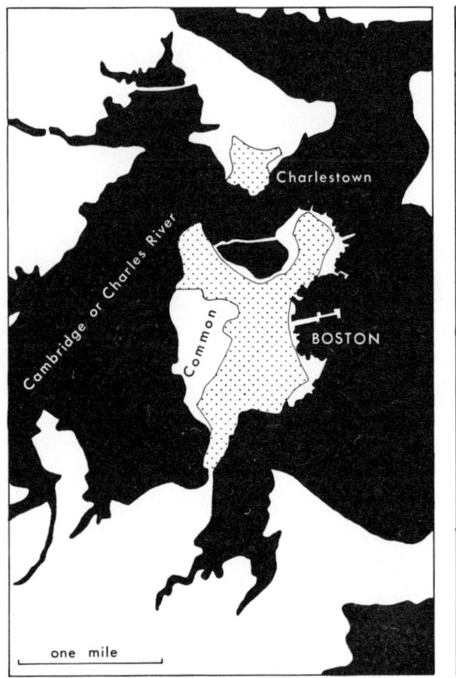

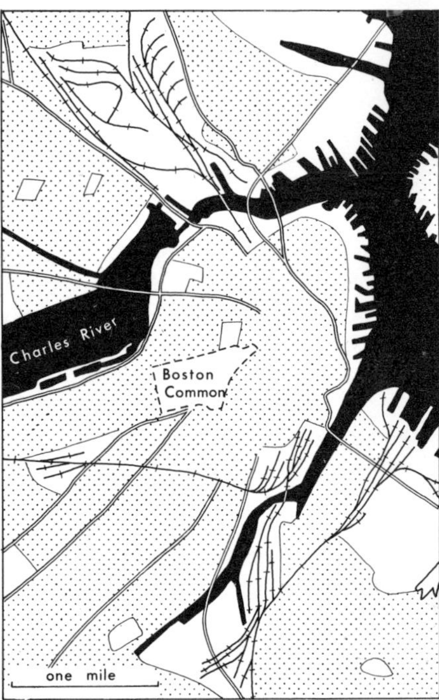

Fig. 3. BOSTON: 1775 AND TODAY

In no other American city has the original site been so modified by man. Extensive railway sidings now occupy what were formerly shallow bays, but the Common remains as a green oasis in the middle of the city. Water is in black, and built-up areas are stippled. Note the slight difference in scale. *Sources: 1775: from a plan published in the 'National Geographic Magazine', August 1962. Today: from the official 1 : 25,000 map.*

apparatus (where skilled labour is at a premium) and printing and publishing. The latter reflects the high standing of Boston as a centre of intellectual life. Among its educational institutions are the Massachusetts Institute of Technology and no fewer than four universities.

In no other American city has the original site been so modified by man. Reclamation of tidal flats has doubled the area of the original peninsula, and restricted the mouth of the Charles river to half its former width. As in New York, the commerce of the port is conducted at open jetties at the river entrance. Boston handles about 20 million tons of cargo a year – more than any other port east of New York, and approximately equal to the tonnage of Montreal. Almost the whole of this consists of imports, for in the export trade southern New England is tributary to New York. Boston concentrates largely on importing the bulky materials needed by the farms and many manufacturing towns of the region, and especially coal, petroleum, cement, and fertilizers.

NEW YORK

Introduction

In population and in commerce one urban region is outstanding in the United States. This is New York. It forms part of the larger urban belt ('Megalopolis') which stretches from Boston to Washington, D.C., but it has had its own separate historical development, and possesses a distinctive 'personality'.

The city of New York has a precise administrative meaning: it consists of five boroughs. Of these, Manhattan corresponds with the island of that name; the Bronx occupies the southern tip of the mainland to the north of Manhattan; Brooklyn and Queens share Long Island; and Richmond corresponds with Staten Island. Together these five boroughs have a population of 7·84 million (estimated, 1964). About 65 per cent. of the total consists of immigrants or their immediate descendants: they include about two million Jews, one million Russians, half a million Germans, and about the same number of Irish.

Beyond the city limits stretches a wider built-up area that extends westward across the Hudson river into New Jersey. The population of this 'Greater' New York in 1960 was 14,114,927. For comparison, the population of Greater London (estimated, 1965) is 7,948,800.

Physical Setting

The New York conurbation occupies a complicated pattern of islands and parts of islands, peninsulas and portions of the mainland – an intricate assortment of land and sea that has resulted from the submergence of a coastal lowland of rather complex structure. Moreover, this drowning of the land represents only the latest stage of a long series of events.

The Hudson river in the neighbourhood of New York follows a major geological boundary. East of it, both in Manhattan Island and in the mainland to the north, the rocks are of Pre-Cambrian age, and represent a continuation northward of the Piedmont Plateau (p. 82). Though they are all extremely ancient, they are not equally resistant to erosion. Two layers of hard metamorphic rocks (the Manhattan Schist above and the Fordham Gneiss below) are separated by a weaker series of limestones – the Inwood Limestone. These layers have been folded along north-and-south axes and subsequently eroded. The tougher metamorphic rocks now form the elevated blocks of Manhattan and the Bronx, while the weaker limestones have been eroded to form the beds of the Hudson and Harlem rivers, and the valleys followed by the Harlem railway and the northern stretch of Broadway (Figs. 4 and 5).

On the western side of the Hudson the rocks are very different. Here

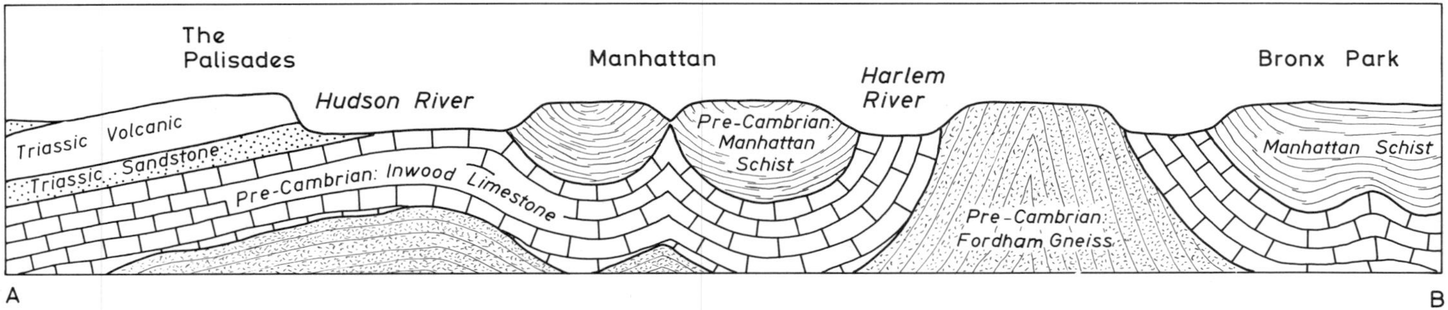

Fig. 4. SECTION THROUGH PART OF NEW YORK CITY

The section passes east and west from the Palisades to the Bronx; its line is indicated on Fig. 5, and its length is approximately five miles. The valleys have been excavated from the relatively weak Inwood Limestone.

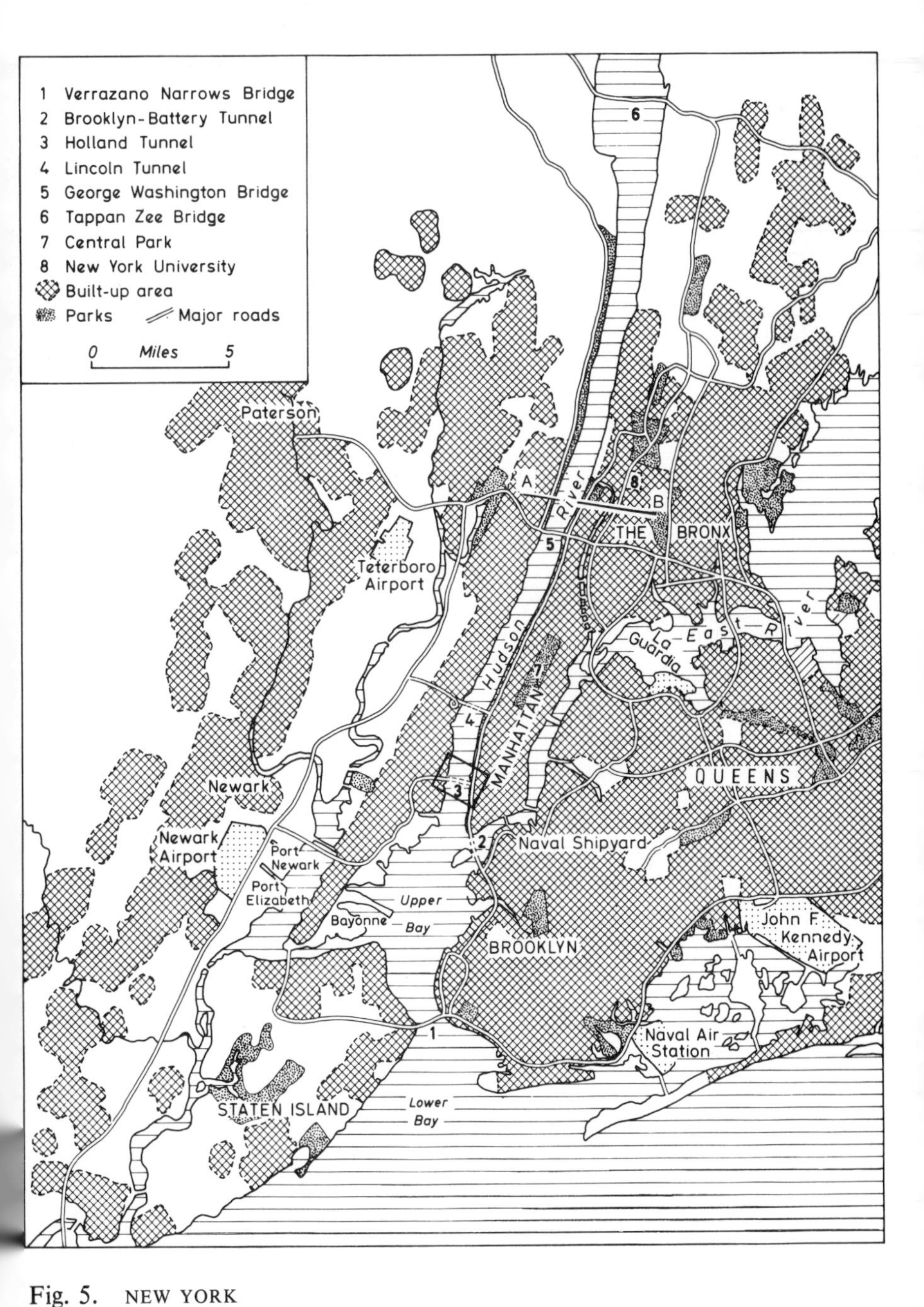

Fig. 5. NEW YORK

The line AB across the north of Manhattan represents the section illustrated in Fig. 4; the rectangle spanning the lower Hudson is represented on a larger scale as Fig. 6.

is a startling break in the succession, for the Pre-Cambrian rocks are overlain by Triassic material, and in particular by sheets of lava such as we have already seen in the Connecticut valley. Their steeply scarped edge forms a bold rampart overlooking the Hudson river for many miles. This barrier (known as the Palisades) effectively prevents any settlement along the edge of the river, but provides a firm base for the western (New Jersey) side of the famous George Washington bridge.

Before the Quaternary ice sheets advanced there was probably already a valley carved out of the limestone by an ancestor of the Hudson. A tongue of ice scoured this valley and left behind it the moraine which now forms the core of Long Island. When the ice sheets receded great volumes of meltwater flushed through the valley, for this was a spillway for the early Great Lakes (p. 30). Then came the land subsidence which drowned the valleys and converted the lower Hudson into a long arm of the sea.

The waterway is naturally deep in that most parts of the port can supply at least 30 feet of water for shipping. A 35-foot channel reaches Newark and serves the East River (Fig. 5). The Navy Shipyard is reached by a 40-foot channel; and the channel on the Manhattan side of the lower Hudson, used by the transatlantic liners, has a depth of 45 feet. But constant dredging is needed to maintain these depths. An important physical advantage of the port is its low tidal range of only $4\frac{1}{2}$ feet; this has made expensive enclosed docks unnecessary, so that all the port business can be carried on at open jetties.

The Development of New York

The first European to discover the mouth of the Hudson river was Giovanni da Verazzano, in 1524. In 1609 the Englishman Henry Hudson entered the bay; but he was in the employ of the Dutch East India Company, and his report on the possibilities of a lucrative fur trade aroused great interest in the newly independent United Netherlands. At once a trading ship was dispatched, and about 1615 a post was established at Albany, a few miles below the Hudson–Mohawk confluence. At the same time a few huts were built on Manhattan Island; and so New York had its modest beginnings.

In 1623 The Dutch East India Company proclaimed the province of New Netherland, and chose as the site of its capital the southern tip of Manhattan Island. Immediately the Dutch began to build a fort and settlement; and in 1626 Peter Minuit, the Director-General of the province, purchased from the Indians the whole of Manhattan Island for goods valued at about £8! By the end of the year New Amsterdam contained 30 bark-covered dwellings.

During this time, however, the English regarded the Dutch as intruders; and it was through the fear of an English attack that the

Dutch in 1653 protected their young capital by a wall whose line is still marked by Wall Street.

Eleven years later Charles II declared the whole area between the Connecticut river and Delaware bay to be an English province, and granted it to his brother, the Duke of York and Albany; so when later in the same year the Dutch were persuaded to surrender, the name of the town was changed to New York.

New York soon became a thriving commercial and shipbuilding centre. By the 1750's its inhabitants owned about 450 vessels, and the conquest of French Canada had opened up the two major routes to the interior – the Champlain and Mohawk valleys. A plan drawn a little later shows the infant city, extending for about three-quarters of a mile from the southern tip of Manhattan. A star-shaped citadel, Fort George, guarded it in the south, and in the north it was bordered by lake and swamp. The port was served by havens and jetties on the east shore. Wall Street bisected the town, and in it was the town hall; the houses had large gardens behind them, and a wide street to the west was named the 'Broad Way'.

About 1800 New York began to take the lead over its rivals, Boston and Philadelphia; and when in 1825 the Erie Canal was opened (p. 32) the cost of carrying goods from Buffalo dropped from 100 dollars to 6 dollars a ton. The city spread from Manhattan to the adjacent mainland, to Long Island and Staten Island, and across the Hudson to the New Jersey shore. New York became, and has remained, the chief gateway of the whole nation, both for commerce and for immigrants.

The Port

We have seen that the low tidal range renders enclosed docks unnecessary, and typically the trade of the port is conducted at finger-like jetties. There are more than 600 of these in New York harbour; their general effect has been to economize in the use of land, which, particularly on Manhattan, is exceedingly expensive; and they have extended the water frontage of the port by at least 200 miles!

Jetties line both sides of the lower Hudson for a distance of about six miles, and continue into Upper bay both in Brooklyn and on Staten Island. In contrast to most European ports, there is an absence of shore-based cranes, and vessels load and discharge with their own gear. Most of these jetties were constructed before the extensive use of lorry transport, and in the few cases where rebuilding has been possible they have been doubled in width to cater for road traffic. Thus the new pier No. 40 (Fig. 6), built by the Holland–America Line, has space for 500 lorries and parking for 1000 cars. Along the Manhattan waterfront the passenger traffic to and from the transatlantic liners benefits from the fast motor road ('expressway') that encircles the island.

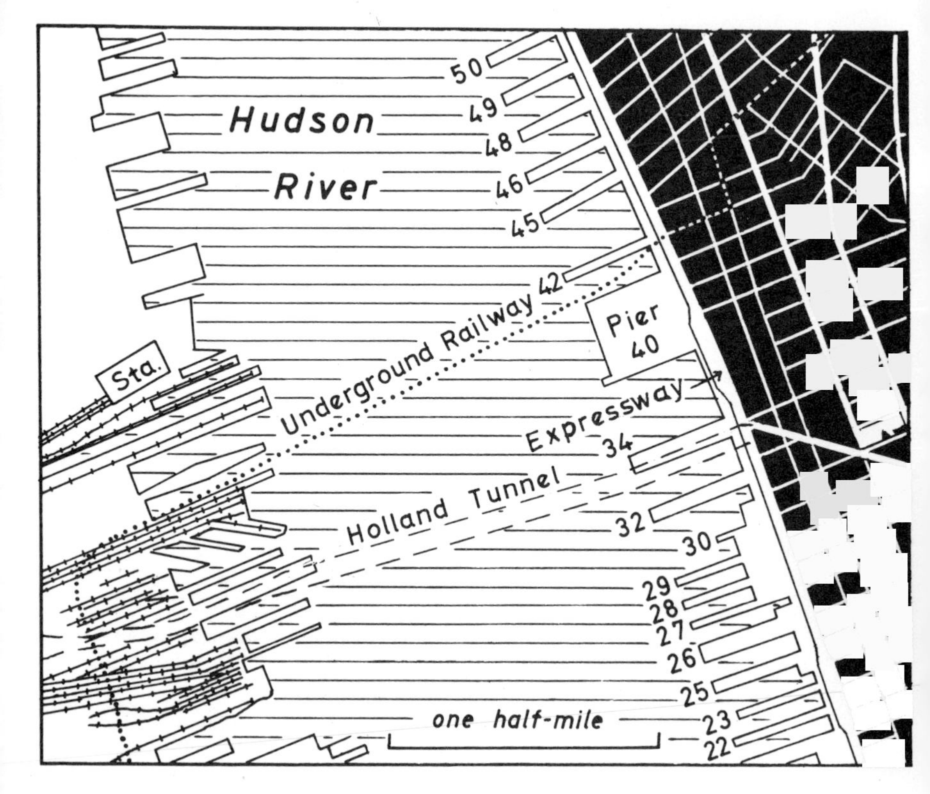

Fig. 6. A PORTION OF NEW YORK HARBOUR

Notice the reconstructed Pier 40 in the midst of older piers, and the expressway behind. The railway terminals on the New Jersey shore give rise to much cross-river traffic, which adds to the congestion of the port. Holland tunnel is a road tunnel.

In the newest extensions to the port, at Newark and Elizabeth, there was more land available for development, and here the traditional jetty system has been abandoned. On land reclaimed from the marshes of Newark bay 63 general cargo berths have been constructed, and generous open storage space has been provided behind the transit sheds. The new facilities represent 40 per cent. of the total general cargo capacity of the port.

Unlike London, there are no great spreads of alluvial flats available for heavy industries. Nevertheless, an important group of oil-refineries operates in Bayonne, on the New Jersey side of the Hudson. In this area too are the great rail terminals and marshalling yards, and these entail much cross-river traffic. A constant stream of car-floats moves back and forth. These are ferries fitted with rails; each carries about a dozen railway trucks, and a tug will push two at a time across the Hudson.

With so many peninsulas and islands, the port and city suffer from difficult access by land. The East River was easily bridged, but for long the Hudson could be crossed only by ferry. In 1927 the Holland tunnel was constructed, and in 1931 the fine George Washington Bridge. In 1964 the Verrazano Narrows Bridge was opened, spanning the entrance to the harbour: this ranks as the largest bridge in the world. There are now two road tunnels below the Hudson, and two more linking Manhattan to Long Island. Congestion, however, remains acute, and it is said that if all the people in the skyscrapers of south Manhattan were to descend at once to the streets, they would stand two layers high!

The concentric street plan of the southern tip of Manhattan Island reflects its seventeenth-century origin, and the site of the citadel is marked by Battery Park. Farther north the roads are laid out in a rectangular grid, with 11 numbered avenues running the length of Manhattan and over 200 streets cutting them at right angles. The avenues are numbered from east to west and the streets from south to north; and between Fifth and Eighth Avenues lies Central Park, the Hyde Park of New York.

The theatre district lies south of the park, and here and to the east are the main hotels. In the north of Manhattan Island is Harlem, the Negro quarter; and in the southern tip is the civic centre.

The skyscrapers lie in two main groups: one is near the civic centre and the other farther north in Manhattan. It is this 'midtown' group that contains the Empire State Building, with 102 storeys and a height of 1250 feet.

With its two cathedrals and its many libraries, museums, and educational institutions, New York is a great centre of culture and religion. It has no fewer than five universities: the largest of them – the University of the City of New York – has over 100,000 students!

New York is the financial centre of the United States, and is the major terminal for the long-distance passenger traffic, handling about 80 per cent. of the total. It has over 30 scheduled sailings with Antwerp, Naples, and Havana, and over 20 with Bremen, Copenhagen, Rio, and Yokohama. While it handles less cargo in terms of tonnage than does the Delaware river, it has no rival in the United States in terms of the value of its foreign trade. In 1961 it handled 37 per cent. of the overseas commerce of the country by value; its nearest rival, New Orleans, could muster only 7 per cent. of the total.

CHAPTER TWO

THE GREAT LAKES AND THE ST LAWRENCE LOWLANDS

The Great Lakes occupy a combined area of nearly 95,000 square miles – a little larger than that of Great Britain and Northern Ireland. Lake Superior, the largest of them (31,820 square miles), is 350 miles long from east to west, and at its widest about 165 miles from north to south: $7\frac{1}{2}$ times as wide as the Strait of Dover. These lake basins form deep hollows in the surface of the earth which, with the exception of the basin of Lake Erie, have been excavated below sea-level (Fig. 7).

The water surfaces of the four upper lakes differ by only 30 feet; their actual heights above sea-level are as follows: Superior, 602 feet; Michigan and Huron, 581 feet; Erie, 572 feet. A major break in level occurs between Lakes Erie and Ontario, and though on extreme occasions it may be as great as 331 feet or as small as 321 feet, it is usually expressed as 327 feet. More than half of this drop is seen at the single mighty leap of Niagara Falls, and most of the remainder is expressed in the turbulent lower Niagara river as it races in its five-mile gorge below the falls. Lake Ontario is still 246 feet above the sea, and most of this height is lost in the Thousand Isles section of the St Lawrence river, where in the space of 100 miles a series of rapids interrupted the early navigation of the river. We discuss later the physical bases of these breaks of slope and examine the canals which bypass them.

From Montreal to the Lakehead harbour of Fort William–Port Arthur the length of navigation is 1211 miles, so that a vessel from Liverpool arriving at Montreal and bound for the Lakehead has still a quarter of its journey to complete. The hinterland of the Great Lakes is computed at about 200,000 square miles; that is, almost as large as France, and far larger than Germany. It includes large tracts of prairie wheatland and Mid-West cornland, the iron-mining ranges of the Lake Superior shores and the new producing districts of Labrador, one of the world's major coalfields in West Virginia and western Pennsylvania, the steel complexes of Chicago, Pittsburgh, Hamilton, and the Erie lakeshore, and many other major cities, including Detroit, Cleveland, Buffalo, Toronto, and Montreal.

During its fall through 600 feet to the sea the water of the Great Lakes is harnessed for the production of electricity.

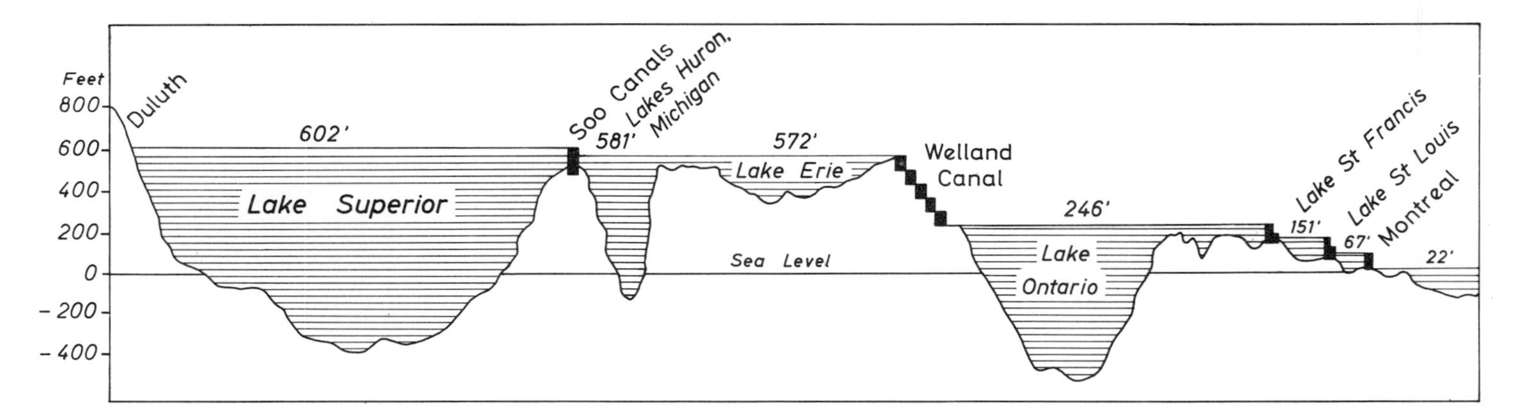

Fig. 7. A SECTION THROUGH THE GREAT LAKES

The lakes occupy deep hollows which, excepting Lake Erie, descend below sea-level. The major difference in level occurs between Lakes Erie and Ontario – a fact that the map alone cannot adequately convey. Notice that in diagrams of this type the vertical scale must be greatly exaggerated. The length represented by the section is about 1500 miles.

With its natural resources of minerals, timber, water-power, and wide areas of fertile soils, with its harbours and its manufactures, the Great Lakes region is the most productive in the continent. It has a greater output than all the Common Market countries put together, and has been described as the greatest industrial and agricultural concentration that has ever existed.

Physical Basis

Lakes are probably the most short-lived features of the physical landscape, and it is clear that the Great Lakes originated only with the retreat of the ice sheets. Their basins, however, must have had earlier beginnings, as shallow valleys etched out of comparatively weak rocks by pre-glacial river systems which flowed southward and south-westward. The advancing ice scoured and deepened these valleys and blocked their southern outlets by depositing masses of morainic material; thus when the ice retreated northward its meltwaters were impounded to form the Great Lakes.

Before we examine the evolution of the Great Lakes it is instructive to notice the close relationship between their shapes and the surface geology. Broadly speaking, the lake basins lie between the Pre-Cambrian shield to the north and the Palæozoic rocks to the south. Lake Michigan, however, thrusts southward into Silurian and Carboniferous strata, while Lakes Erie and Ontario are bordered both to the north and the south by older Palæozoic strata of Ordovician to Devonian age.

Lakes Michigan and Huron in their shapes reflect in part the underlying structure. The peninsula between them consists of an almost symmetrically circular basin which has been planed off by erosion, so that Upper Coal Measures are exposed in its centre, and progressively older formations are arranged in narrow concentric bands. The more resistant of these form outfacing scarps, and the shores of both lakes are related to the strike of the geological formations.

One resistant formation in particular can be traced for many miles through shorelines, peninsulas, and islands: this is the famous Niagara Limestone, of Middle Silurian age (Fig. 8). It can be recognized first in Indiana, a few miles south-east of Chicago, whence it extends in a gentle curve parallel to the western shore of Lake Michigan. It forms the Door

---

Fig. 8. THE GREAT LAKES

The map indicates two geological formations that have influenced the shapes of the lakes, and it names the towns, rivers, and other features that are mentioned in the text. The American Mississippian corresponds with the English Carboniferous Limestone.

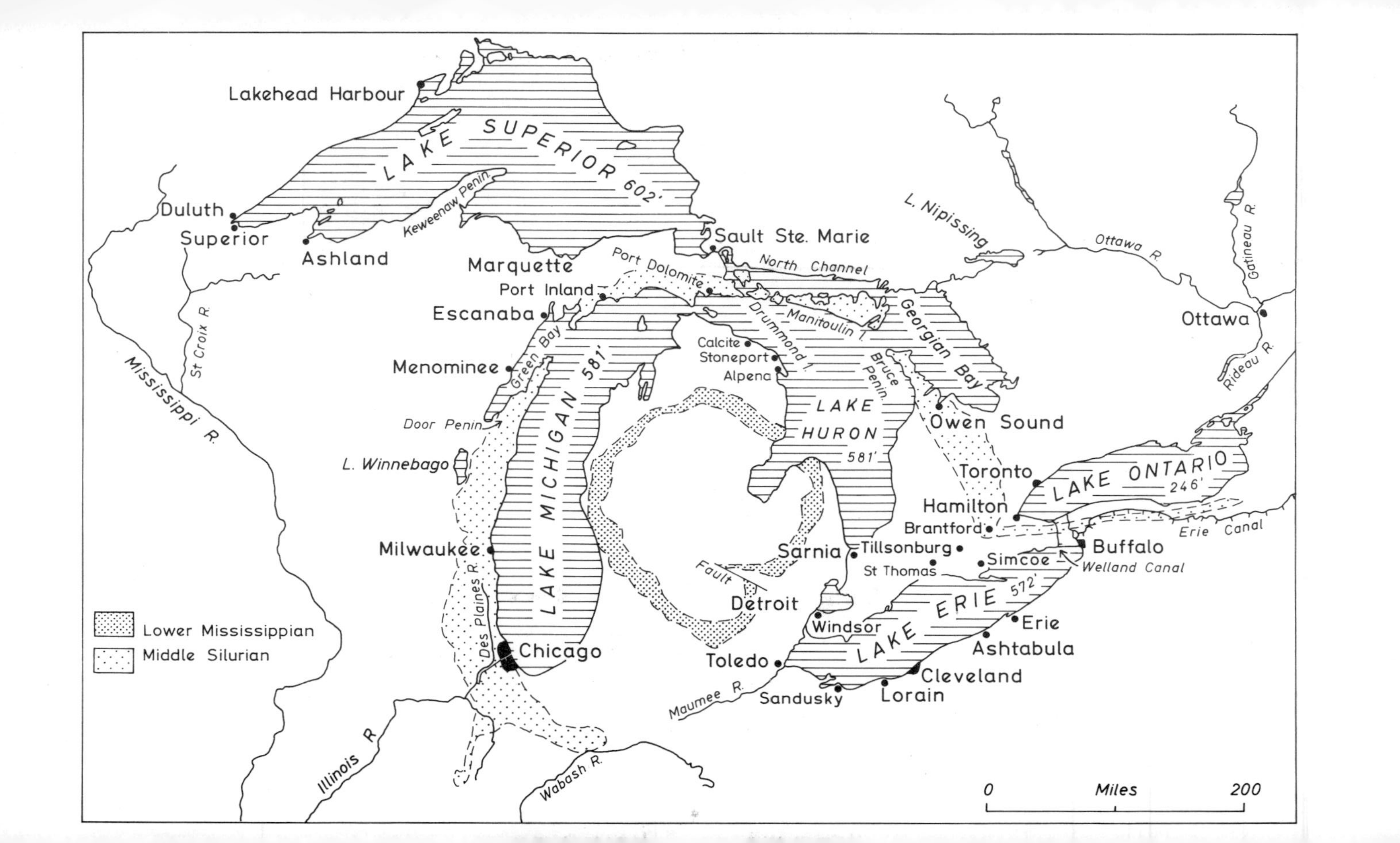
Lakehead Harbour
LAKE SUPERIOR 602'
Duluth
Superior
Ashland
Keweenaw Penin.
Marquette
Sault Ste. Marie
North Channel
L. Nipissing
Ottawa R.
Gatineau R.
Ottawa
Rideau R.
Port Dolomite
Port Inland
Escanaba
Drummond I.
Manitoulin I.
Georgian Bay
St Croix R.
Mississippi R.
Menominee
Green Bay
Calcite
Stoneport
Alpena
Bruce Penin.
LAKE MICHIGAN 581'
LAKE HURON 581'
Owen Sound
Door Penin.
L. Winnebago
Toronto
LAKE ONTARIO 246'
Hamilton
Brantford
Erie Canal
Milwaukee
Tillsonburg
Buffalo
Sarnia
St Thomas
Simcoe
Welland Canal
Fault
Detroit
LAKE ERIE 572'
Des Plaines R.
Windsor
Erie
Ashtabula
Lower Mississippian
Middle Silurian
Chicago
Toledo
Cleveland
Maumee R.
Sandusky
Lorain
Illinois R.
Wabash R.
0
Miles
200

peninsula with its associated islands, which separate Green bay from the main body of the lake. Green bay and the small Lake Winnebago to the south have been developed from a weaker Ordovician material, which likewise can be traced for many miles in a great arc beyond the Niagara Limestone.

The Limestone forms the southern part of the narrow neck of land between Lakes Superior and Michigan, and accounts for Drummond, Cockburn, and Manitoulin islands, together with the Bruce (or Saugeen) peninsula of Lake Huron, which cuts off Georgian bay from the main body of the lake. Structurally the North Channel and Georgian bay of Lake Huron correspond with Green bay of Lake Michigan. The scarp runs southward, and near Brantford it turns eastward, to run parallel with the southern shore of Lake Ontario. The Niagara river, formerly tumbling over it, now trenches it in a deep gorge. The bed of Lake Ontario has been hollowed from the same soft Ordovician material as that which floors Georgian and Green bays, and structurally forms a continuation of them.

While the hollows must have been of pre-glacial origin, the lakes themselves were consequent upon the northward retreat of the ice sheets. Several different stages have been recognized in this retreat, and the emerging lakes have had different outlets at different times. For long they drained to the south-west: the incipient Lake Michigan (known as Lake Chicago) drained into the Illinois river, and the incipient Lake Erie (Lake Maumee) into the Maumee and Wabash rivers. When Lake Superior began to appear (Lake Duluth) it too drained to the south-west, by way of a headstream of the Mississippi, the St Croix river. All these former outlets have provided easy lines of communication – for portages, roads, canals, and railways.

A further retreat of the ice allowed the meltwater to form the 'finger' lakes of New York state, and these at one stage overflowed southward across the Appalachians by way of the Susquehanna river. When the ice cleared from the Mohawk valley this lower route provided an outlet for the lower lakes (Fig. 9; see also Fig. 55, p. 137). A tongue of ice still occupied the St Lawrence valley; but when this cleared as far as the site of Montreal the Mohawk was abandoned as an outlet in favour of the Champlain route. Finally this too was abandoned, and for the first time the whole of the Great Lakes water spilled out through the St Lawrence.

Fig. 9. A STAGE IN THE EMERGENCE OF THE GREAT LAKES

Lakes Duluth and Chicago (ancestors of Superior and Michigan) are draining to the Mississippi; the remaining lakes drain to the Hudson. Today these old spillways form important lines of communication. Other stages in the development of the Great Lakes are shown in Fig. 55 (p. 137).

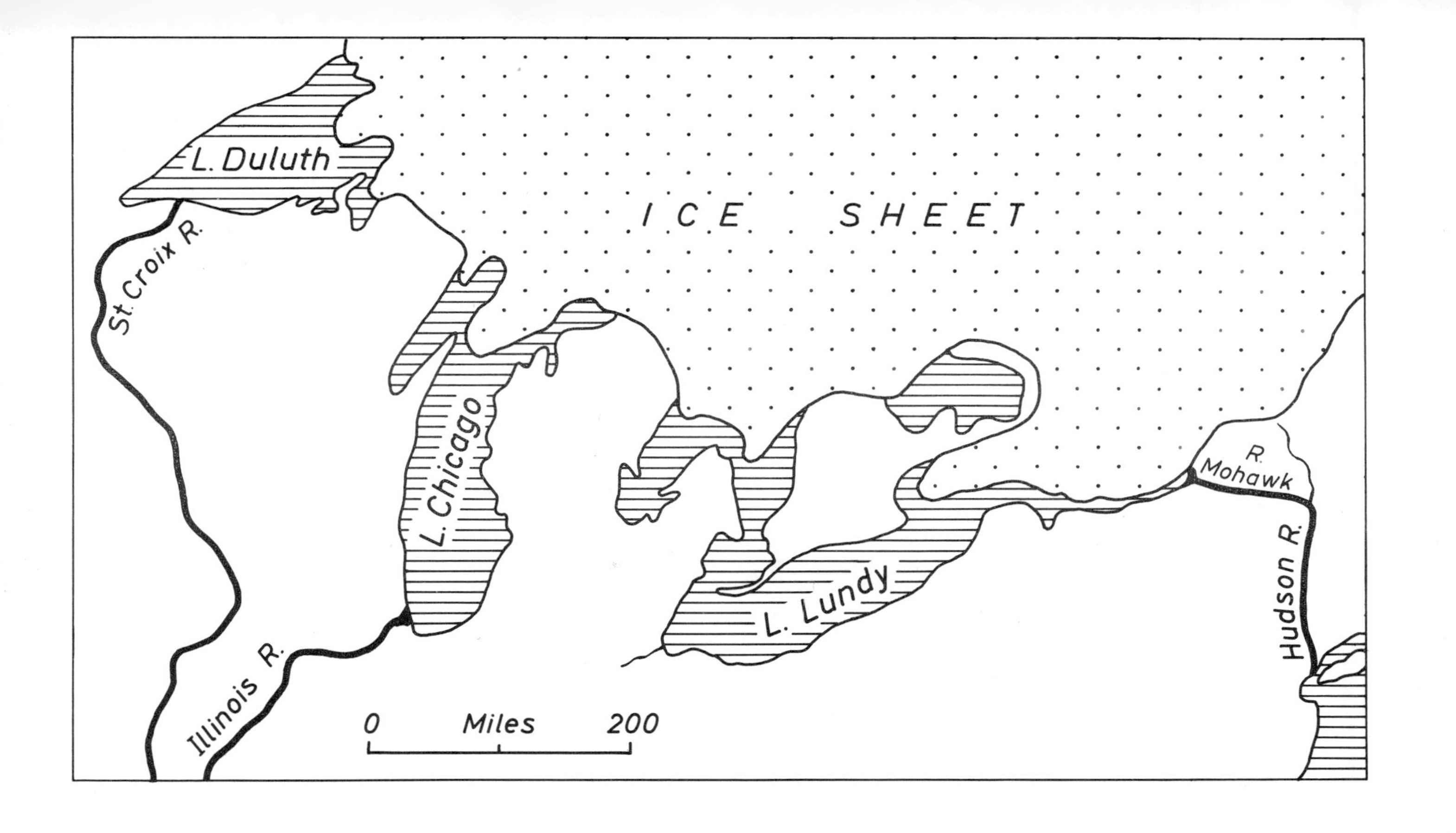
L. Duluth
ICE SHEET
St. Croix R.
L. Chicago
L. Lundy
R. Mohawk
Hudson R.
Illinois R.
0 Miles 200

The Improvement of Navigation

In a state of nature, through navigation of the Great Lakes system was interrupted in three districts. Between Lake Superior and Lake Huron a short stretch of rapids existed at Sault Ste Marie (the word 'sault', which appears so commonly in Canadian place-names, is derived from the French word *saut*, meaning a jump or leap, hence a waterfall). Here the St Mary's river drops about 20 feet as it cuts through Cambrian sandstones and limestones. Between Lake Huron, Lake St Clair, and Lake Erie the differences in level are of only a few feet, and this presented no difficulty for navigation; but there has always been a major barrier in the Niagara river, which plunges 170 feet at the falls and descends a further 115 feet in the gorge below. The third difficult stretch of the system lay between Lake Ontario and Montreal, where the river is cutting through the Pre-Cambrian rocks of the Laurentian Shield. In a 45-mile stretch the river descends through a whole series of rapids (the International rapids) to the level of Lake St Francis, which is 95 feet below that of Lake Ontario; and a further series of four rapids occurs between Lake St Francis and Lake St Louis. Finally the river drops 50 feet in the dramatic three-mile-long Lachine rapids to descend to a mere 20 feet above sea-level at Montreal; and thence it pursues a leisurely course to the sea.

All these barriers to navigation were bypassed during the course of the nineteenth century. Sailing-vessels and steamers were already in use on the lakes before there was any outlet for shipping, but it was clear that the traffic could be greatly increased if there were access to the sea. The Americans made the first move, with the intention of attracting the Lake Erie traffic into New York state. Theirs was an ambitious scheme for a canal 363 miles long from Buffalo to Albany, following essentially the former spillway by which the lakes had overflowed eastward. But it had to cross many rivers and descend 500 feet, and it required 18 aqueducts and 83 locks. This, the Erie Canal, was built, largely with Irish labour, during the years 1816–25. It was an immediate success. The cost of carrying goods between Lake Erie and New York fell from 100 to 6 dollars a ton, and soon there were 4000 canal boats in use. Originally 40 feet wide and 4 feet deep, the canal was deepened ten years later to 7 feet; improvements continued until 1916, and by then the width had been increased to 123 feet and the depth to 12 feet, while the number of locks had been reduced to 36.

Even before the Erie Canal was opened the Canadians on their side were preparing to bypass Niagara Falls, to replace the traditional 25-mile portage by a canal. This, the Welland Canal, would then tempt the Lake Erie traffic to remain in Canada, and there is little doubt that it was the spur of American competition that hastened its construction.

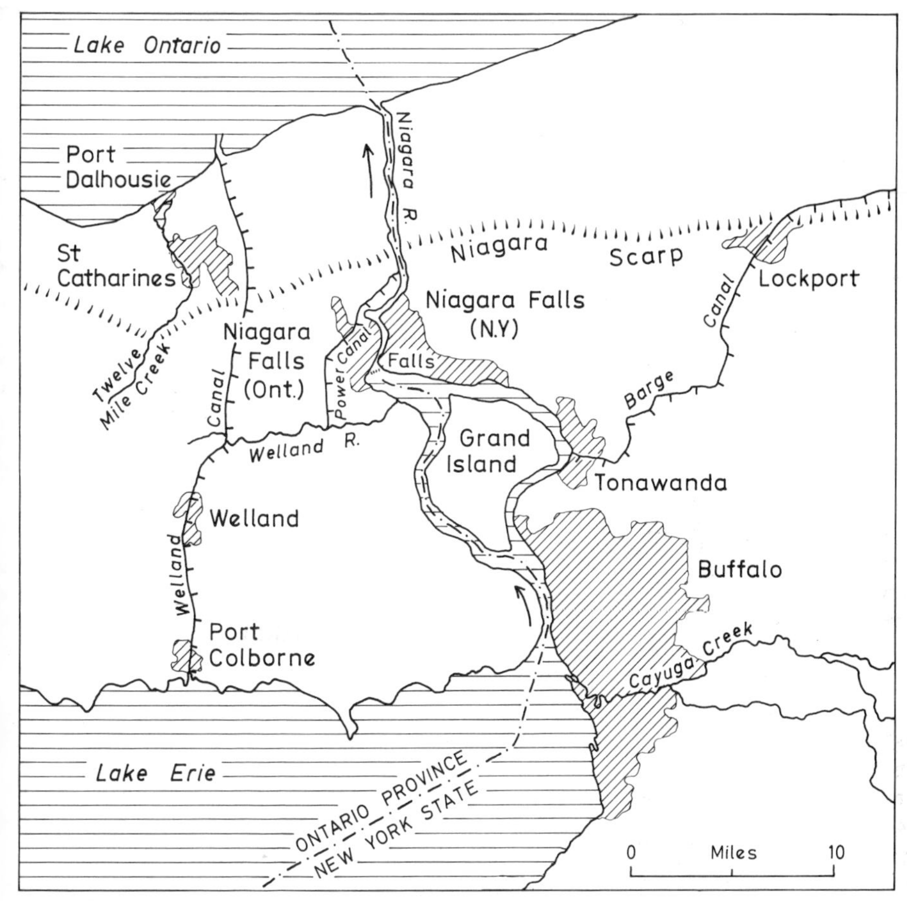

Fig. 10. THE NIAGARA FALLS DISTRICT

The map illustrates the 'retreat' of the Falls from the scarp to their present position; it shows the courses of the Welland Canal and the Barge Canal (formerly the Erie Canal) and the site of Buffalo. The first Welland Canal followed the valleys of Twelve Mile Creek and the Welland river.

Its original route was from Port Dalhousie on Lake Ontario, along the valley of Twelve Mile Creek (Fig. 10). A staircase of 39 locks raised the boats 325 feet to the crest of the Niagara scarp, and they reached Lake Erie by way of the Welland and Niagara rivers. The first Welland Canal was built in 1825–29, and its limiting depth was 8 feet. It too was progressively improved, until in 1932 the fine new Welland Ship Canal was formally opened.

With five locks (three of them twinned), each 859 feet long and 30 feet deep, the new canal foreshadowed the dimensions of the St Lawrence Seaway. Its traffic, as the following table indicates, has grown phenomenally, and its former rival, the Erie Canal, has been left far behind.

Cargo carried through the Welland Canal

Year	*Million tons*
1901	·6
1928	7·4
1932	8·5
1940	12·9
1950	14·7
1960	29·2
1966	59·2

The latest project in the improvement of the Welland Canal is to complete the twinning of all the locks, so that two-way traffic will be possible throughout its length; this is scheduled for completion in 1968, and is expected to increase the capacity of the canal by 60 per cent.

The barrier between Lakes Superior and Huron consisted of a mere 20-foot waterfall. For generations loads of furs had been carried round the falls, until in 1797 a lock with a lift of 9 feet was constructed by the Canadians. It had only a short life, for the Americans blew it up in the war of 1812. For 40 years goods were then carried round the falls by a horse-drawn tram on the American side. But about 1840 rich deposits of copper and iron were discovered on the shores of Lake Superior and some improvement was clearly essential.

The demand for transport on Lake Superior became so great that vessels were actually dragged round the falls on rollers and sledges: eight ships were thus manhandled in 1845–47, and another five in 1850–53. The problem was solved in 1855, when a fine canal a mile long and 12 feet deep, containing two locks, was opened on the Michigan side of the river. For the first time there was through navigation from the head of the lakes to the Atlantic, either by way of the Erie Canal and the Hudson river or by the Welland Canal and various stretches of canal between Lake Ontario and Montreal.

The Sault Ste Marie Canal (usually known as 'Soo') immediately prospered. In 1856, 11,000 tons of iron ore passed through the locks, together with 2¼ million dollars' worth of copper; upstream went cargoes of manufactures and equipment to help in the development of the mineral districts. Enlargement and duplication were almost inevitable. After the Civil War the canal was deepened to 16 feet; in 1895 a second canal was built, on the Canadian side; the following year the two American locks were condensed into one. By 1905 the Soo canals were carrying twice as much traffic as the Suez Canal, and the volume of shipping has remained high ever since.

The Soo Canal now consists of five parallel locks, four of them on the American side and one on the Canadian. The latter is 900 feet long, 60 feet wide, and 22 feet deep. The largest of the American locks is 800 feet long and 31 feet deep; but another is being lengthened to 1200 feet and deepened to 32 feet well in advance of Seaway dimensions. This is appropriate to the status of the Soo Canal, for it ranks as the world's busiest waterway: in a shipping season restricted to seven or eight months it carries as much as the combined traffic of the Suez, Panama, and Manchester Ship canals.

The Great Lakes Traffic

Several features distinguish the commerce of the Great Lakes from other branches of shipping. First is the specialization on a few bulk cargoes. There are, it is true, many cargoes which are regularly handled, such as timber, package freight, and passengers; but by far the greater part of the cargoes consists of four commodities. In order of tonnage these are: iron ore, coal, limestone, and grain.

Second is the fact that traffic is interrupted by the freezing of the canals and harbours and of the edges of the lakes between December and April, so that the long-distance traffic at least is confined to a seven or eight months' season. Icebreakers carve out a narrow channel through the ice in April, and the long procession of freighters begins. Even when the season has been opened, an April gale has been known to pile up the ice in restricted bays, and so trap the vessels for a week or more. There is also an element of risk at the close of the season, and in 1965 four ocean vessels were caught by ice and forced to spend the whole winter in the Great Lakes.

All this has encouraged the development of specially designed freighters and speedy methods of handling cargoes. Grain and ore are loaded by gravity; grain is discharged by suction as if it were a liquid; limestone and coal are discharged by self-unloaders, which stow away in the vessel: they consist of a series of conveyer belts which conduct the cargo from the vessel to the shore. The world's records for cargo-handling are set up on the Great Lakes.

Third is the immense volume of cargo that is carried in this shortened season. No other shipping route can approach the quantities of cargo that traverse the Lakes. On their shores are the world's greatest ore port (Duluth–Superior), the world's greatest coal port (Toledo), its greatest limestone port (Calcite), and its greatest grain port (Fort William–Port Arthur, lately renamed Lakehead Harbour).

Fourth is the fortunate fact that in many instances there are return cargoes available: grain and ore travel 'down-stream' and coal moves 'up-stream', so that important economies are possible in the operation of Great Lakes shipping. Fifthly and lastly, there are real savings in distance in many cases when cargoes are shipped via the Lakes, compared with the corresponding journey by land. It is estimated that to haul corresponding loads of coal by rail would be six times as expensive, and the haulage of ore would be seven times as costly compared with movement by lake freighter.

We now discuss the four leading cargoes carried on the Great Lakes. First is the iron-ore traffic.

Iron Ore

The progressive improvements in the navigation of the Great Lakes system took place as a result of the pressing needs of industry. Foremost among these were the demands of an expanding iron and steel industry for ever-larger quantities of iron ore. Its raw material originally had been supplied from workings in the east, particularly in the Adirondack mountains. But explorers had long heard of the tales of rich mineral deposits in the lands bordering the upper lakes, and from the 1840's onward these deposits were gradually located, surveyed, and developed.

In 1844 John Hays discovered metallic copper at Cliff Mine, close to the tip of the Keweenaw peninsula; soon other deposits were found nearby, harbours were opened, and small craft chartered to carry the ores eastward. They had to be portaged round the St Mary's Falls, then reloaded to other vessels below the Falls. Other deposits were discovered at Bruce Mines, on the North Channel of Lake Huron. These could be shipped direct, and by the 1850's 300 immigrant miners were operating 12 shafts at this mine.

In the late 1830's the newly established (1837) state of Michigan began to survey her land south of Lake Superior. By 1844 the surveyors were at Negaunee (a few miles west of the present port of Marquette), when the compass whirled and fluttered madly, and the men found chunks of rich iron ore at their feet. They had discovered the Marquette Range. Five years later the port of Marquette was founded, and it became the outlet for a whole group of mines 12 to 30 miles from the shore. Ore moved to the dock at the rate of 30 to 40 tons a day, first by horse tram, and later by steam locomotive: and its output was stimulated in 1855, when the barrier at the St Mary's Falls was overcome.

Shipments from Marquette had climbed to about 2 million tons a year by 1898 (that is, nearly 6000 tons a day), and reached a peak of nearly 4 million tons in 1916. In 1941 there was a record shipment of nearly 6 million tons; this was not maintained, but later output has usually been greater than 4 million tons annually.

With the surveyors systematically at work it could not be long before new ranges were revealed. In 1849 they arrived at a rocky ridge, 1000 feet high and 80 miles long: it was the western extension of the Keweenaw peninsula, composed of Pre-Cambrian volcanic material. This was the Gogebic Range, and everywhere there were traces of iron. Three years later the Vermilion Range was discovered. Its glistening ore, at first thought to be gold, proved to be 'fools' gold – sulphide of iron – but more valuable than the precious metal itself to the developing iron and steel industries of the east. The Menominee Range was found about the same time.

It did not prove easy to persuade the eastern financiers that railway connections were essential to make full use of these storehouses of iron; but rail links were completed from the Vermilion Range to Two Harbors in 1884 and from the Gogebic Range to Ashland in 1885.

Menominee Range was operating by the late 1870's, and shipping its ore from Escanaba – an established sawmilling port near the mouth of Escanaba river, on Green bay (Lake Michigan). Shipments from this port reached 6 million tons a year soon after 1900, and have remained at about that level ever since.

The largest and richest of all the ranges – Mesabi – was discovered latest. The credit belongs to three lumbermen, the Merritt brothers: they acquired 141 leases in 1890 and managed to obtain financial backing for a railway. This was built to Superior, and the first load of ore arrived at the lakeside in 1892. The earliest discoveries were towards the east of the ridge, and named by the Merritts 'Mountain Iron'. Hibbing, which proved to be the centre of the Range, was named after a German immigrant who helped to uncover it.

The ore at Mesabi is loose and easily excavated by power shovel; it is covered by only a few feet of glacial material which can be easily stripped off; and it ranks 64 per cent. pure – the richest of all the lake ores. Many great pits now scar the ridge, and a whole row of towns now serve the needs of the miners (Figs. 11, 12). Largest of all is the Hull Rust pit, 4 miles long and up to a mile wide, and about 350 feet deep. It contains 75 miles of railway track, and the ore is lifted by giant shovels, 15 tons at a scoop, into the waiting railway trucks. In 1921 the town of Hibbing itself was moved to a new site 1½ miles away so that the ore beneath it could be mined.

Duluth–Superior quickly rose to become the world's greatest ore-shipping port, which it has remained ever since. By 1900 it had surpassed the ports of neighbouring ranges. It shipped 10 million tons in 1904, 20 million in 1907, 35 million in 1917, and 55 million in 1942. During the 1940's and 1950's shipments ranged betwen 40 and 60 million tons a year, while Two Harbors, tapping the eastern end of the Range, contributed an additional 15 to 20 millions.

But this tremendous rate could not be expected to continue indefinitely, and with the removal of the most accessible deposits a steep decline has taken place: from a peak of 80 million tons in 1953, production fell to 49 million in 1964. Fortunately there exist in the eastern part of the district further large reserves of a harder, leaner ore known as taconite. It contains up to 30 per cent. iron; it has to be crushed and

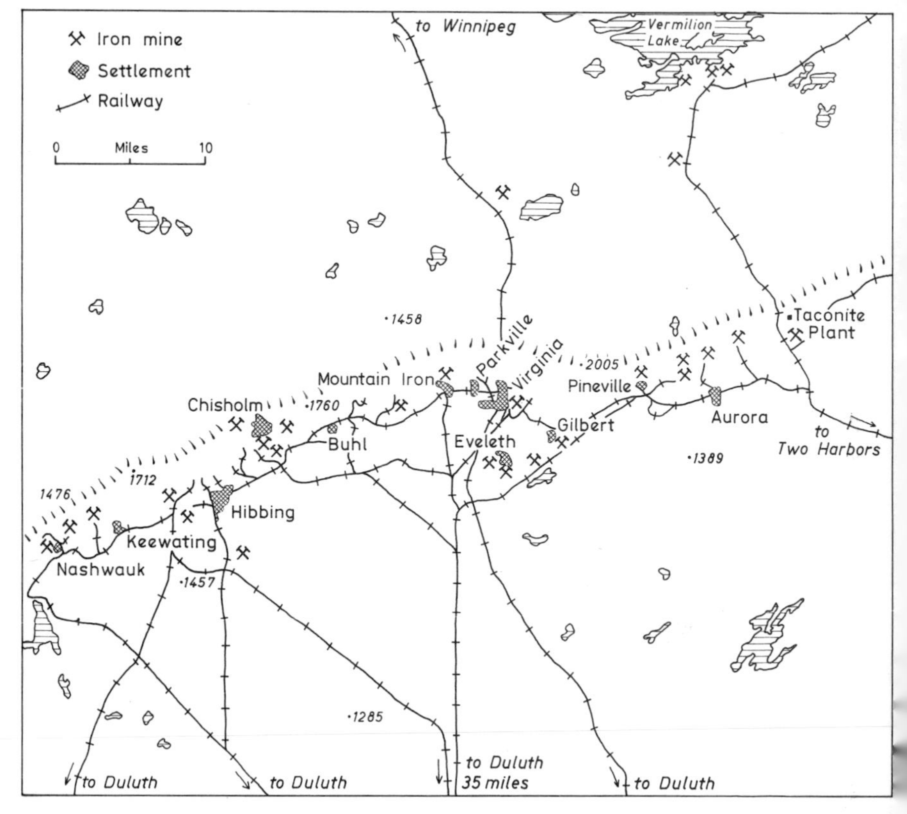

Fig. 11. PART OF MESABI RANGE

Mining is almost continuous throughout the whole 75 miles of the length of the Range, and there is a succession of mining villages, pits, and waste dumps. In the section illustrated there are 12 settlements and 23 mines in addition to the great excavation at Hibbing. The railways send off 'feelers' into each pit, and all this ore is carried southward to the Great Lakes. Some of it is shipped at Two Harbors, but most of it is sent to Duluth. The mining activity is in a setting of woodland and lakes, characteristic of the Laurentian Shield. The hachures represent the steep northern edge of the Range; lakes are indicated by horizontal ruling. For the sake of simplicity the rivers are omitted. *From the official 1:250,000 map, 1954.*

sorted, and emerges in the form of pellets with an iron content of 70 per cent. In its new form this raw material is therefore decidedly richer than the original Mesabi ore, and the steel-makers reap the benefit. Taconite is now challenging imported ore. Two new ports have been developed for the pellet traffic: they are Taconite Harbor (1957) and Silver Bay (1956). A tax concession of 1964 has encouraged the new venture; four plants are under construction, and it seems that the eastern Mesabi Range has a long span of life ahead.

Iron ore is by far the greatest single cargo handled on the lakes:

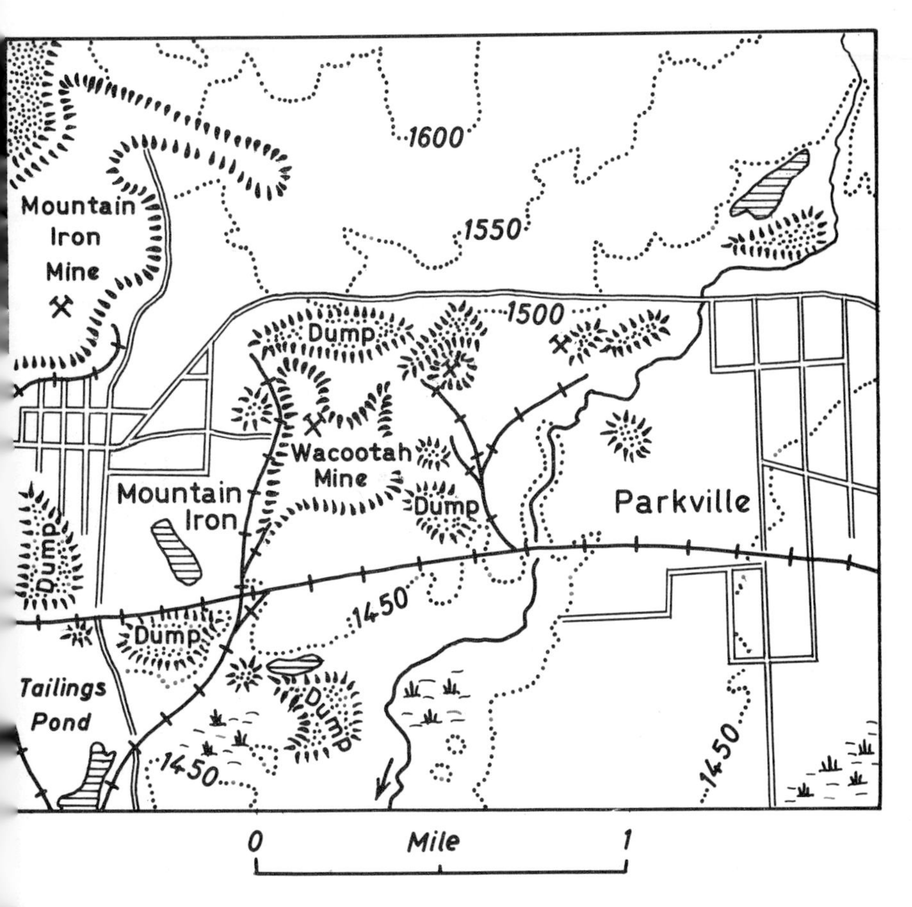

Fig. 12. THE LANDSCAPE OF MESABI RANGE

This is an untidy landscape, in which a confusion of forest, lake, and marsh is interrupted by great pits, waste dumps, and mining villages, tied together by roads and railways. *Based on the official 1:24,000 map, 1951.*

total shipments in 1960 were about 75 million tons, compared with coal, about 43 million; limestone, 25 million; petroleum and grain, each about 13 million tons. These quantities, however, fluctuate quite considerably from year to year.

Whether it is carrying grain, ore, limestone, or coal, a Great Lakes freighter is essentially a self-propelled cargo hull. Almost everything in its design is sacrificed to speed of loading and discharging its cargo. The bridge and accommodation are for'ard, the machinery aft, and between them are the cargo holds in a long row, with automatically controlled hatches, and nothing to impede access. The dimensions of the vessels are customarily related to the locks of the Welland Canal and the St Lawrence river sections of the Seaway, so that they can then trade anywhere within the Great Lakes system. Their size does not prohibit them from ocean navigation, but they are not designed to withstand the Atlantic gales, and it is rare for a 'laker' to leave the lakes.

The Seaway locks are 768 feet long, and the largest of the bulk carriers are 730 feet in length: these are very large ships – nearly three-quarters the length of the *Queen Elizabeth* (1031 feet long), and their appointments rival those of the luxury liner. A vessel of this order carries 18,000 tons of ore, and this is normally loaded in about $3\frac{1}{2}$ hours, though *record* loading times are very much shorter. Loading is by gravity. As the vessel enters the ore port her cargo is waiting in the railway trucks above her berth: these discharge through floor openings which lead to chutes, and so into the vessel's hold. In a battery of docks at Superior there are 1352 chutes, at which 16 freighters can load simultaneously.

Discharging is always a longer process, but it has been greatly speeded by the use of giant scoops which operate at the end of steel arms and travel on rails. Unloading a full freighter takes eight to ten hours; she will then be away again to the upper lakes for another cargo. The round trip usually takes a week.

Let us take a bird's-eye view of the iron-ore traffic during a specimen season (Fig. 13). If we assume that the average freighter carries a little more than 15,000 tons, then to transport a million tons will require the services of about 60 of them, and in a 30-week season this will represent an average of two loads a week. These are round numbers, but they will not be far from the truth.

We should see a crowd of freighters moving in and out of the upper lake harbours. Duluth (shipping 40 million tons a year) is loading 80 vessels a week – 11 or 12 a day – and its neighbour Two Harbors (15 million tons) 30 a week. Port Arthur, the outlet for the Canadian mines of Steep Rock, supplies eight freighters a week, and Silver Bay loads the same number with pellets concentrated from taconite. On the south shore of Lake Superior, Marquette handles ten vessels, and Ashland eight a week. In all 144 ore freighters are loading in Lake Superior each week, and converge on the St Mary's river. Four of them discharge at the Sault Ste Marie steel-works; the rest continue by way of the Soo Canal.

The stream of vessels enters Lake Huron, where nearly a third of

---

Fig. 13. THE GREAT LAKES: IRON-ORE TRAFFIC

The map indicates the iron ranges and the ore ports. The shipping ports are those on Lake Superior together with Escanaba on Lake Michigan; the receiving ports are those on Lake Erie together with Chicago, and all of them have steel-works. The width of the black band is proportional to the volume of ore handled at each port in 1960.

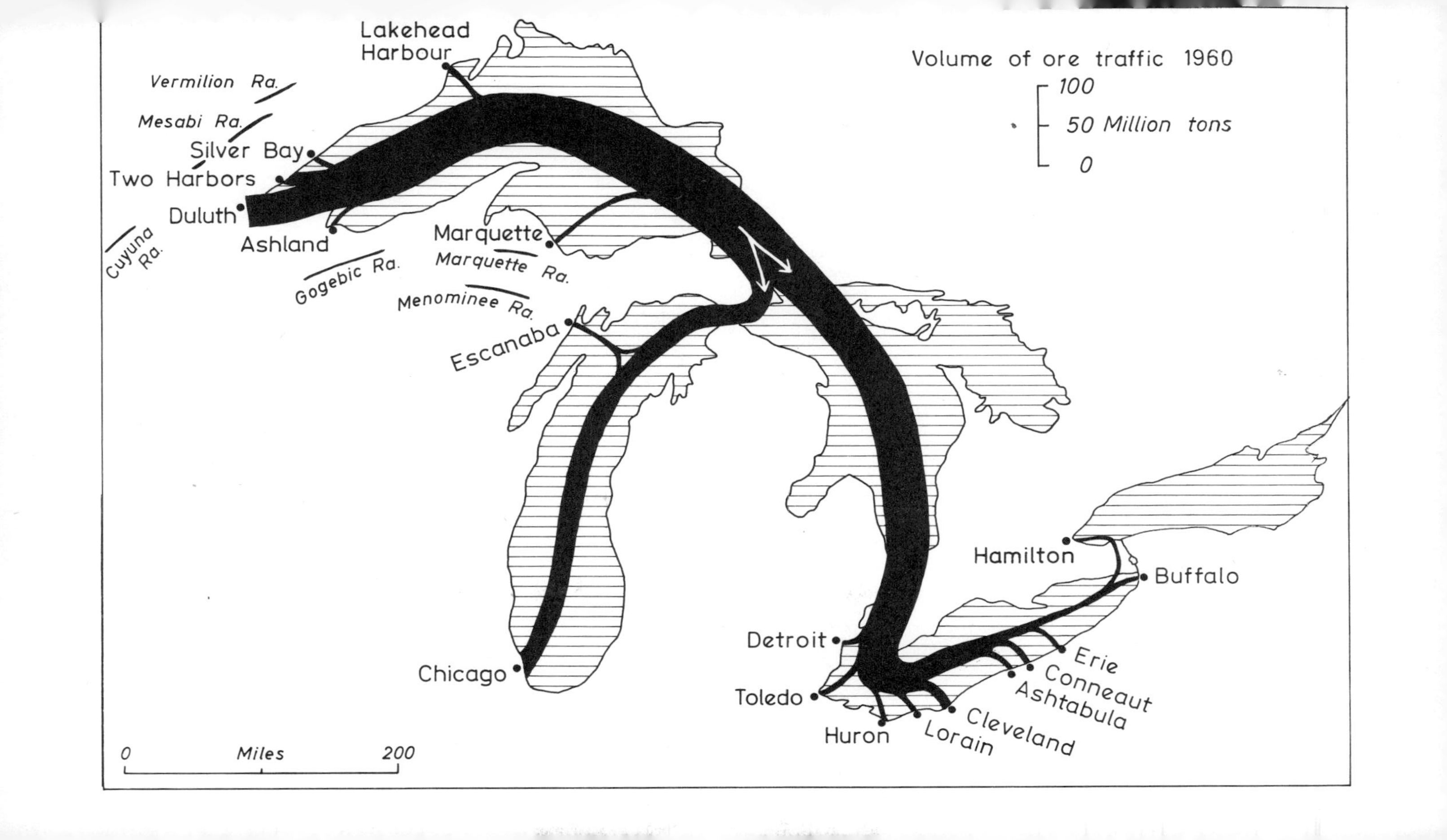

Volume of ore traffic 1960
100
50 Million tons
0
Lakehead Harbour
Vermilion Ra.
Mesabi Ra.
Silver Bay
Two Harbors
Duluth
Cuyuna Ra.
Ashland
Gogebic Ra.
Marquette
Marquette Ra.
Menominee Ra.
Escanaba
Chicago
Detroit
Toledo
Huron
Lorain
Cleveland
Ashtabula
Conneaut
Erie
Hamilton
Buffalo
0
Miles
200

them branch off to the west into Lake Michigan, to supply the steel-works of the Chicago district. On the way they come into contact with a trickle of ten ships a week which have loaded at Escanaba, on Green bay. The main procession, however, continues through the length of Lake Huron, and carefully negotiates the St Clair river, where there is little depth of water to spare. It sheds ten of its number each week to feed the steel-plants of Detroit.

So the fleet of ore-carriers, now somewhat depleted, enters Lake Erie. Here it supplies a whole row of steel-works along the southern shore of the lake, and provides a surplus for the Pittsburgh district. Eight vessels berth at Toledo each week, and 4 at Huron, another 8 at Lorain, 22 at Cleveland, 14 at Ashtabula and another 15 at Conneaut, 6 at Erie, and 12 at Buffalo. A mere trickle of 6 vessels a week remains to pass through the Welland Canal for the steel-works of Hamilton.

The numbers may vary slightly, but they give a fair picture of the shape of the traffic. A new element since the opening of the Seaway is the small but growing stream of vessels entering with ore from Labrador. Seven Islands is handling about 22 ore-carriers a week, but at present most of them are moving eastward.

Coal, Limestone, and Grain

The coal traffic differs in several respects from the ore trade. The average journey is shorter, for much of the coal traffic takes place within Lake Erie. In many cases there is a relatively longer haul from the coal-fields to the lakeshore compared with the corresponding journey from the ore-field. The railway therefore seriously competes with the lake carrier for the coal traffic, and the Chicago steel-works are in fact supplied by rail in spite of their frontage on Lake Michigan.

Nevertheless, the row of Lake Erie ports from Toledo to Erie is busily engaged in shipping coal, usually in the same vessels which have discharged ore. Toledo ships by far the largest quantities, and handles nearly half of all the coal loaded on the lakes: its dominating position is due partly to its location near the largest and expanding sections of the Appalachian coalfields – in southern West Virginia and eastern Kentucky and Tennessee. But Toledo enjoys the additional advantage of a southerly latitude; the port itself is open throughout the winter, and its extensive trade with the Detroit area proceeds the whole year round.

Almost every other port on the lakes receives coal: Hamilton, Detroit, and Sault Ste Marie for their steel-works, the others for power stations, factories, and domestic heating. Detroit, receiving about 10 million tons annually, is the largest unloader; Chicago and Duluth each receive between 5 and 10 million tons; Toronto, Sault St Marie, Green Bay,

Milwaukee, Buffalo, and Montreal each receive more than a million tons.

The limestone traffic has its own distinct character. Limestone is widely distributed through the continent, but for steel-works with a lake frontage it is economic to transport their fluxing limestone over long distances once the initial expense of quarrying and loading is covered. The limestone of the Great Lakes commerce is all quarried in the district of northern Michigan close to the junction of the three upper lakes; the rocks on the north shore consist of the Niagara Limestone (Silurian) and on the south shore of Devonian Limestone.

The trade is handled by six large private ports, of which Calcite is the chief: nearly 15 million tons of crushed limestone are loaded annually at this busy port, representing about 30 freighter-loads a week during the season; and this must certainly be the world's greatest limestone port. The other ports are Stoneport and Alpena (a few miles east of Calcite), Port Inland and Dolomite (on the north shore of Lake Michigan), and Drummond Island (fronting the North Channel of Lake Huron). Each of them handles between 1 and 5 million tons annually. Many ports receive comparatively small quantities of stone for cement and chemical industries, but the main consumers are the steel centres of Chicago, Detroit, Buffalo, and the Lake Erie ports.

The grain traffic too has its own character. In contrast to the ore trade, it is competing with other routes, for, as we shall see, more than half of the prairie grain moves westward by rail to the Pacific, and small quantities are sent northward to Churchill (p. 274). Unlike the other three cargoes, the destination of most of the prairie grain lies overseas and not within the Great Lakes region. The traffic is largely in Canadian hands, for more than half the total carried on the lakes is shipped at the Lakehead Harbour (Fort William–Port Arthur). Handling about 7 million tons annually, this is the world's leading grain port.

The largest of the grain freighters carry cargoes of about 27,000 tons (over a million bushels), which is equivalent to the crop grown over 50,000 acres of prairie-land. The entire season's movement through Lakehead Harbour is roughly equal to the loads of 1170 trains, each comprising a hundred 60-ton wagons. In terms of port traffic, it represents about 14 freighters a week.

Grain is shipped also at Duluth, Chicago, and Toledo, but the proportions are smaller, and wheat gives place to maize and soya flour. Duluth ships about 4 million tons, Chicago 1 million, and Toledo about half a million. The grain-carriers mingle with the main stream of ore-carriers, and many of them discharge at Buffalo, which is one of the world's largest flour-milling ports: it supplies the cities of the eastern United States with their bread. Most of the grain destined for overseas markets continues through the Welland Canal and the St Lawrence

Seaway, to be transhipped into ocean carriers at Montreal and (in smaller quantities) at Sorel, Trois Rivières, and Quebec. Though ocean vessels can and do trade throughout the Great Lakes system, there is no sign that they will take over any significant share of the grain traffic.

The St Lawrence Seaway

In the strict sense, the St Lawrence Seaway is that part of the great inland waterway which extends from Montreal to Lake Ontario; but though the main construction and dredging have taken place in this relatively short stretch of the St Lawrence valley, deepening of the shipping channel has been necessary in other parts of the system and in almost every harbour, so that the effects of the Seaway have been felt throughout the whole of the Great Lakes system.

We may preface our remarks on the Seaway by a glance at the earlier works in the St Lawrence river above Montreal. Here, as we have seen (p. 32), the river is cutting through a narrow neck of Pre-Cambrian rocks which join the Adirondack mountains to the Laurentian Shield. About 1818, men began to clear away some of the larger rocks that obstructed navigation at the rapids: small boats had previously 'shot' the rapids downstream, and now they could be towed upstream. But the Erie Canal pointed the way, and in the year of its opening (1825) the Canadians inaugurated a more modest waterway to bypass the Lachine rapids. It was 9 miles long and provided with seven locks, and it accepted boats of 4½ feet draft.

The remaining four sets of rapids were not overcome till the 1840's, when a stretch of 26 miles of the river was improved by the building of the Cornwall Canal, Farran's Point Canal, and Galops and Rapide Plat canals (Fig. 14). All five were remodelled and enlarged during the 1880's to a depth of 14 feet; and until the building of the Seaway this limited the size of the vessels trading between Lake Ontario and Montreal, or entering the Great Lakes from the Atlantic. Large lake freighters could not reach Montreal, and their cargo was transferred at Port Colborne into 'canallers', designed to fit the St Lawrence canals. Transhipment itself was costly; and the canallers, moreover, could carry only about 100,000 bushels of grain – ten of them were needed to do the work of one of the largest lakers. An important economic advantage of the Seaway is that it has overcome this expensive process, and it is clear that most of the canallers are destined for the scrapyard.

Coupled with the need to improve navigation was the immediate and growing necessity for power: indeed, it is doubtful whether the Seaway would ever have been built without the desperate need for energy in northern New York state and southern Ontario. Yet in the International rapids section of the St Lawrence there was over 2 million horse-power of potential energy running to waste.

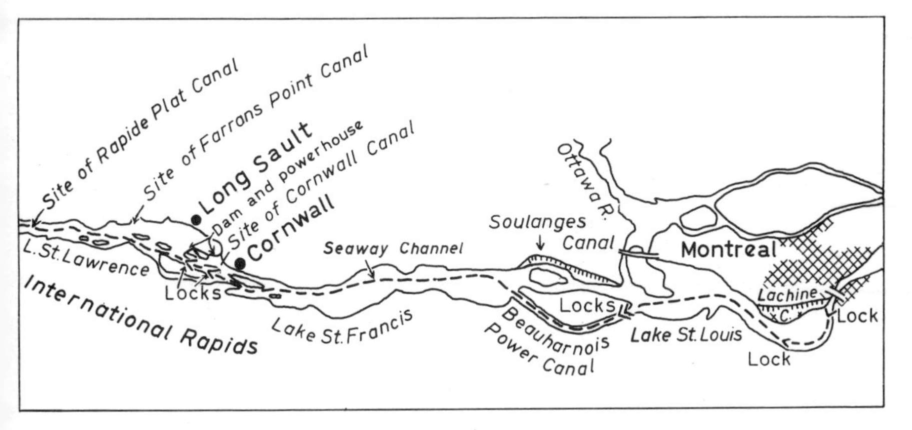

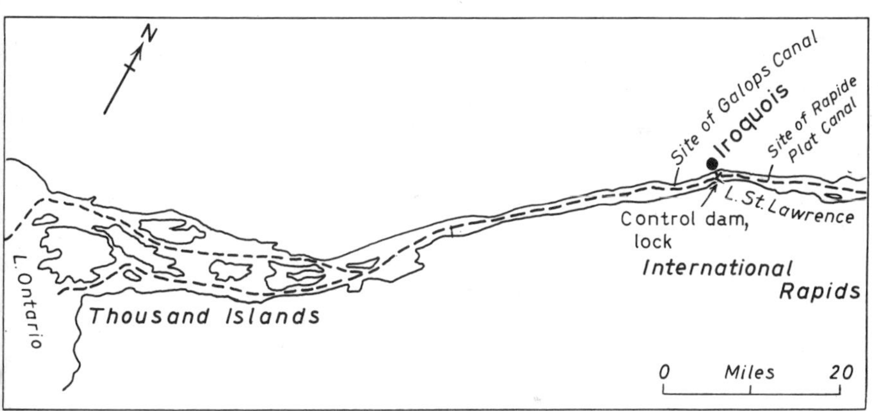

Fig. 14. THE ST LAWRENCE SEAWAY

The 187-mile Seaway is illustrated from Montreal (*upper diagram*) to Lake Ontario (*lower diagram*) with a slight overlap of about 13 miles in the two diagrams. The old canals on the north (Canadian) side were built in the 1840's to avoid several sets of rapids in the St Lawrence; they were later deepened to 14 feet. Only two of them remain in use: the others have been flooded or interrupted by the Seaway works. The broken line indicates the course of the Seaway channel.

The idea of the Seaway can be traced back at least to the 1890's, when Narcisse Cantin campaigned for a ship canal: in 1919 he published his plan for a 30-foot waterway linking together the Great Lakes and connecting with Lake Champlain and the sea. The power potential of the rapids was early recognized; and immediately the Ontario Hydro-Electric Power Commission was formed (in 1906) it set its engineers to survey the rapids.

The first joint examination by the United States and Canada took place in 1926, and after a year's investigation they presented a comprehensive report; but no action followed. On the Canadian side, however, two important projects paved the way for the Seaway. Reconstruction of the Welland Canal (1913–32) was carried out with the dimensions of a Seaway in mind; and the company building the Beauharnois Power Canal was required by the Government to provide at the same time a navigation channel 27 feet deep and 600 feet wide. This canal, opened in 1929, was eventually incorporated in the Seaway.

It is clear that the main impetus for the Seaway was originating from Canada. The Second World War delayed the project; but at its conclusion the Canadian Government felt that it now had sufficient resources to proceed with the Seaway – if necessary, alone. In 1950 Canadian statesmen made this public, and in the following year Parliament enacted the legislation necessary to enable work to begin. At last the United States was roused into action; but another four years passed before the way was clear to begin. In August 1954 the men and machines of both nations began to labour together in the great project, and in April 1959 the Seaway was open.

A vessel from the Atlantic enters the Seaway at Montreal, in the form of a great man-made trench 200 feet wide and over 50 feet deep cut into the south side of the river, where there is little urban congestion. The artificial cut passes alternately over land and through lakes (Fig. 33). The first two locks, near the Lachine rapids, raise the ship 21½ and 36½ feet. Thirty-one miles from Montreal the vessel enters the Beauharnois Canal by two more locks, which raise it to the level of Lake St Francis. Above the lake the former International rapids have disappeared below a reservoir covering 100 square miles; so have the old 14-foot canals, 225 farms, 6 villages and towns, 35 miles of highway, 40 miles of railway, and the homes of 6500 people. Only a desperate shortage of power could justify so drastic a remedy: this power is produced near Cornwall, Ontario, from two identical power-houses, one each side of the international boundary, and each with a capacity of 1·1 million horse-power. Thus the power is shared equally between the United States and Canada.

Two more locks lift the ship 80 feet into the new St Lawrence Lake, and at its far end a final lock raises it a further 6 feet or so to the level of Lake Ontario, whose height is now governed by a control dam at Iroquois.

Above the main works a great deal of dredging was needed. Systematic deepening was undertaken in the 65-mile stretch of beautiful wooded islands (the Thousand Isles); the Welland Canal, formerly maintained at a depth of 25 feet, was dredged to 27 feet; and the Detroit and St Clair rivers were appropriately deepened too. To reap the full benefits of the Seaway most of the lake ports needed to dredge their main berths. By 1962 this had been accomplished at Duluth–Superior, Lakehead, and Buffalo. Toledo attained it in 1963 and Cleveland in 1965.

Small ocean vessels have been trading with the upper lake ports for many years: there were regular sailings between Manchester and Chicago and Cleveland long before the Seaway was built; but from 1959 large ocean vessels were able to trade directly with the lake ports: it is estimated that now 80 per cent. of the world's shipping has access to the lakes. Some vessels are being built especially for the Great Lakes trade, such as the *Manchester Commerce* (8724 gross tons), built in 1963, and the largest vessel to be owned in Manchester. Labrador iron can now move in large ore-carriers from Seven Islands and from other Quebec North Shore ports to Hamilton and the Lake Erie ports; and, as we have seen, grain can now reach Montreal in large freighters without a break in bulk.

As soon as the Seaway opened, the volume of cargo using the waterway between Lake Ontario and Montreal rose from 11·8 million tons (in the 1958 season) to 20·1 million tons (in 1959), while there was a corresponding increase in the Welland Canal traffic (from 21·7 to 26·9 million tons). Ninety-one per cent. of the cargoes using the Lake Ontario-to-Montreal waterway were in bulk.

New large freighters are being built; the lake ports are flourishing; foreign vessels are appearing in larger numbers; new cargoes are appearing, and the volume of traffic is expanding, as the following figures show:

St Lawrence Seaway: Cargoes carried, Montreal to Lake Ontario

Year	*Million tons*
1961	23·4
1962	25·6
1963	30·9
1964	39·3
1965	43·4
1966	49·2

Unfortunately, the toll charges were based upon an over-optimistic estimate of the rate of increase in traffic, and some revision of the financial basis has been necessary; there have been delays at the opening and closing of the season, but this should be rectified when current improvements on the Welland Canal are complete. It is clear that the construction of the Seaway has justified the faith of its early promoters and the energy of their successors.

TOWNS

We cannot examine the setting and functions of all the many lakeside and riverside towns of the Great Lakes system, but it is necessary to discuss some of the more important ones. We begin at the head of the lakes and work gradually 'down-stream'.

The Lakehead Cities (Fort William–Port Arthur)

In 1958, by an Act of the Federal Parliament, the two harbours of Port Arthur and Fort William were combined to form a single port, so giving legal recognition to what had for long been an established fact. The port lies on Thunder bay, 35 miles long and 10 miles wide, and sheltered from the main expanse of Lake Superior by a peninsula and group of islands (Fig. 15).

Fort William began as an Indian encampment. Close by was built the headquarters of the fur-trading Northwest Company, the rival of the Hudson's Bay Company until 1821, when the two merged. It stands at the mouth of a considerable stream, the Kaministiquia, whose navigable lower section is now bordered by grain elevators and coal and oil docks. The future of the town was assured when the main line of the Canadian Pacific was routed through it; and soon the prairie wheat, collected at Winnipeg, was being shipped from this point.

The commercial centre of Port Arthur lies about four miles north of Fort William. Formerly an open roadstead, it is now sheltered behind five miles of breakwaters. The two towns are of almost equal size, and have a combined population of 77,000. Despite its rather small population, this is the world's largest grain port and, in terms of the volume of its shipping, the third port of Canada.

We have already mentioned the grain and ore traffic; the forest resources of the district add to its commerce. There are four pulp and paper mills and two sawmills in the area, and the port ships about half a million tons of pulpwood annually. Nearly half a million tons of petroleum products from the prairies are handled, and in 1964 came the first experimental shipments of potash, from mines in Saskatchewan.

The Seaway has greatly stimulated the trade of the port: the 11 million tons of cargo handled in 1958 had risen by 1964 to 19 million tons, and the 28 ocean vessels to 126. In 1962 a fine new cargo terminal was opened, covering 500 acres.

Duluth–Superior (1960 population: 144,763)

Duluth and Superior, at the most westerly point of Lake Superior, face each other across the mouth of the St Louis river, one town being in Minnesota and the other in Wisconsin. In 1860 there were only 70 white inhabitants at this spot, and its rise to become the world's greatest iron-ore port was a result of the exploitation of the Mesabi Range. In 1915 a steel-works was established, following a promise that ore used locally would enjoy lower taxes than that shipped beyond the state border. Coking coal arrives from the Lake Erie ports as a return cargo for ore;

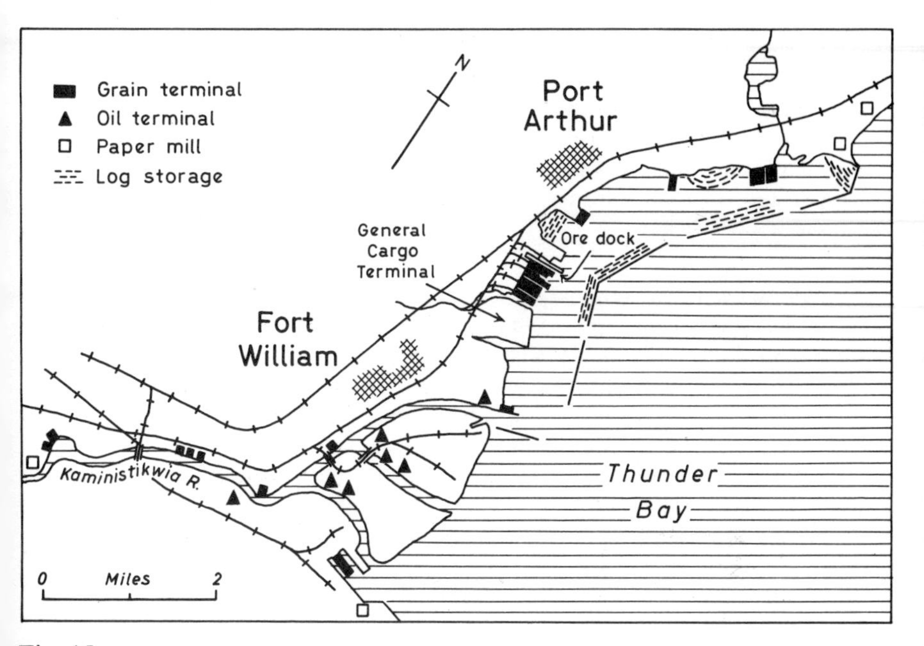

Fig. 15. LAKEHEAD HARBOUR

The built-up areas of Port Arthur and Fort William have now merged; cross-hatching indicates the commercial centres of the two towns. Essentially this is a grain port: it possesses 26 elevators with 129 loading spouts; but it is also the outlet for the iron ores of Steep Rock, and the diagram indicates other port activities. The general-cargo terminal was opened in 1962 to accommodate the increasing traffic in general cargo following the completion of the Seaway.

but Duluth suffers from a location far from the established markets for steel, and its expansion has been less than that of more favourably placed centres. Its capacity is about a million tons annually.

Duluth–Superior is also a considerable grain port, and a record cargo of 173 million bushels (1962) allows comparison with the 450 million or so shipped annually from Lakehead Harbour.

Sault Ste Marie (population: about 50,000)

First an Indian village, later a trading-post and mission station, Sault Ste Marie owes its modern growth to the harnessing of the St Mary's Falls. As early as 1902 a power-station was built and a steel-works established to utilize some of the power; in the early years of the century this helped to supply the enormous demand for steel rails in the expanding prairie railway network. To some extent the Sault Steelworks have continued this interest: their present capacity is about $1\frac{1}{2}$ million tons a year.

Associated companies mine iron ore about 100 miles to the north, transport it over their own railway system, and ship it in their own vessels from the port of Michipicoten. This is a growing enterprise for which 200 new rail trucks and two large new ore-carriers have been built. The commerce of the town may well expand with the growing importance of road transport, for there is only one other land crossing of the upper lakes.

Milwaukee (1960 population: 741,324)

A mere village in 1835, Milwaukee (Wis.) received its city charter in 1846. It became the landing-point for immigrants, many of them German, and was soon shipping grain from the newly opened American Middle West. Like many other lake cities, it has grown round a river-mouth, but the civic authorities have wisely focused their port development on the lake frontage rather than on the congested river-banks.

The port traffic is relatively small: it handles about half a million tons per annum compared with the 19 million at the lakehead. About half the total of exports consists of grain, and half of general cargoes. In spite of inadequate depths for the largest vessels, since the opening of the Seaway the number of scheduled oversea services has grown from 26 to 48. Deepening of the main channels from 21 feet to 28 feet began in 1965, and will undoubtedly be reflected in increased commerce.

Milwaukee is primarily an engineering centre: its manufactures include diesel and petrol engines; electrical, mining, and road machinery; cranes, shovels, tractors and farm machinery.

Chicago (1960 population, metropolitan area: 6·8 million)

Chicago, the second city of the United States, is outstanding on several counts: it is at the same time the world's largest stock market and its greatest railway centre, its biggest steel-producer and its largest inland port.

Yet in thc 1820's what is now a metropolis was only a hamlet of 14 dwellings. The site, where the Chicago river joins Lake Michigan, was first occupied in 1804, when the United States Government established Fort Dearborn as a frontier military post in Indian territory. It became a county seat in 1831, when its population was less than 100, and a 'city' in 1837, when pigs were still roaming the streets and the water-supply was from a single well.

The seeds of its later commercial importance were sown in the 1840's when the mouth of the Chicago river was improved and the old glacial meltwater channel to the south-west was utilized for the construction of a canal. Rail connection with the east was established in 1852, and the stage was set for the future growth of the city.

The rise of Chicago from a centre of 307,000 in 1870 to one of 1·7 million in 1900 was due to two main assets in its general setting. On the one hand the opening up of the Middle West made Chicago, the port at its eastern limit, the focus of a great trade in farm products, and in particular livestock. On the other, its situation near the southern end of Lake Michigan made it a focus of land routes as they rounded the lake, and in particular of railways. As a market for the Middle West the city developed its vast stockyards and its immense meat-packing industries: and as a centre for transport it became the terminal for 33 trunk railways, established locomotive works, and later became an important airway centre.

Its position in the middle of the nation has made it the most convenient location for conferences, and the same advantage has led to the establishment here of the three largest mail-order firms in the country. In the later phases of its growth Chicago has relinquished some of its food-processing functions in favour of other Middle West cities, but it has increased its commercial, industrial, and port activities. With a total traffic of 60–70 million tons of cargo, Chicago is the leading port on the Great Lakes, though Duluth–Superior, with over 50 million tons, is not far behind. While Duluth is almost entirely an exporter, most of the traffic of Chicago is inward.

The original port was at the mouth of the Chicago river, and this area, protected by breakwaters, still handles large quantities of Canadian newsprint, and of coal, sand and gravel, and cement. But only about 4 per cent. of the total trade of the port is now handled here.

The successor to the old Illinois and Michigan Canal is the Chicago Drainage Canal, opened in 1900, and its Chicago terminals handle large quantities of petroleum products, coal, sand and gravel – in all about 10 million tons annually.

Nevertheless, the major part of the port has developed on the southern outskirts of the metropolis, where there are three distinct harbours. All are concerned particularly with raw materials for the steel industry: ore from Lake Superior and limestone from north Michigan.

The mouth of the Calumet river was selected in 1880 as the site for the first steel-works of the region: now this section of the port handles about 24 million tons of materials a year. A few miles to the east is Indiana Harbor: essentially this is a short length of ship canal, protected by breakwaters and lined by chemical plants, oil terminals and refineries, and two large steel-plants. Indiana Harbor receives ore, limestone, and coal, and ships petroleum products: in all it handles about 18 million tons of freight.

Still farther east, in Indiana, is Gary. Here in 1907 the United States Steel Corporation opened an immense steel-works and named it after its chairman, Judge E. H. Gary. With a capacity of about 8 million tons, and covering 4500 acres, this is among the largest steel plants in the world. Its port handles over 7 million tons of cargo a year.

The Chicago district is the greatest of all the American steel centres. Its total capacity is 27 million tons a year – larger than that of the whole of the United Kingdom. Its lakeside situation allows it to import its ore and limestone cheaply, but its coking coal arrives by rail from Kentucky and Tennessee. The industry supplies the locomotive works of the city, and the local demand for constructional steel, the steel sheets needed in a thriving canning industry, and the engineering requirements of the great farming region to the west.

Detroit (1960 population: 1,670,144)

We have already noticed the rise of the automobile industry at Detroit (p. 6), and may now examine its activities in relation to the Great Lakes. The early name of the city suggests its origin: Fort Pontchartrain du Détroit – that is, Fort Pontchartrain of the Strait. It was founded as early as 1701 – a fortified fur-trading post where a narrowing of the channel between Lakes Erie and Huron gave the opportunity for a ferry crossing. Its growth has been connected largely with transport industries. The stimulus of the Erie Canal was of great benefit to Detroit, whose population doubled every decade between 1830 and 1860.

Detroit produced steam-engines in the 1860's, locomotives in the 1870's, and began to manufacture the early automobiles in the 1890's. By 1904 it had emerged as one of the leading car centres in the United States; now it is the greatest vehicle centre in the world. Side by side with the automobile industry have developed shipbuilding and the steel industry. The city is well placed to assemble the fuel and raw materials, and finds an inexhaustible market in the vehicle trade. The combined capacities of its four steel plants amount to nearly 8 million tons per annum, and this is the largest of the Lake Erie steel centres.

The shipping lane between Toledo and Detroit is not interrupted in winter, and Detroit receives 10 million tons of coal a year – more than any other port on the lakes. Four-fifths of the trade of the port is linked with the needs of the steel industry. There is an important local resource in the shape of a 34-foot bed of rock salt 1100 feet below the city, and this has aided the rise of manufactures of both pharmaceutical products and heavy chemicals.

Toledo (1965 population, estimated: 363,297)

Toledo (Ohio) received its name only in 1833, and the reason for this choice is not apparent. The town compares with Chicago in its general position, in that both are at the beginning of former lake spillways, and

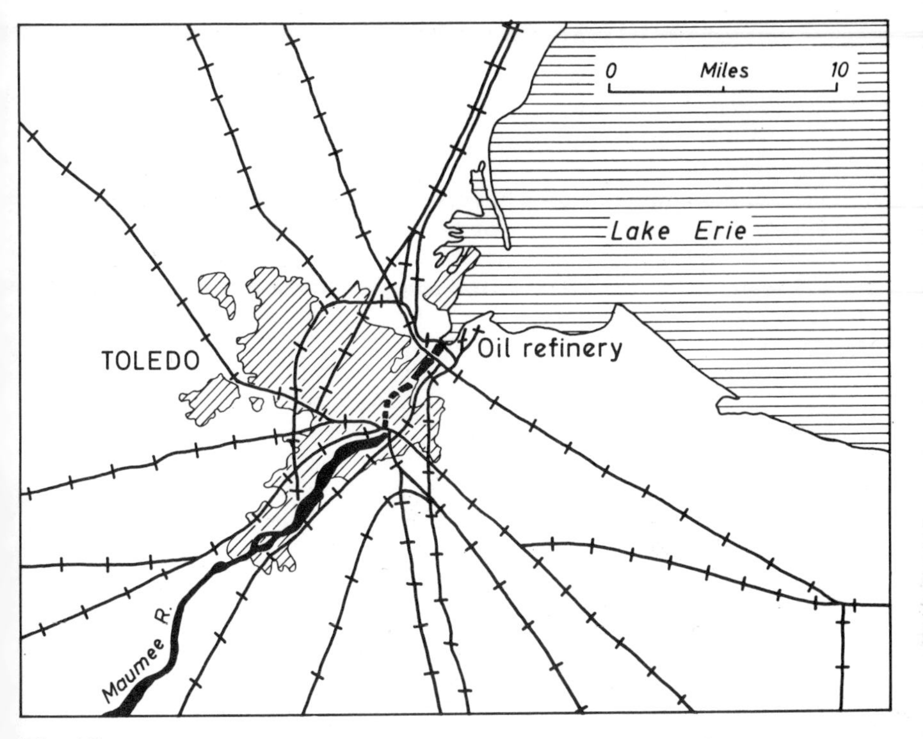

Fig. 16. THE SETTING OF TOLEDO

Land routes are forced to round the lake so that they converge on the site of Toledo; westward communication has been facilitated by the former spillway, now occupied by the Maumee river. Toledo is the world's greatest coal-shipping port.

so in addition to their lake frontages have easy communications to the west. The eastern portion of the Lake Erie spillway is now occupied by the Maumee river, which is the largest affluent of the Great Lakes; and Toledo grew up about five miles from its mouth, where a narrowing of the river decided the lowest crossing-point (Fig. 16).

The town has developed miscellaneous engineering industries together with shipbuilding and oil-refining, and the occurrence of local high-quality glass sands has encouraged the establishment of glass-making. Commercially Toledo is of interest as the world's greatest coal-shipping port (p. 42): its 1964 shipment of $31\frac{1}{2}$ million tons has created a new world record. Other outward cargoes include $1\frac{1}{2}$ million tons of grain and 2 million tons of petroleum products from the seven local oil-refineries. Inward, the chief cargo is iron ore (about 5 million tons annually). Since the opening of the Seaway the port authority has constructed six new berths at the mouth of the Maumee, specially designed for the overseas traffic.

Cleveland (population of urban area, 1960: 1,784,991)

In 1786 a trading-post was established where the Cuyahoga river entered Lake Erie, and ten years later a town was laid out there by the agent of the Connecticut Land Company, Moses Cleaveland. The town did not grow to any size until communications with the interior were improved. The first stage was the building of a canal, making use of the valley of the Cuyahoga: this, the Ohio Canal, reached Akron in 1827 and the Ohio river in 1832. At the same time the harbour was improved, and

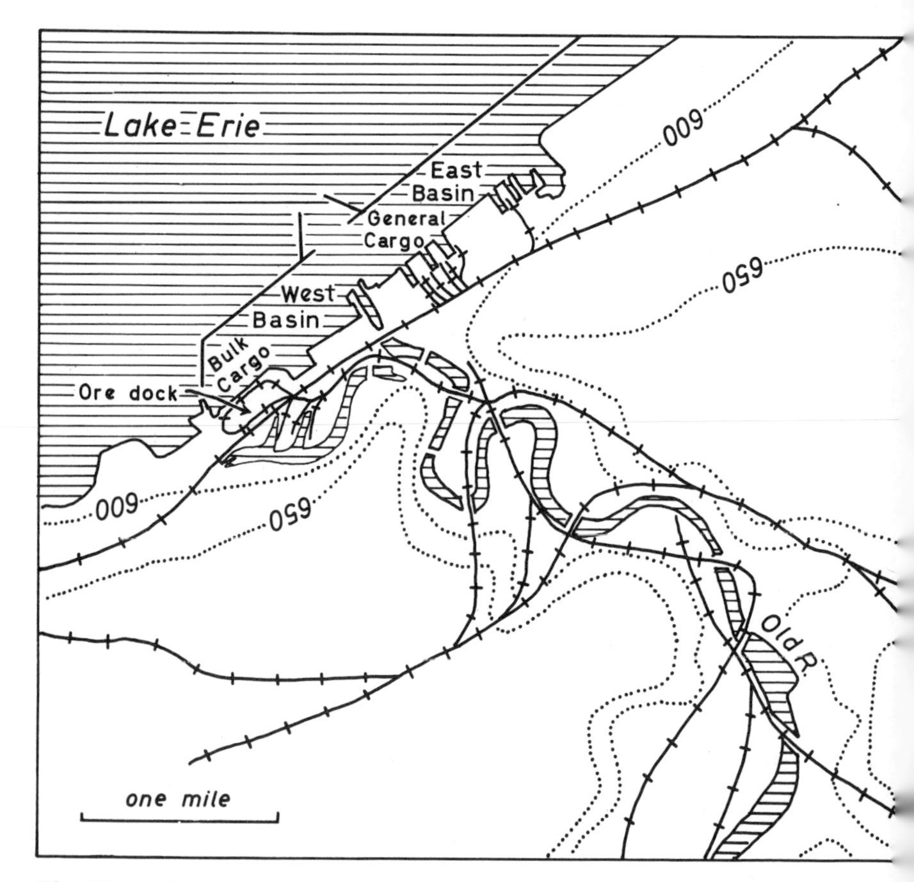

Fig. 17. THE CORE OF CLEVELAND

The river is the Cuyahoga: it has been provided with a new mouth, and its old course has bee converted into a dock. The newer docks front the lake. The West Basin is the main ore dock, an supplies the local steel-works, which are situated about five miles up-stream; it also forwards larg quantities of ore inland. Almost the whole of the area in the figure is built up, and represents only small part of the modern city.

Cleveland now became the outlet for the farm produce and the coal of the productive districts to the south. The building of railways in the 1850's strengthened the city's link with its hinterland, and its population grew rapidly, from a mere 1076 in 1830 to 43,417 in 1860, and 261,353 in 1890.

In modern Cleveland we see a port arrangement which is common to several lake cities (Fig. 17). By the river-mouth is the older, congested section of the port; here the wharves are mainly linked with industrial plants – steel-works, cement-works, flour-mills, chemical plants, and oil installations. The newer section of the port is its lake frontage, protected behind five miles of breakwater: here are the bulk-cargo basin, dredged to 28 feet, and the general cargo terminal, dredged to 27 feet. In contrast, the river wharves in 1965 had limiting depths of 23 feet.

Cleveland has an important steel industry (capacity about 5·4 million tons), but it imports far more ore than it uses: the surplus is for the Pittsburgh and neighbouring steel districts, and to these we now turn our attention.

The Appalachian Coal and Steel Districts

The northern flanks of the Appalachians do not drain to the Great Lakes but to the Gulf of Mexico by way of the Ohio river; but their economic fortunes are so closely linked with the navigation of the lakes that we have no hesitation in discussing them here.

No other major coalfield in the world can compare in physical advantages with those of West Virginia and western Pennsylvania. The chief seam – the Pittsburgh Seam – is close to the surface and lies almost horizontal over wide areas.

In western Pennsylvania it is rare for a shaft to descend more than two or three hundred feet, while in the United Kingdom many shafts are ten times as deep. Moreover, the river systems have entrenched themselves into the plateau, so that the coal seams are often exposed in the valley sides (Fig. 18). Vertical shafts are then replaced by horizontal galleries – conditions which are virtually unknown in Britain.

The Pittsburgh Seam is approximately six feet thick. This is ideal, for when the coal is removed the miner can comfortably stand in the gallery which takes its place. If the seam were much thicker it would be difficult to prop up the roof. Since the seams are horizontal and uninterrupted by faulting it is possible to make the maximum use of mechanical cutting and loading. All these advantages result in important economies in mining, so that the output per man is far greater than in the United Kingdom coal industry.

The river systems have been rejuvenated, so that all the main streams are flanked by level terraces, well above the reach of possible floods: these provide attractive sites for mining villages and level routes for

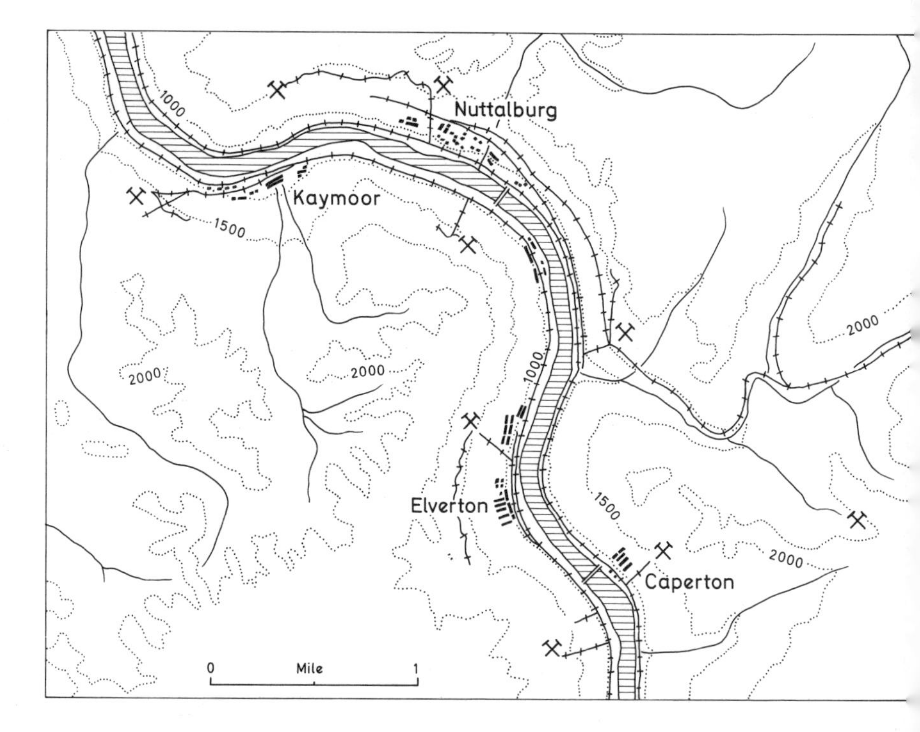

Fig. 18. CONDITIONS IN THE APPALACHIAN COALFIELDS

The map illustrates the New River district of West Virginia, just east of Fayetteville. The river ha entrenched itself 1000 feet below the plateau surface and the chief coal seam outcrops in the valle sides at about 1500 feet above sea-level. Galleries are driven in at this height, and the coal is lowere by short stretches of railway track to the main line in the valley. This and the mining villages stan on the river terrace about 50 feet above water-level. *Based on the official 1 : 62,500 map.*

roads and railways. In many instances the coal is brought to the surface above the terraces, and can thus be loaded by gravity into the railway trucks. Two of the major streams of the district have been canalized – these are the Youghiogheny and the Monongahela – and they carry a heavy coal traffic. Close to their junction with the Ohio stands Pittsburgh, which is therefore exceptionally well served by roads, railways, and navigable rivers.

Pittsburgh (population, 1960: city, 604,332; metropolitan area, 2,405,435)

The first permanent settlement on the site of Pittsburgh was the French Fort Duquesne, which was established in 1754. Captured by the English four years later, it was rebuilt and renamed Fort Pitt after the elder Pitt. The civil settlement that grew round it became in the early nineteenth century a river port and outfitting centre for pioneers moving westward by boat along the Ohio river.

From about 1850 onward the town grew rapidly, for the area was rich in natural resources of timber, brick clays, glass sands, petroleum, and natural gas; above all, it was close to the richest and most accessible deposits of coal in the whole continent. When the Lake Superior ores were developed, Pittsburgh became the headquarters of the United States steel industry, and it remains a very large producer of steel, though it has now been surpassed in capacity by the Chicago district.

The original site of the settlement, strategically placed in the angle between the Monongahela and Allegheny rivers, now is occupied by the business centre of the city. With its skyscrapers, this is the 'golden triangle'. Industry and working-class houses occupy the valley floors, while the residential suburbs are on the hillsides and plateau tops. There are three universities in this great city.

Pittsburgh lies within a few miles of productive mines which yield a high-quality coking coal: 'Connellsville coke' is named from the small town 40 miles south-east of the city. Its iron ore, originally produced locally, is now shipped a thousand miles or so by freighter from the Lake Superior ranges, and transferred into railway wagons at Cleveland or Ashtabula to travel the final 130 miles to Pittsburgh. The coal is relatively cheap, compared with other steel centres; the iron ore is relatively expensive.

The total capacity of all the Pittsburgh steel-plants amounts to about 20 million tons per annum – approximately equal to that of all the Lake Erie shore towns, but rather less than that of Chicago (*cf.* p. 52). Steelmaking has extended into the neighbouring valleys, and there are plants at Weirton and Steubenville on the Ohio lower down-stream, and at Monessen and Johnstown nearer to the Appalachians, as well as a large industry at Youngstown, halfway to Cleveland. The total capacity of all these plants is equal to that of the whole steel industry of the United Kingdom.

Pittsburgh steel supplies the locomotive and motor-car industries and the electrical engineering, mining, and oil industries; and it is nearer than most other steel-making districts to the concentrations of population from which these demands arise.

While the coal of western Pennsylvania is linked closely with steelmaking, that of the West Virginia field, which is focused on the Kanawha river and its tributaries, is transported to other areas for use. Much of it is sent by rail to Toledo, and reaches all parts of the basin of the Great Lakes: large quantities are also forwarded by rail to Chicago for use in the steel industries there.

Buffalo (population of urban area, 1960: 1,034,370)

The key to the importance of Buffalo (N.Y.) lies in its situation in relation to Niagara Falls (Fig. 10, p. 33). It was the first lake port above this barrier, and it sent a stream of immigrants westward. It was the barrier of the Falls which acted as a spur to the construction of the Erie Canal.

The town was laid out in 1801–02 where the small and winding Cayuga creek reaches Lake Erie. In 1825 a harbour was constructed to act as the western terminal of the newly opened Erie Canal (p. 32), and soon Buffalo became an important transhipment centre. The steel industry began about 1900, when the former Lackawanna Steel Company left Scranton (eastern Pennsylvania) in search of a site which offered cheaper ore and an expanding market. Its choice of Buffalo has been justified, for the recent expansion of the steel industry has been far greater in the lakeshore districts than in older inland areas.

Until the opening of the Seaway much of the Canadian wheat was sent eastward by rail through the Mohawk valley for shipment from New York. The export traffic now uses the Seaway; but prairie grain destined for the Atlantic cities is milled at Buffalo, which has become one of the largest milling centres in the world.

The Buffalo district is one of expanding population and, close to the power-plants of Niagara, of cheap electricity. The city harbour has been deepened to 27 feet, and since the opening of the Seaway its trade has been greatly increased.

Hamilton (population, 1961: 273,991)

Hamilton (Ont.) has an importance greater than its relatively small size might suggest. With less than a sixth of the population of Toronto, it is the busiest harbour on Lake Ontario, and the value of its industrial output places it third among the Canadian cities.

Standing at the western tip of the lake, Hamilton has grown as a meeting-point of land routes which skirt the lake. The city occupies a series of former lake terraces which overlook the present lakeshore and are backed by the Niagara scarp. This formerly limited the expansion of the city, but has now been overstepped. At the western end of the Niagara fruit belt (p. 66), Hamilton has become a large market and commercial centre for this district (Fig. 19).

The major industrial activity of Hamilton is steel-making; with a capacity of about 3 million tons, this is the chief steel centre of Canada. The industry dates from 1895. Its coal is supplied by the Appalachian fields by way of the Welland Canal; formerly based on the Lake Superior ores, now the works are using larger quantities of Labrador ore which the Seaway has made more accessible. Fluxing limestone is quarried locally in the Niagara scarp; and the scarp has been of value

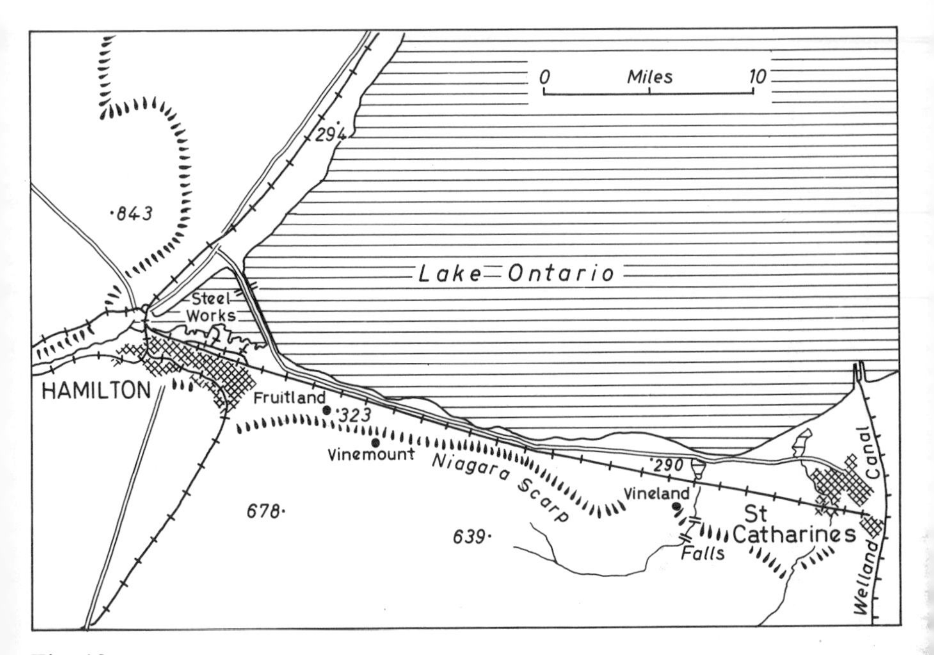

Fig. 19. HAMILTON AND THE NIAGARA FRUIT BELT

Situated at the western end of Lake Ontario, Hamilton became a focus of land routes rounding the lake. Its modern economic importance stems from its steel-works, which are the largest in Canada; but the city is also the commercial centre for the Niagara fruit belt. The hachures indicate the position of the Niagara scarp. *Based on the official 1 : 250,000 map of the United States Geological Survey.*

to the city in another way, for Hamilton derives some of its power from the De Cew Falls, at the scarp about 30 miles to the east of the city.

Hamilton harbour has been developed behind an enclosing sandspit four miles long: it is therefore sheltered, but has required much dredging. Like many other lake ports, its traffic has expanded since the opening of the Seaway: in 1964 it totalled 9·2 million tons, and nearly one-third of the arriving vessels were engaged in the overseas trade. The port is improving its facilities in the shape of a heavy lift crane and new transit sheds.

Toronto (population, metropolitan area, 1966: 2,158,496)

It is not always easy to explain why one settlement grows to metropolitan dimensions while another nearby remains of modest size. The site of Toronto has no compelling advantages which might have marked out this place to become the second city of Canada; and there are no nearby raw materials.

The choice, however, was not fortuitous. To the north the land rises from the lake level at 246 feet to over a thousand feet: this forms the

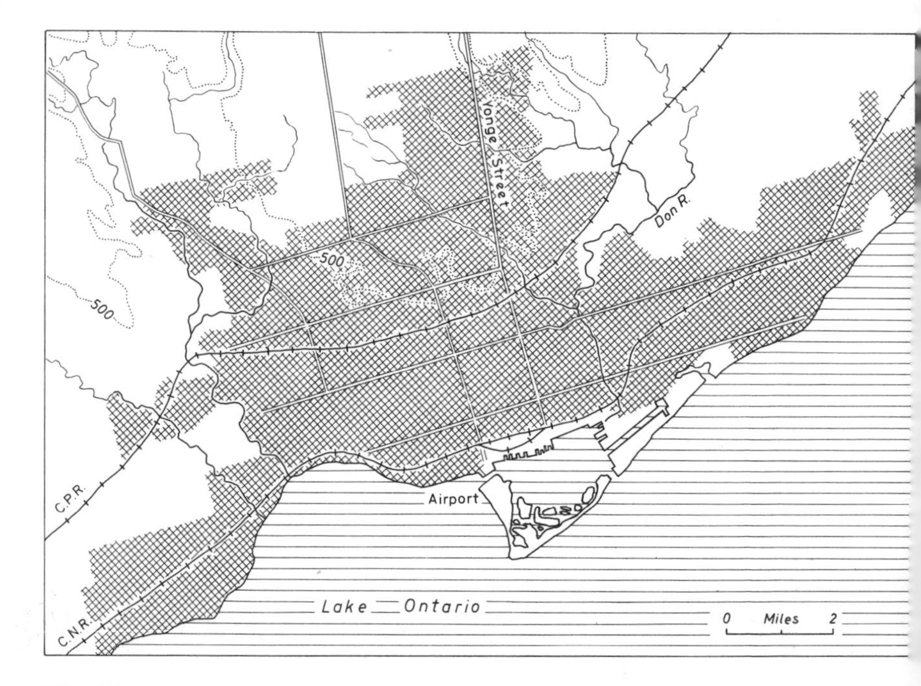

Fig. 20. TORONTO

The settlement was planned where an overland trail from the upper lakes reached Lake Ontario a a deep and sheltered bay.

divide between Lake Ontario and Lake Simcoe, which is tributary to Georgian bay, Lake Huron. This short cut to the upper lakes was early followed by a trail which departed from Lake Ontario at a square-shaped bay protected by a sandspit. The Indian name 'Toronto' signifies 'meeting-place'.

In 1749 the French established a fortified trading-post close to the bay, and 40 years later the administrator Colonel Simcoe realized the potential importance of this site. The water in the bay was 18–30 feet deep, and it did not readily freeze in winter. In 1794, when the population was less than 500, Simcoe proclaimed the centre the capital of Upper Canada. A chequerboard plan of streets was laid out, the surveyors cheerfully neglecting the relief of the site, so that roads now cross great ravines by means of expensive viaducts. The old Indian trail has become the chief highway to the north, beginning in the city as the commercial avenue, Yonge Street; and the first railway, which arrived in 1853, ran parallel to it (Fig. 20).

Upper Canada became in 1867 the Province of Ontario, and the building of a system of roads and railways converging on its capital aided its rise as the industrial, commercial, and financial centre of the province.

The shores of the bay have been profoundly altered. Along its northern edge a strip of land half a mile wide has been reclaimed from the lake, and now provides the site for a row of docks and wharves, backed by large railway yards. Former marshland to the east has been converted into coal and oil quays, and on reclaimed land at the tip of the sandspit a small airport has been built. (Toronto International Airport is situated in the north-western part of the metropolitan area.) The port handles a slightly smaller tonnage than Hamilton, but has a greater variety of cargo.

Until the 1880's the expansion of the city was limited eastward by the deep valley of the Don and northward by steep bluffs which mark the edge of the old lake floor. Since that time both these limits have been overstepped. The commercial core has shifted a little to the north-west of the original nucleus; industry concentrates in the former marshland area to the east, and in narrow zones along the railway. Modern Toronto is a city of varied manufactures, and, with its large and famous university, a city of culture as well as skyscrapers.

NIAGARA FALLS

The name Niagara river is given to that part of the Great Lakes–St Lawrence system which links Lake Erie with Lake Ontario. A mere 34 miles long, its spectacular falls have made this river world-famous.

The first European to see the falls is believed to have been Fr Hennepin, in 1678. He writes: 'The waters which fall from this horrible Precipice do foam and boyl after the most hideous manner imaginable making an outrageous Noise more terrible than that of Thunder.' He was witnessing a volume of water 85 times as great as the Thames at London plunge 170 feet over a thick ledge of resistant limestone into the gorge below.

Originally the falls were fully seven miles north of their present position, as is clear from their location in relation to the Niagara scarp (Fig. 21). They were uncovered by the retreating glaciers, 30,000 or more years ago, and continued erosion at their crest has left on the downstream side a deep and narrow gorge.

Niagara Falls provide one of the greatest tourist attractions in North America, and are visited annually by about 2 million people. In addition they represent a major source of hydro-electricity, which was first tapped as early as 1879, when power from the falls lit the lamps in Prospect Park. Most of the energy of the river is released at the actual falls: but the Niagara river descends a further 100 feet as it hurtles along through the gorge: at the Whirlpool it is forced through so narrow a

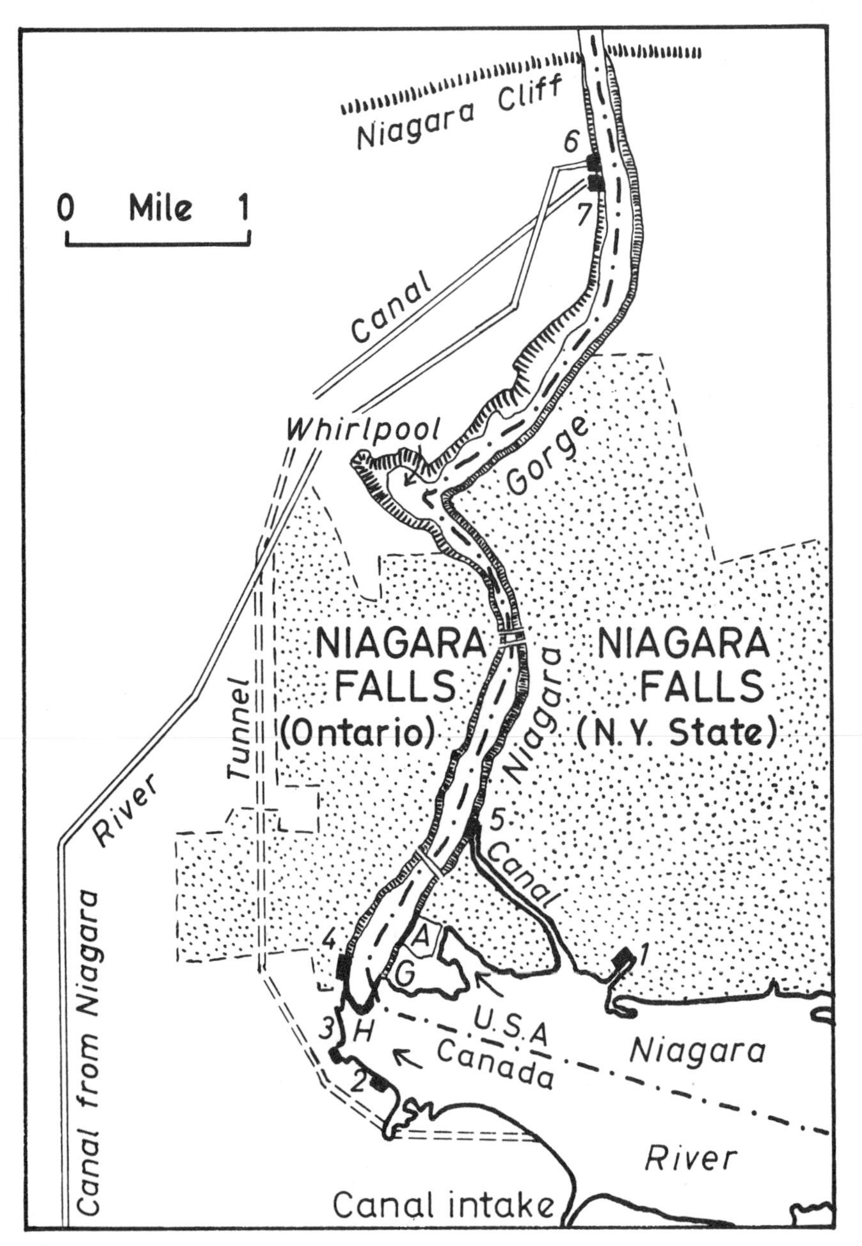

Fig. 21. NIAGARA FALLS AND POWER-PLANTS

It is clear that Canada has taken the initiative in the development of power from Niagara Falls. T key to the initials and numbers is as follows: H: Horseshoe Falls; G: Goat Island; A: Americ Falls; 1: the Adams Plant; 2: the Toronto Plant; 3: the Canadian–Niagara Plant; 4: the Onta Plant; 5: the Schoellkopf Plant; 6: the Queenston–Chippawa Plant; 7: the Sir Adam Beck No. Plant, completed in 1958.

passage that its surface bulges like that of a glacier, with its centre 20 feet higher than its edges.

The early hydro-electric projects tapped the energy only at the falls, but in the present generation schemes have been devised to utilize the additional energy released in the gorge. As many as seven power-plants are operating simultaneously. The Adams station (Fig. 21) first delivered power in 1895, and is still in use: water diverted from the falls descends into pits set 177 feet below ground-level; it operates 21 turbines and empties into the gorge by way of a tunnel below the American city of Niagara Falls. This plant served as a model for others on both American and Canadian sides.

Later stations were built at the lower end of the gorge to utilize a greater head of water, but had to be supplied by long diversion canals. The Canadian Queenston–Chippawa plant, opened in 1922, was in its day the largest in the world. The newest plant, also in Canada, is the Sir Adam Beck No. 2: fed by 7½ miles of canal (most of it in tunnels below the Canadian town), it utilizes a head of 295 feet, and produces over 1000 MW. It was opened in 1954.

The combined capacity of all the Niagara plants is about 2300 MW, so that these falls are one of the world's most productive sources of hydro-electricity. It appears that the limit of power-development has now been reached if the scenic value of the falls is to be retained. In 1950 the two nations agreed by treaty to define the maximum volume of water which may be extracted by the two hydro-electric authorities: this is greater by night than by day, so that it has been possible to incorporate a pump storage scheme in the latest plant.

Power from Niagara Falls supplies the aluminium, carbide, and abrasive industries of the two towns of Niagara Falls (N.Y.) and Niagara Falls (Ont.); in addition it is distributed over 30,000 square miles, which includes half the population of New York state. It is also transmitted to Buffalo and Toronto, and even as far as Sarnia, 240 miles away.

FARMING IN SOUTHERN ONTARIO

The Lake Peninsula, which is bounded to the north and west by Lake Huron and to the south and east by Lakes Erie and Ontario, is one of the most productive farming regions in Canada. While there is much local variety in climate, relief, and soils, there is in the region generally a measure of uniformity in these elements.

The lakes exert a moderating influence on temperatures and add moisture to the atmosphere, particularly in summer. The soils are all of glacial origin, and range in physical character from sands to clays, so that they present opportunities for a variety of crops.

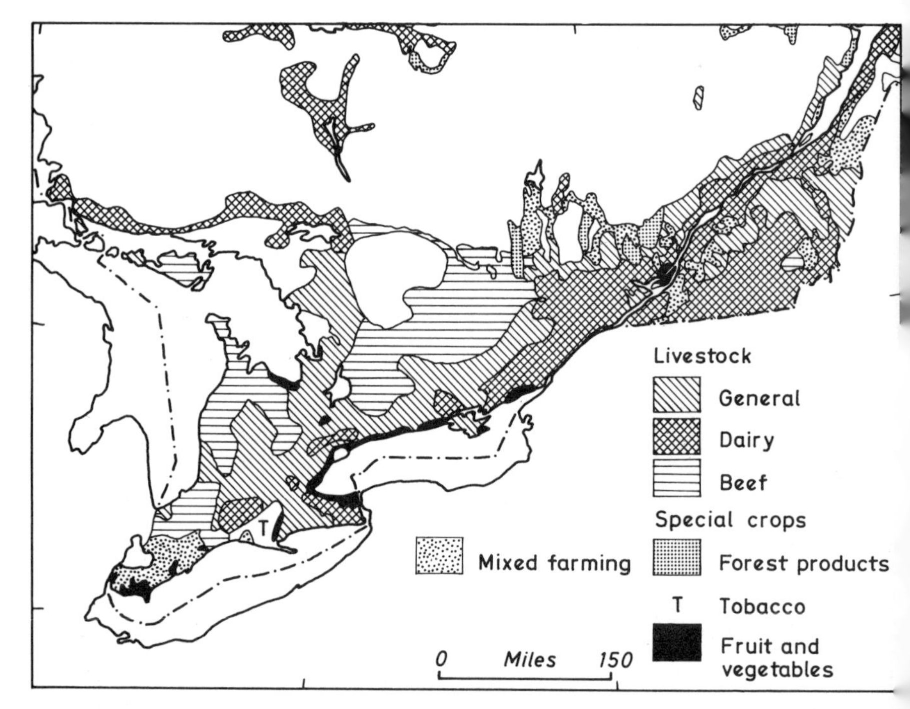

Fig. 22. FARMING TYPES IN ONTARIO AND QUEBEC

In general the dairy farms are closest to the urban markets, while the beef-cattle farms are farther from the markets. Fruit and vegetable production is confined to narrow strips bordering the lakes where there is an extended growing season.

In spite of the presence of many towns, and of the growth of manufactures, farming remains the greatest industry of southern Ontario. Compared with the neighbouring parts of the United States, the region has few great cities, for there are no really good, large harbours on the Canadian shores of Lakes Huron and Erie.

Southern Ontario was chiefly concerned with grain-production until the development of the prairie lands to the west: the farmers of the Lake Peninsula then turned towards stock-farming and the cultivation of specialized crops. Dairy farms are widely distributed throughout the region, but they reach their highest concentration in the neighbourhoods of Toronto and Hamilton, where they supply the metropolitan demands for fresh milk. Farther north and east the milk is converted into cheese, Jersey, Guernsey, and Ayrshire cattle have helped to build up the dairy industry, but an even greater contributor is the black-and-white Friesian (here called the Holstein).

Pig-farming often accompanies dairying, since the pigs can be fed on the whey from cheese-making and the skimmed milk from butter-making; and Ontario produces more than one-third of all the Canadian pigs.

Beef cattle also are widely reared, but there is a concentration in the west, where the hillier land is less suitable for dairy cattle, and where imported feeding-stuffs are more accessible from the Mid-West through the port of Owen Sound (Fig. 22).

The Tobacco Belt

Virtually the whole of Canada's tobacco – about 95 per cent. of it – is grown in Ontario. It forms an immensely valuable crop, not only four times as valuable as all the fruit crops but surpassing in value all the fruit and vegetable crops combined.

Thirteen counties share in the production of tobacco, but the greatest concentration is in a relatively small triangular area to the south-east of London, with a base of 50–60 miles fronting Lake Erie. Here the soils are predominantly sandy and are derived from deltaic material deposited by ancestors of the Thames and Grand rivers at the late stage in the northward retreat of the glaciers.

Climatically this is a particularly favoured district with a long frost-free period (153 days) and early spring (the average growing season begins on April 14th), and a relatively low rainfall (34 inches per annum). Essex county, in the far south-west, has an even more favourable climate, yet has specialized in fruits and vegetables; and it is likely that the crucial physical advantage in the tobacco belt is its sandy soil, which warms up quickly in spring.

The district consists of a low plateau rising from about 600 feet along the lakeshore to over 900 feet in the latitude of London, and deeply dissected by many short streams which flow to the lake. It still carries a more than average share of woodland, particularly on the steeper slopes; formerly the whole of it was regarded as waste land. Yet in the space of a single generation a flourishing tobacco industry has been established, with several thousand small, specialized tobacco farms. They require considerable capital: hothouses must be built to rear the seedlings; cultivating and transplanting machinery must be bought; drying kilns must be constructed for the curing process. Tobacco manufactures play an important part in the economic life of Simcoe, Tillsonburg, and St Thomas; the last-named, with 55 establishments, may be regarded as the organizing centre of the whole industry.

Fruit and Vegetables

Ontario produces about half of all the Canadian fruit and half of all the vegetables. While most counties in the region produce *some* fruit and vegetables, the bulk of the produce is from two relatively small areas:

Fig. 23. LAND USE IN THE NIAGARA FRUIT BELT

The curving northern boundary of the map represents the shore of Lake Ontario, and the Niaga fruit belt in the strict sense extends between this and the scarp. Here almost the whole of the land either under fruit and vegetables or is built up. The scarp itself is mainly wooded. The drift-covere plateau south of the scarp is an area of mixed farming, and on to its northern border the vineyar and orchards of the fruit belt have been extended.

these are the Niagara fruit belt, bordering the south-western shore of Lake Ontario, and Essex county, in the far south-west of the Province.

The Niagara fruit belt consists of a narrow strip of land, about 50 miles long and between one and eight miles wide, confined between the lakeshore and the Niagara scarp, and extending from the neighbourhood of Hamilton to the international border (Fig. 23).

The soils consist mainly of sandy loams; they are largely derived from the floor of the former enlarged Lake Ontario, but are diversified by outwash material and recent alluvium. Sheltered by the Niagara scarp and moderated by lake water, the district has an enviable climate. At 31 inches the mean annual rainfall is adequate but not excessive; the average frost-free period is 158 days, and the growing season begins about April 11th.

Toronto, Hamilton, and other lakeshore cities provide a lively local demand for fresh fruit, but also compete for the land. Even so, about half the fruit and increasingly large quantities of vegetables are destined for the canneries. Peaches and grapes are the two chief crops of value – unexpected fruits for Canada. Others include cherries, pears, plums, raspberries, and strawberries. The local village names of Fruitland, Vineland, and Vinemount suggest the main economic activity of their districts.

Essex county, south of Lake St Clair, is the most southerly and the most westerly district of Ontario. Its latitude of 42° N. corresponds to that of Rome and Barcelona. It has the lowest rainfall of the province (28·1 inches per annum), the lowest snowfall, and the longest frost-free period (167 days). Its soils are predominantly sandy loams, which warm quickly, and as a result of this combination of favourable circumstances its vegetables are ready for the market between one and three weeks earlier than in other areas. A corresponding region of the United Kingdom would be the Scilly Isles (though these are eight degrees farther north). The products of the district include lettuces, radishes, cabbages, melons, and tomatoes (*cf.* Plate 1).

A Farm in Southern Ontario

We may illustrate the agriculture of southern Ontario from a farm near the village of Hillsburgh, 40 miles north-west of Toronto. It comprises the greater part of two rectangular lots, which originally formed separate units (Fig. 24). The farm lies to the west of the Niagara scarp, so that the land is somewhat elevated, ranging between 1450 and 1525 feet above sea-level. The underlying rock consists of Silurian Limestone (the same material whose edge forms the scarp), but this is masked by morainic deposits, mainly sandy and gravelly in character, and strewn with boulders. One steep-sided gully crosses the farm, and reminds us that on steep slopes there is a risk of soil erosion. The rainfall, at 35 inches per annum, is not unduly great; but it is liable to arrive in violent torrents. Only 50 miles away, in the Niagara fruit belt, the frost-free period is 167 days long; but at Hillsburgh it has fallen to 126 days. While the total area of the farm amounts to 315 acres, nearly 100 acres remain in woodland and rough land.

This is essentially a grass farm: of 20 fields, in a specimen year all but $5\frac{1}{2}$ are yielding either pasture or hay. The farmer has many interests: his major object is the rearing of pedigree shorthorn (beef) cattle; but in addition he raises pedigree Suffolk lambs, he fattens crossbred lambs,

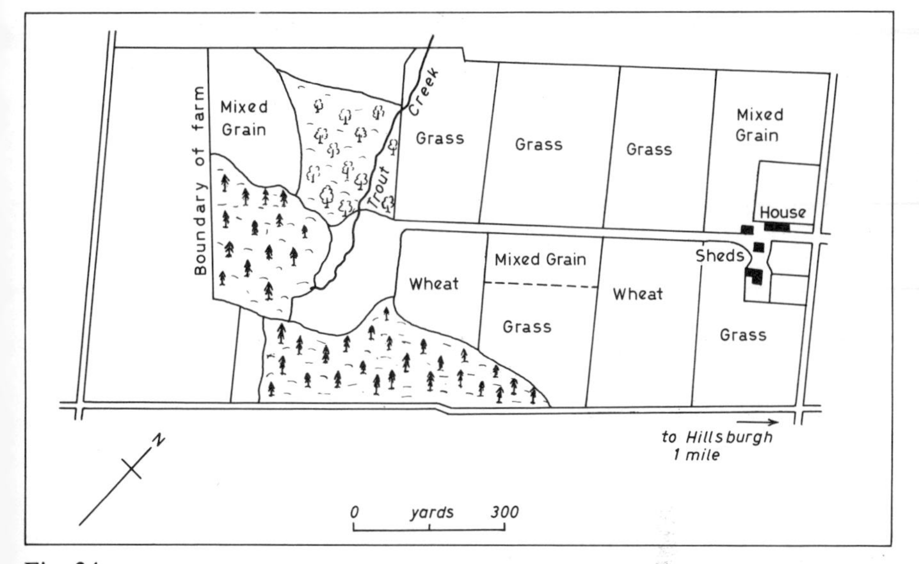

Fig. 24. A FARM IN SOUTHERN ONTARIO

This is essentially a stock farm: the farmer breeds and fattens beef cattle, sheep, pigs, and poultry. Only half the farm is illustrated here – there is another similar block farther north. *By courtesy of the Association of Agriculture.*

he breeds young pigs, he fattens pullets as table birds, and he grows high-quality oats and barley to be sold as seed.

With a limestone subsoil, the farm is somewhat deficient in running water, but this is less vital in a breeding farm, and helps to explain why there is no milk produced here, in spite of the nearby Toronto market. The farmer devotes 65 to 70 acres to his seed grains; he also grows small quantities of maize for feeding his stock, either in the form of grain or as silage. The farm is not particularly well endowed by Nature, and its remarkable success is due largely to the enterprise and skill of the farmer and his son: there is no hired labour.

Plate 1. A DISTRICT IN THE LAKE PENINSULA OF ONTARIO: CEDAR SPRINGS (NEAR CHATHAM)

This district, east of Lake Clair and fronting Lake Erie, is bordered by the intensive fruit area of Essex county to the west and the tobacco belt to the east. The landscape has developed on the flat bed of the enlarged Lake Erie of late glacial times. This is one of the most southerly districts of Canada, with a latitude corresponding to that of Rome and Barcelona. The soils consist mainly of clay and gravelly loams. The characteristic crops are soft fruits, early vegetables, soya beans, tobacco, maize, and winter wheat. The photograph suggests an intensive agriculture with an extremely high proportion of orchard and arable land, a close rural settlement, and a net of first-class roads. Roads and field boundaries clearly reflect the work of the land surveyer (p. 262). The scale is approximately 1·5 inches to 1 mile.

Photo Royal Canadian Air Force. Crown copyright reserved

THE ST LAWRENCE CITIES

Montreal (population, metropolitan area, 1966: 2,436,817)

Montreal is the largest urban centre of Canada and her major gateway to the world market; it is also the chief focus of railways in the Dominion, and its leading manufacturing district. With two universities, it is a major centre of intellectual life. Two-thirds of the population of Montreal speak French, and Montreal constitutes (after Paris) the second largest French-speaking metropolis in the world.

The setting of Montreal is of great interest (Fig. 25). A large port was almost bound to arise here, for the Lachine rapids form the first obstruction to up-stream navigation on the St Lawrence river. Ocean vessels were halted at this point, and their cargoes perforce discharged. Two other natural routeways focused on this spot. From the west led the Ottawa river, forming a highway from the upper lakes; this was the route favoured by the early traders, for hostile tribes inhabited the Lake Erie district and the Niagara area was not easily negotiated. Southward a short overland journey of only ten miles brought the traveller to the Lake Champlain navigation, and so to the Hudson valley and New York.

There were distinct local advantages too. Near the Lachine rapids the St Lawrence divides into three main channels, enclosing two large islands. The larger, more southerly, of the two fronts the deepest of the three channels; a stretch of terrace land offers a firm, dry site for settlement and is sheltered from the north by Mount Royal (769 feet), a large igneous intrusion. Nearby is a significant narrowing of the main stream, which in early days suggested the possibility of a bridge.

Jacques Cartier found a native Indian town here when he ascended the river in 1535. The European settlement was founded in 1642 as a fortified Catholic outpost in the New World, and it soon became the headquarters of the fur trade and the starting-point of many military and exploring expeditions.

The original gravel terrace site now houses the central business district, with its banks, shops, and 40-storey office blocks, and the two railway stations. Below is the port, with its shipyards, coal tips, and grain elevators; above are the schools and colleges, and the well-to-do residences.

The harbour handles far more traffic than any other Atlantic port of Canada. The main shipping area remains close to the entrance of the Lachine Canal, between the two lowest bridges, and since this is well above the tidal limits there is no need for enclosed basins. Ice interrupts the work of the port for four months, and to allow a continuous flow of crude oil for the Montreal refineries a pipeline has been constructed from the ice-free terminal of Portland (Maine).

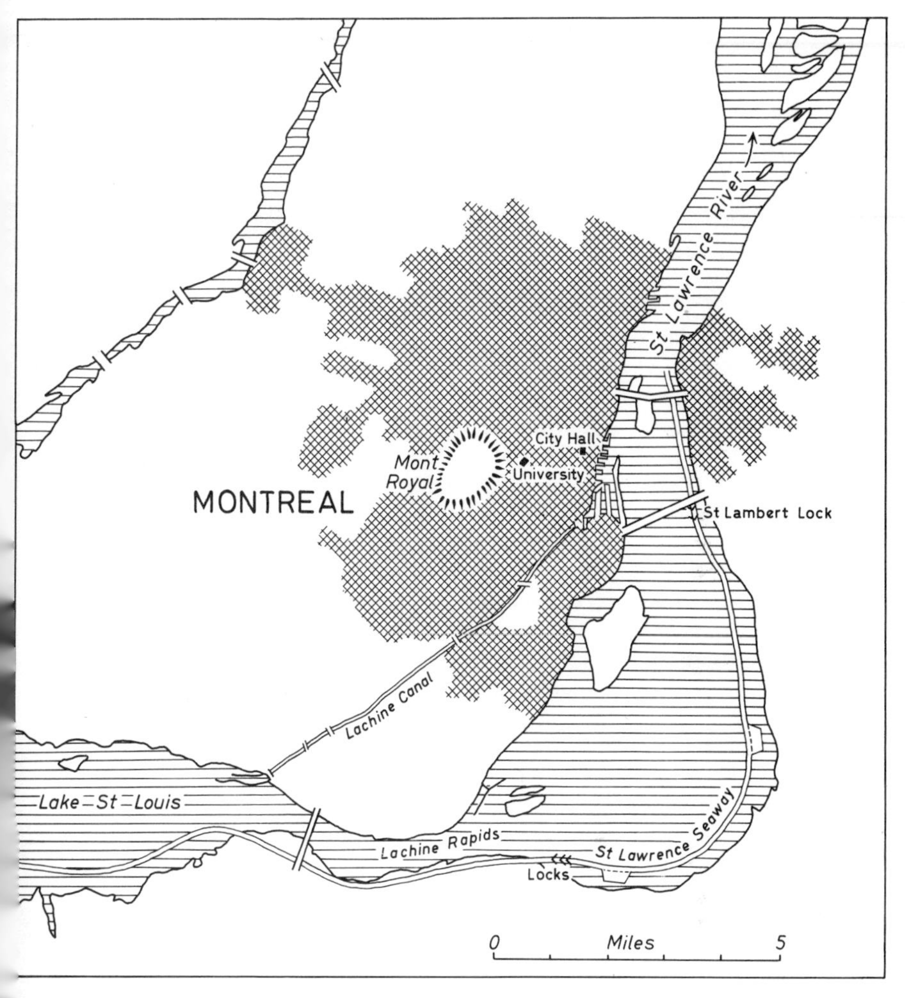

Fig. 25. THE SITE OF MONTREAL

The Lachine rapids formed the first up-stream obstruction to navigation on the St Lawrence river, and here the cargoes had to be transhipped. The narrowing of the river a few miles below the rapids provided the opportunity for a bridge, and Montreal remains the lowest bridge point. The early city was built on a gravel terrace at the foot of Mont Royal. The falls were bypassed by the Lachine Canal, which carried all the water traffic to and from the lakes until the opening of the Seaway in 1958. The course of the Seaway is indicated by a double line.

How will the St Lawrence Seaway affect Montreal? Direct overseas shipments, which bypass Montreal, at present form only a very small proportion of the total Seaway traffic; the reduction in transport costs has provided an immense stimulus to economic activity in the region as a whole, which can only be to the advantage of its major manufacturing centre.

Quebec (population, metropolitan area, 1961: 331,307)
With only one-sixth of the population of Montreal, Quebec is nevertheless a city of great historic interest and a growing commercial, manufacturing, and cultural centre.

Translated from the Algonquin, its name means 'where the river narrows', and this summarizes its essential position: here the St Lawrence markedly changes both its width and its direction, and Quebec stands at the place where the river turns into an estuary.

The settlement was founded by the French about 1608 as a fortified fur-trading post, at the foot of the cliffs of a high peninsula pointing north-east into the St Lawrence (Fig. 26). Walls and gates were constructed in 1716 on the high ground at the tip of the peninsula: and in 1823–32 these were remodelled and enlarged by the British, who at the same time constructed the strong citadel at the southern end of the circuit of walls. Quebec is the only walled and gated town left in Anglo-America, and with its narrow streets, its university, and many religious houses, it forms the religious centre of French Canada and an almost unrivalled tourist attraction.

In the days of the sailing-ship, navigation farther up-stream proved to be difficult, so that Quebec grew to become the ocean port for Canada. It shipped large quantities of timber and developed a flourishing shipbuilding industry. Quebec was the chief immigrant port of Canada, and welcomed a million newcomers between 1829 and 1865. For long this was the largest city of Canada; for nearly a generation (1841–67) it was the capital, and when a trans-Canada railway was planned Quebec was chosen for its eastern terminus.

But with the change from wooden to iron, and later steel, vessels the shipbuilding industry languished, for Quebec was far from the established iron and steel centres. When steam replaced sail the difficulty of navigating above Quebec was overcome, and dredging of the river as far as Montreal to a depth of 30 feet shifted the head of deep-water navigation away from Quebec. The hinterland of the city is limited, for it cannot compare with Montreal as a route focus; consequently its port traffic is far smaller – about 4 million tons a year compared with the 20 million at Montreal.

Yet recent trends seem to indicate a quickening in the economic growth of Quebec. It is developing as an outport for the passenger trade of Montreal, rather as London is served by Tilbury. The region has abundant resources of hydro-electricity, while those of the Montreal district are limited. Quebec is the outlet for the world's largest asbestos-producing district, 50 miles to the south, at Thetford Mines, and it is

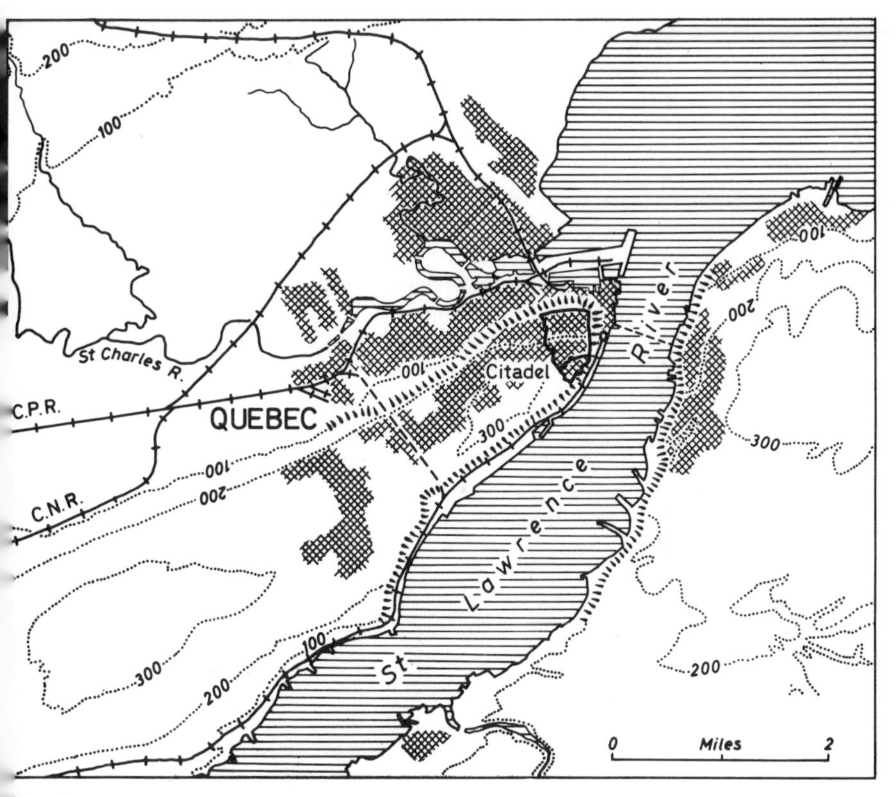

'ig. 26. THE SETTING OF QUEBEC

he narrowing of the St Lawrence in this area facilitated a crossing by ferry. Farther up-stream it as difficult to navigate large sailing-vessels, so that it became usual to tranship their cargoes here. 'he precise site of the city was a steeply scarped peninsula, which offered the opportunity for defence. 'he circuit of the town walls can be seen near the tip of the peninsula.

the nearest large city to the Labrador ore deposits and the many other mineral resources of the North Shore and the Gaspé peninsula. The city may yet add mineral industries to its existing clothing, textile, and timber and paper manufactures. Quebec can look to the future with some confidence.

Ottawa (population, metropolitan area, 1961: 429,750)

The Federal capital stands at the head of navigation of the Ottawa river, the chief affluent of the St Lawrence, and at the point where it receives two important tributaries, the Gatineau from the north and the Rideau from the south. The site was a natural centre for native trade, and the name itself in Algonquin signifies 'trading-point'.

Early explorers followed the Ottawa up-stream and after a short portage reached the Mattawa river; this by way of Lake Nipissing led them to Georgian bay on Lake Huron. This direct route to the upper lakes is followed today by the Canadian Pacific Railway and by the Transcontinental Highway. Northward from the Mattawa an easy passage leads to the Clay Belt, astride the Ontario–Quebec boundary: this offers moderately good farming prospects amid an otherwise unpromising region.

Below Ottawa the valley widens and allows easy communication both eastward to Montreal and southward to Lake Ontario. It was this last possibility that resulted in the emergence of the town. In 1826 Colonel John By was entrusted with the task of building a canal to bypass the St Lawrence above Montreal: this was desirable for strategic reasons, since the United States was potentially hostile. The Rideau Canal was opened in 1832, and the village at its northern terminal was named Bytown.

Its remarkable nodality soon asserted itself: its rise was aided by water-borne traffic, and it became a major centre for the lumber industry. In 1847 its population numbered 6000; in 1854 it was incorporated as the city of Ottawa. Since it was on the border of Quebec and Ontario – and therefore centrally placed for the then settled parts of Canada – it was chosen in 1867 as the capital of the new Dominion.

Pulp and paper industries are still important, and are favoured by the abundance of hydro-electric power, but Ottawa is now primarily a centre of administration, with 25 per cent. of its gainfully employed persons engaged in Government service. There are two universities, one English-speaking, the other bilingual, and there are Anglican and Catholic cathedrals. The French part of the city is Hull, across the river. The Ottawa area exhibits a happy blend of English and French traditions.

CHAPTER THREE

APPALACHIA

Any regional division of a continent has its shortcomings, for the boundaries between adjoining regions are often indistinct. Even worse, there may be a clear area of overlap, so that the same district may appear in two or more regions. This is the difficulty that faces us in our discussion of Appalachia. On a purely physical definition the region would extend to include New England and the Atlantic Provinces of Canada. For the sake of convenience we examine the maritime provinces elsewhere (pp. 218–252), and we feel that New York and New England are of sufficient importance to require separate study. In the north-west the region extends beyond Pittsburgh almost to Lake Erie; but this district is so clearly linked with the economy of the Great Lakes that we discuss it in that context. South-westward the region thrusts far into the Cotton Belt, so that in this direction overlap is unavoidable.

Yet in spite of its ties with neighbouring regions, 'Appalachia' remains a unit with its own 'personality'. It has a common geological history and a common structure, so that, broadly speaking, a transverse section remains the same whether it is taken in the latitude of Richmond, Virginia, or Atlanta, Georgia, though these are 500 miles apart. As one moves southward the type of farming changes, but these changes are less fundamental than those which occur within shorter distances on a journey from east to west.

We interpret 'Appalachia' widely to include the Atlantic coast plain and the Piedmont Plateau, in addition to the folded Appalachians and the Cumberland Plateau. It is a region of great variety, for it includes on the one hand coastal marshes, and on the other peaks over a mile high; metropolitan cities and deserted ridges; mining and steel districts such as Pittsburgh and Birmingham, and plantations of cotton and tobacco. The home of the original Thirteen Colonies, it has played a vital part in the historical evolution of the United States. In modern times the activities of the Tennessee Valley Authority in the south-western part of the region have set a standard for regional planning that has never before been reached.

Climate

Stretching across 20 degrees of latitude, and including within its limits tidal flats, plains, plateaux, and high ridges, Appalachia is bound to experience great differences in climate within its borders. The general direction of movement of disturbances is from the Gulf of Mexico towards the Great Lakes and the Atlantic, so that, other things being equal, it is the more southerly districts which receive the greater rainfall. The region derives little benefit from the Gulf Stream, for the winds are generally from the south-west, and in any case the warm current is separated from the shore by a belt of relatively cool water.

As we move southward in the coast plain we find that the growing season (that is, the period free from killing frost) increases from about 175 days in New Jersey to more than 210 in North Carolina and more than 270 in Georgia. Mean temperatures steadily increase southward: in New Jersey the average July temperature is 70°–75°F., in North Carolina, 78°–80°; and in Georgia, 80°–82°. These temperatures represent averages of day and night, so that at about 2 P.M. we must expect temperatures in the 80's in New Jersey, and in the 90's farther south. Since the mean annual rainfall (everywhere more than 40 inches) is ample for farming, it is clear that the coast plain is capable of growing a wide variety of crops; and these range from the temperate vegetables in the north through tobacco, maize, and cotton in the centre and south, even to oranges and bananas in the extreme south-east of Georgia.

Moving west into the hills, we find that the growing season shrinks to 130–165 days in Pennsylvania, 150–180 days in North Carolina, and 190 days in Georgia. Cotton-growing is out of the question in the north, and risky in the south. Farther west still, in the Cumberland Plateau, Pennsylvania experiences 120–150 days free from killing frost, appropriate to wheat, oats, and barley, while in Kentucky the growing season lasts 180–200 days – suitable for maize and tobacco, but risky for cotton.

In most districts the rainfall is well distributed, with a slight summer maximum. Most of Pennsylvania receives 40–46 inches per annum; most of North Carolina, 46–52 inches, with more than 60 inches in the hills. The ridges of eastern Tennessee receive up to 80 inches a year, and this is the heaviest rainfall of the eastern United States. Even where the rainfall is not excessive in total it can be extremely destructive in character, for it arrives not in the form of the steady drizzle that is often found in Atlantic Britain but in torrential downpours, which can hasten soil erosion in hilly areas and cause serious flooding down-stream. To this we return below (p. 99).

STRUCTURE AND GEOLOGY

We may readily divide Appalachia into five structural units: from the coast westward, these are the Coast Plain, the Piedmont Plateau, the

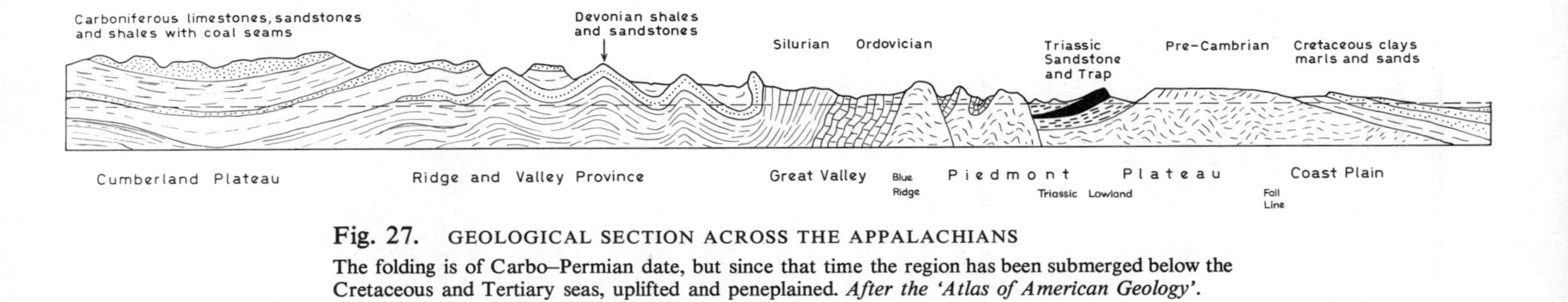

Fig. 27. GEOLOGICAL SECTION ACROSS THE APPALACHIANS

The folding is of Carbo–Permian date, but since that time the region has been submerged below the Cretaceous and Tertiary seas, uplifted and peneplained. *After the 'Atlas of American Geology'.*

Great Appalachian Valley, the Ridge and Valley Province, and the Cumberland Plateau (Fig. 27). While the details of the structure may be conveniently discussed under these separate heads, there are some general characteristics which are common to all.

In the region there is a great variety of rocks, ranging from Pre-Cambrian to Tertiary in age – in fact, the only major period not represented in the area is the Jurassic. These rocks are not scattered haphazardly but are arranged in distinct longitudinal zones, and these zones (or at least some of them) extend in a great curving belt from the neighbourhood of Birmingham (Alabama) to that of Quebec, a distance of about 1250 miles.

The Piedmont Plateau, composed mainly of Pre-Cambrian material, represents the stumps of an ancient continent whose rocks have been folded, peneplained, submerged below the Cretaceous seas, arched, again peneplained, elevated once more, and then subjected to tens of millions of years of erosion.

Resting upon these oldest rocks, with a startling unconformity, are the remains of a former extensive cover of Cretaceous and Tertiary sediments: these form the coastal plain.

West of the Piedmont Plateau we see first the Great Valley and then the Ridge and Valley Province. Here the strata range in age from Silurian to Carboniferous; they were compressed to form a series of parallel and tight folds in Carbo-Permian times, and there are some structural similarities with the Mendips, south Wales, and south-west Ireland, where the effects can be seen of the same mountain-building movements.

Farther west the folds die away quite suddenly and their place is taken by a plateau composed of horizontal or only slightly tilted strata, of Carboniferous age. This is the Cumberland Plateau. Its surface has been deeply entrenched by the rivers, and in their valleys coal seams are often exposed. The Cumberland Plateau terminates northward in the Mohawk gap, but other elements in the structure continue. The coastal plain is represented by Staten and Long islands and the Cape Cod peninsula; the Pre-Cambrian rocks of the Piedmont Plateau disappear temporarily in New Jersey, but they are seen again in Manhattan, and their western edge, the Blue Ridge, reappears beyond the Hudson in the form of the Taconic mountains of eastern New York state. In a similar manner the Great Valley of Pennsylvania, Virginia, and the Carolinas turns northward to reveal itself as the trench of the Hudson river and its continuation, the Lake Champlain lowland.

For convenience in regional description, however, we limit ourselves here to the Appalachian province south and west of the Mohawk–Hudson gap.

The Atlantic Coast Plain

Geologically speaking, the Atlantic coast plain is one of the youngest portions of the continent. It is composed of strata of Cretaceous and later periods which dip gently south-eastward and are traversed by many broad and smooth-flowing rivers. In the north the lower reaches of the rivers have been drowned to produce the complex indentations so well illustrated in Chesapeake bay: these are very different from the rias of County Kerry and south Cornwall, for the coast is low-lying and the peninsulas do not rise far above the intervening inlets. Bordering the shore is a wide belt of marshland which is deserted.

The rivers were navigable and the early settlers penetrated well inland. They found a climate rather more extreme than they had experienced in Western Europe; but the coastal belt enjoyed milder winters than the land to the west; severe falls of snow were rare, and the harbours were open throughout the year.

In a state of nature most of the land was wooded, typically with long-leaf pine; and a large proportion of the area remains in woodland, heath, or marsh. The soils are predominantly sandy and not in themselves particularly fertile; but they warm up quickly and are easily cultivated, and when carefully managed they are potentially highly productive.

In the northern part of the plain is a belt of large cities stretching from Boston to Washington. It has been named by Professor Gottmann 'Megalopolis': it is the largest continuous urban and suburban belt in the world, and it contained in 1960 a total population of about 37 millions.[1] We are directly concerned here with only a portion of this belt, whose development will be examined later (pp. 107 ff.). But Megalopolis has influenced the agriculture of the coast plain by providing an almost unlimited demand for dairy produce, pork and bacon, eggs and poultry, and fruit and vegetables of all kinds.

Farming in this northern part of the coast plain is closely linked with the supply of urban needs, and it has been named the 'truck crop' belt. It is true that door-to-door transport by lorry is an essential part of the economy of the region; but in this case the word 'truck' apparently derives from its meaning of 'barter' or 'exchange', for in the early days it was customary to market vegetables in small lots.

Since the sandy soils warm quickly in spring, the fruits and vegetables mature quickly, and they benefit from the longer growing season of the coastal areas. They are treated with liberal doses of fertilizer, and the land receives more fertilizer per acre here than anywhere else in the United States. It has been said that the soil is regarded as a mouth through which the crops can be fed! It is significant that it was in this district – at Baltimore – that the American fertilizer industry was born.

[1] J. Gottmann, *Megalopolis*, 1961.

This city remains a very important centre in the industry: it makes use of local supplies of fishmeal, and receives large quantities of phosphates.

A great variety of vegetables is produced. It includes all the temperate vegetables known in the United Kingdom, such as potatoes, lettuce, tomatoes and cucumbers, cabbages, sprouts, carrots, onions, peas, beans, and spinach, and many less common ones, like sweet corn, asparagus, artichokes, melons, pumpkins, peanuts, soya beans, and sweet pepper.

Many farms now contract to have their fields sprayed with chemical insecticides and fertilizers from the air. This is a speedy and effective method, for a low-flying helicopter can cover up to 50 acres an hour: in some cases five applications are made annually.

Throughout the district there are canneries and frozen-food plants. Thus Cambridge (Maryland) has canning industries; Exmore (Virginia), near the southern tip of the peninsula between Chesapeake and Delaware bays, has a frozen-food plant; and nearby Cheriton has a tomato cannery which dispatches daily 20 railway wagons laden with tins of tomato juice, tomato soup, and tomato sauce.

Associated with vegetable-growing is the rearing of poultry. The little state of Delaware is the leading producer of broiling fowls in the United States, and this industry accounts for 70 per cent. of its farm income. It has grown only during the last generation or so: in 1929 there were 2·1 million chickens sold in Delaware; by 1949 the figure had risen to 71·9 million, representing 10 per cent. of the United States total. This is an exceedingly localized industry, for 90 per cent. of all the broiler fowls were reared in the single Delaware county of Sussex.

The chicks are reared in about 30 hatcheries in the state. At one of these, near Dover (in the north-centre of the state), are six incubators with a total capacity of 400,000 eggs; they raise 3 million chicks a year, and these are 'packed' into cardboard containers and loaded in a large lorry which carries 27,000 at a time to the poultry farms.

Many coast-plain farmers rear beef cattle, dairy cows, and pigs. In Virginia tobacco becomes a leading crop; and beyond the southern boundary of North Carolina vegetables and tobacco are joined by cotton. North Carolina raises two-fifths of the nation's output of tobacco, and is its chief producer. The plant grows well on these light, sandy soils, and Wilson, centrally placed near the inner border of the coast plain, is the chief marketing centre of the industry. Here the auctioneers, moving in a great shed among hundreds of piles of golden-brown tobacco leaves, will sell up to 3 million pounds (about 1350 tons) a day during the autumn sales.

A unique feature on the coast plain from North Carolina as far as Georgia is the existence of the so-called 'bays': these are circular or oval-shaped, shallow, flat-floored hollows up to two miles long and a mile

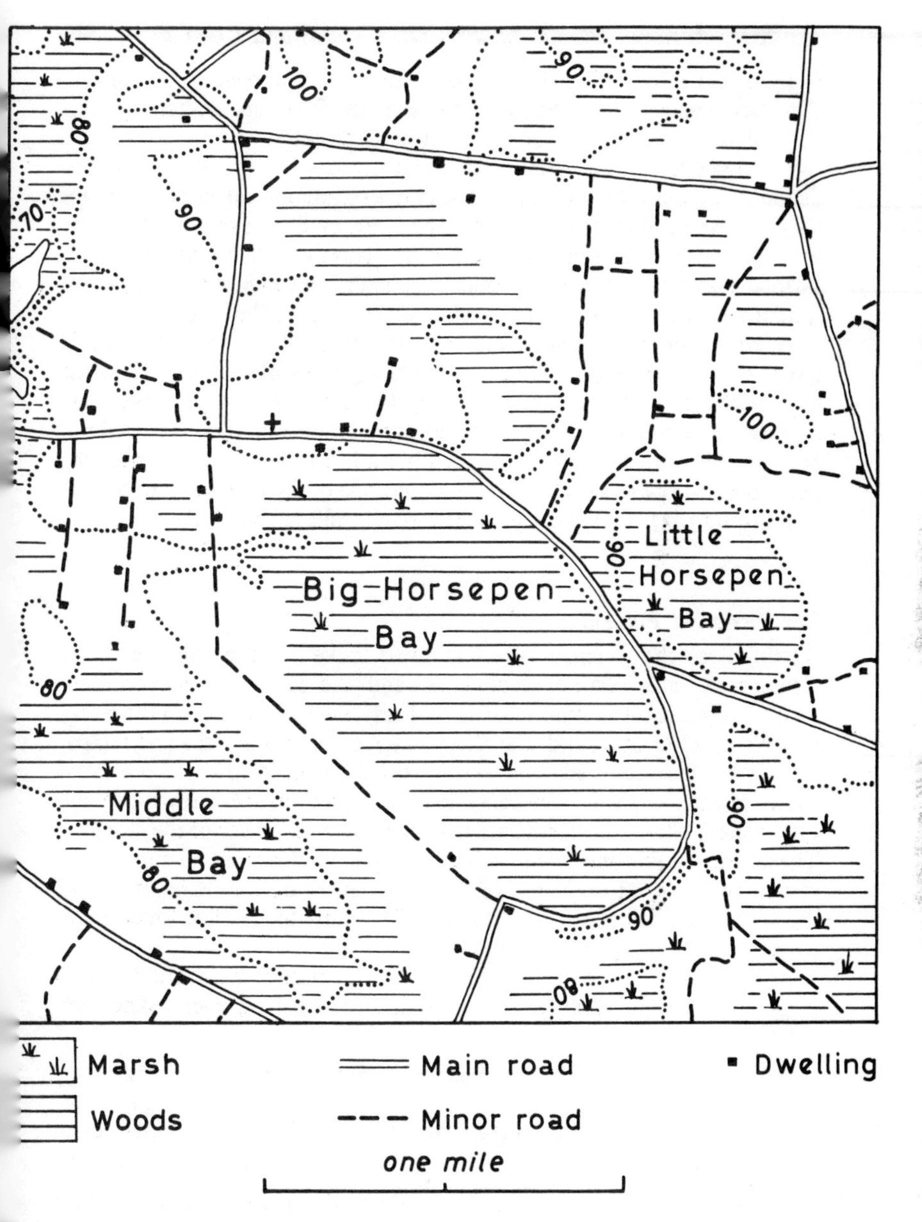

ʼig. 28. THE LANDSCAPE OF THE COAST PLAIN OF SOUTH CAROLINA

ʼhe map illustrates the strange 'bays', whose origin appears to be due to a shower of meteorites. lthough there is much marsh and woodland, the available land is intensively settled and farmed and ıere is a close network of roads. *Based on the official 1 : 24,000 map, Mullins quadrangle, Marion ɔunty.*

wide. Some have well-defined rims, so that they appear to be craters; their bottoms are occupied by marsh (Fig. 28). They are scattered over a wide area amounting to about 25,000 square miles.

No obvious normal agent of erosion or deposition can be found to account for these features; and the only explanation appears to be that they represent meteorite craters. They are of little agricultural value, and form negative areas in an otherwise closely settled and intensively farmed lowland; but in North Carolina thousands of turkeys are fattened on the pastures on the edge of the 'bays' (Plate 2).

A characteristic but scattered industry of the Atlantic coast ports is paper-making. It originated in a Savannah (Georgia) mill in 1937, when the southern pine was first used for the manufacture of newsprint; another large mill operates farther north in Charleston (South Carolina), and has been greatly expanded. Two more in the Savannah district produce kraft (brown paper) containers, and one of them, with an output of a thousand tons a day, is the largest paper-mill in the world.

The Piedmont Plateau

Resting on the ancient Pre-Cambrian base of the continent are Cretaceous and Tertiary sediments, and the junction between them forms a significant human boundary. Early settlers, sailing up the rivers in their small craft, found that their way was barred by falls and rapids. Here they disembarked, and some settled in the district to serve the needs of later arrivals. On every river of consequence a town became established, later to take advantage of the potential power of the streams. These are the fall-line towns, which comprise a dozen or so substantial settlements and cities. Some of these, however, are a mile or two from the actual geological boundary, and at Baltimore the fall line touches the coast. The list is given on page 84.

The general level of the Piedmont Plateau rises from about 500 feet in the east to 900–1000 feet in the west. Into its rolling, rounded surface

---

Plate 2. A PORTION OF THE ATLANTIC COAST PLAIN IN JENKINS COUNTY, GEORGIA

Jenkins county lies in eastern Georgia, close to the border of North Carolina. Two 'bays' are seen in the photograph (bottom, right) – *a smaller and a larger. These are shallow elliptical depressions with wooded rims and marshy floors. Their origin is obscure* (see *p. 80 and Fig. 28*). *The land was originally under pine forest, and much of this remains. The soils consist of thin, sandy loams, and are not inherently fertile; nevertheless, where it has been cleared, the land is closely settled, and there is an efficient network of major and minor roads. The main cash crop is cotton.*

Photo by courtesy of the U.S. Department of Agriculture, Agricultural Stabilization and Conservation Service

The Fall Line Towns

Town	*River*
Montgomery	Alabama
Columbus	Chattahoochee
Macon	Ocmulgee
Augusta	Savannah
Columbia	Congaree
Camden	Wateree
Raleigh	Neuse
Richmond	James
Washington	Potomac
Baltimore	(coast)
Philadelphia	Delaware
Trenton	Delaware

the rivers have cut deep and wide valleys (Fig. 29), and above the general level stand residual hills, clothed in forest; these rise to between 1500 and 2200 feet. The western edge is higher still, and appears to have been raised by block-faulting; this, the Blue Ridge, rises to about 2400 feet in some parts, but in the Smoky mountains of North Carolina to 6617 feet.

Though the underlying rocks of the plateau are Pre-Cambrian, they have been exposed so long to the forces of erosion that a deep and mature soil has developed, unaffected by the ice sheets, which did not penetrate so far south. The soils are relatively productive, the land is closely settled, and many small towns have developed, with characteristic and thriving manufactures. Often these have achieved outstanding reputations (Fig. 30).

Thus at High Point, in west-central North Carolina, a furniture industry has evolved which was based originally on the local fine stands of timber. There are now about 90 factories, and the district within about 125 miles radius produces two-fifths of all the bedroom and dining-room furniture of the United States. Its products are displayed annually in a 14-storey building at High Point, and attract 5000 buyers.

About 18 miles to the north-west of High Point is Winston-Salem, one of the major centres of the United States tobacco industry. Here are the headquarters of the R. J. Reynolds Company, which controls over 140 factories and warehouses; the town also produces cigarette-making machinery.

North Carolina produces 60 per cent. of all the nation's tobacco manufactures, and nearly all the tobacco companies have factories there. An important associated activity is the production of cigarette paper, and most of the world's supply is made in a single plant near Asheville, in the far west of the state, close to the Blue Ridge.

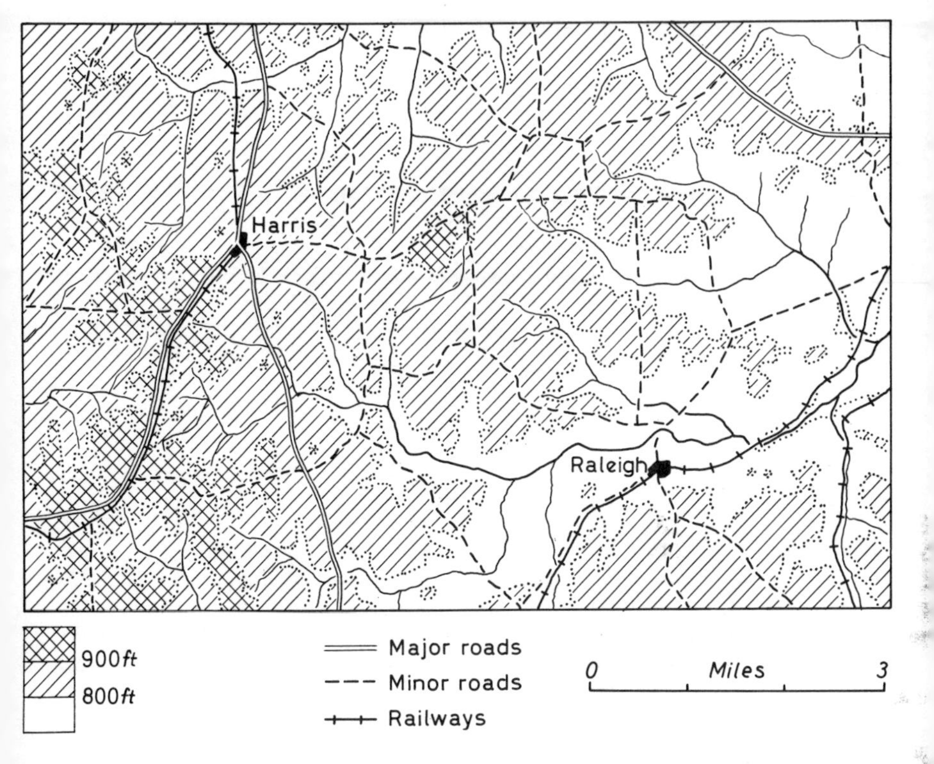

Fig. 29. THE LANDSCAPE OF THE PIEDMONT PLATEAU

The soils are based on Pre-Cambrian schists. About half the area shown is occupied by woodland, which tends to remain on the steeper slopes. The close network of subsidiary roads suggests an intensive occupation of the land. This district lies about 55 miles S.S.W. of Atlanta, Georgia. *Based on the official 1:62,500 map, Warm Springs quadrangle, 1934.*

While tobacco manufacture forms a considerable industry, even more outstanding is the production of textiles. Beginning over a century ago with the spinning and weaving of the local cotton, the industry has since extended its scope to include wool (most of which is imported), rayon (based on local woodpulp), and nylon (a coal-tar product). The core of the industry lies in the Piedmont of the Carolinas, but it spills into the coast plain and the Great Valley, and it extends into neighbouring states, and, indeed, as far as Tennessee and Mississippi. In all the South produces about 75 per cent. of the nation's textiles.

The greatest centre of the industry is probably Greensboro, in the Piedmont of North Carolina: here are the headquarters of the Burlington Mills Corporation, the largest producers in the world of denims, and, in addition, manufacturers of nylon and rayon cloth. Nearby Winston-Salem, in addition to its tobacco activities, is a leading producer of

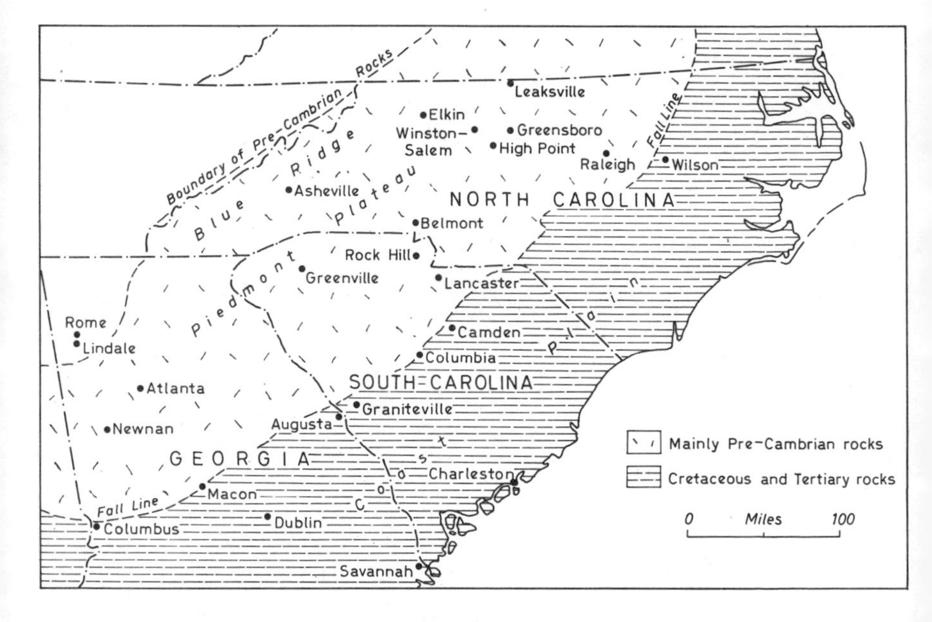

Fig. 30. SOME MANUFACTURING TOWNS OF APPALACHIA

The activities of these towns are described in the text. The geological boundaries are in fact exceedingly complex, and it has been necessary to generalize them.

knitted underwear; and High Point, together with its furniture, produces nylon stockings. Near the southern border of the state is Belmont: only a small town, it nevertheless contains 15 cotton-spinning mills, 5 hosiery mills, a dye-works, and a finishing plant, together with many small firms which engage in related work.

South Carolina too has its textile centres. Near the northern border are Rock Hill and Lancaster. The former produces cotton and woollen cloth, hosiery, and synthetic yarn; the latter claims the largest textile mill in the world under a single roof, with 7000 looms. At Greenville, in the west of the same state near the Blue Ridge, various synthetic fibres are woven in a factory containing 2000 looms; and at Graniteville the first important cotton mill to be built in the South (erected in 1845) has grown into a giant factory which produces 56,000 miles of cloth a year!

The textile industry extends into Georgia and Alabama, though the centres are not always in the Piedmont province. Lindale, in the north-west of Georgia near Rome, lies in the Great Valley, and has large cotton mills. In Alabama a works at Sylacauga (40 miles south-east of Birmingham) has developed new techniques in the use of low-grade cotton, and in the production of non-woven material bonded with resin.

Woollen-mills are less common than those producing cotton or synthetic material; but Dublin, in the coast plain of Georgia 50 miles south-east of Macon, manufactures woollen cloth. At Elkin, near the Blue Ridge of North Carolina, an old-established blanket factory is the mainstay of the town; and Leaksville, in the same state, close to the Virginia border, specializes in carpet-making.

The Blue Ridge. The elevated western edge of the Piedmont Plateau forms the Blue Ridge. From a height of 1200 feet the land rises, forested and virtually uninhabited, to elevations of up to 5000 feet or more. Part is preserved for the nation as parkland; all is of great scenic beauty, and much of it is threaded by a highway for the use of the tourist. Remnants of the pioneer stock wrest a precarious living from the inhospitable mountain country. To the student of farming techniques the district ranks as an 'agricultural slum'; but its inhabitants live a life that is probably as full as that of more prosperous regions. We illustrate from the Blue Ridge of North Carolina.

Here the quarrying of mica and feldspar are still important activities, and there are many other ways of earning a living. John Hutchins is the local gunsmith; Ed Whetstine weaves baskets from oak and hickory; Lusk Edwards operates a printing press, and is also the local dentist; Kelse Boone is the blacksmith; Roby Buchanan cuts and sets gems gleaned from the local abandoned mines. Bill Blevins, at 75, is part-time farmer and occasional Baptist preacher. He grows a few acres of tobacco; he quarries building-stone; he hunts and sells the pelts of deer, bear, squirrel, and skunk; he supplies eastern herb companies with ginger root; he is a carpenter, and also builds chimneys.[1]

The Great Appalachian Valley

For over 800 miles from Alabama to New Jersey the ancient rocks of the Piedmont and the Blue Ridge are flanked to the west by a structural trough which has been named the Great Appalachian Valley. It is occupied by portions of many rivers, and different parts of it carry different names. In eastern Pennsylvania it appears as the Kittatiny, the Lebanon and Cumberland valleys; in Virginia a medial ridge appears, and separates the two 'forks' of the Shenandoah river (Fig. 31); farther south it is named the valley of east Tennessee, and in Alabama and Georgia it is occupied by the Coosa river.

The Great Valley has been etched out of a persistent band of rela-

[1] John Ross, 'My Neighbours hold to Mountain Ways', *National Geographic Magazine*, June 1958.

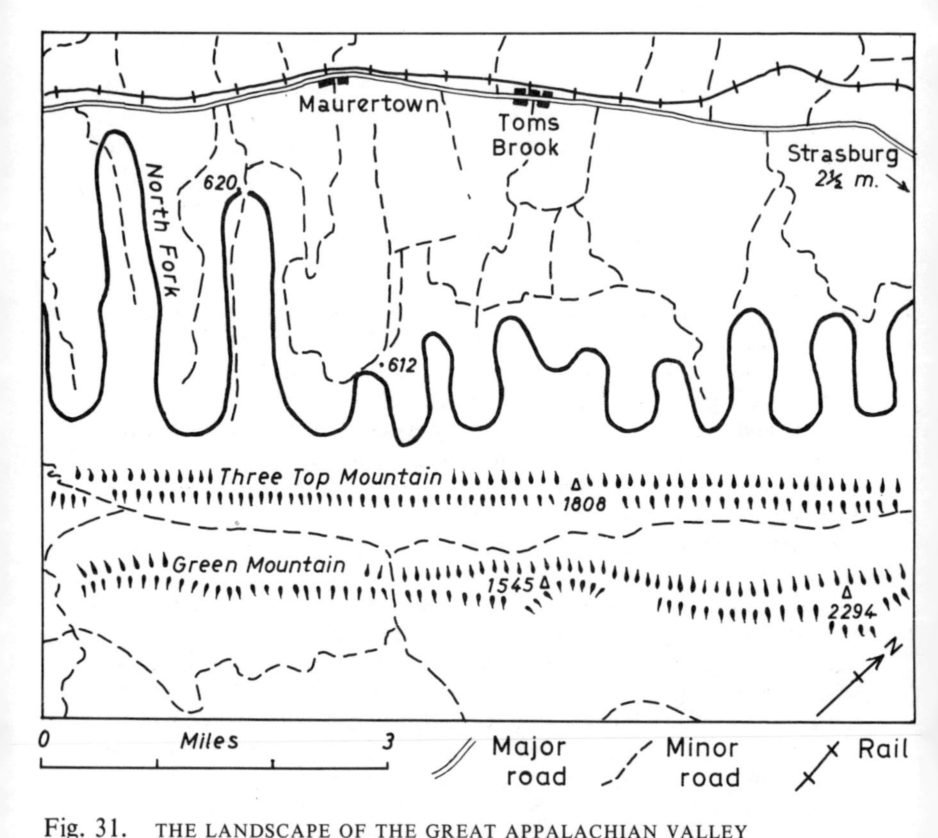

Fig. 31. THE LANDSCAPE OF THE GREAT APPALACHIAN VALLEY

This portion of the Valley is occupied by the North Fork of the Shenandoah. The soils, based on Silurian limestone, are fertile, and support a close settlement, as the network of roads indicates. *Based on the official 1:62,500 map, Strasburg quadrangle, Virginia, 1947.*

tively soft Silurian limestone, which dips north-westward at a sharp angle. It weathers into a fertile soil, so that in this narrow strip we find a prosperous farming community, a belt of relatively dense population, and a string of thriving towns.

The towns have their characteristic industries, and we illustrate them from the northern part of the valley, in Maryland and parts of the nearby states. Chambersburg and Timbersville produce apple purée and juice from the apple orchards for which the valley is famous. Hagerstown uses local maple, walnut, and spruce timber for organ parts, and supplements these by imported materials. Front Royal and Waynesboro have rayon industries based on local pulp. The limestone itself is quarried on a large scale for flux and for use in the glass, paper, paint, and synthetic-rubber industries. Below the surface are strings of caverns, and a major highway (the Valley Pike) makes these accessible to the motorist, so that a thriving tourist industry adds to the resources of the Great Valley.

The Ridge and Valley Province

To the west of the Great Valley is a sub-region where long, narrow, and steep-sided ridges alternate with deep longitudinal valleys. This strange topography can hardly be paralleled anywhere else in the world. It is the result of the erosion of strata of differing resistance, which have been thrown into tight folds, so that their limbs dip steeply. Often the folds themselves have been tilted along their axes (that is, they are pitching folds), and this betrays itself on the surface by a series of zigzag ridges (Fig. 32). The drainage has accommodated itself to this bold pattern of

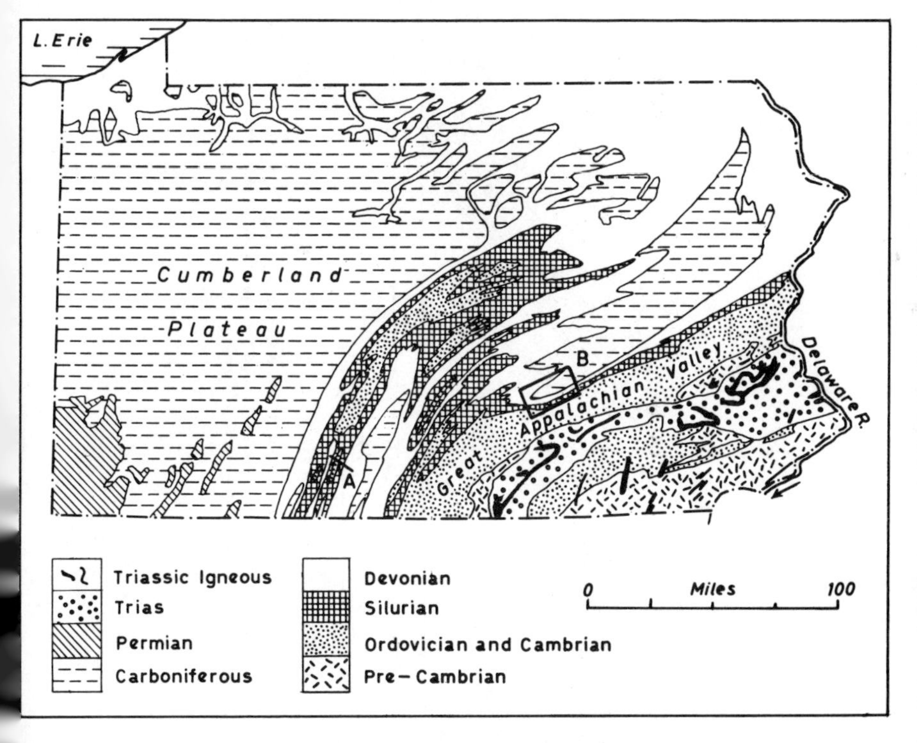

Fig. 32. THE SURFACE GEOLOGY OF PENNSYLVANIA

The diagram illustrates the level strata of the Cumberland Plateau and the intricate zigzags of the Ridge and Valley Province. The Great Appalachian Valley is here formed of Ordovician and Cambrian material; the Piedmont Plateau is largely replaced by the Triassic lowland. The structure along line A is shown in Fig. 33; the topography and structure in rectangle B are illustrated on a larger scale in Figs. 34 and 35. *Based on the 'Atlas of American Geology'.*

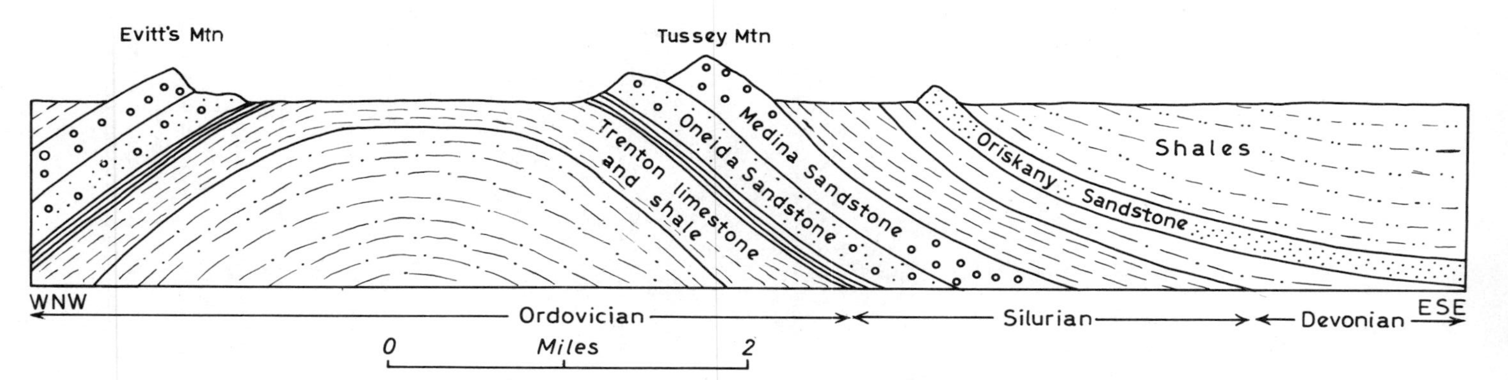

Fig. 33. CLOSE FOLDING IN THE RIDGE AND VALLEY PROVINCE

This section across an upfold in the Ridge and Valley Province of Pennsylvania illustrates the simple but close folding that is typical in this part of the Appalachian ridges. Its line is indicated on Fig. 32. *Based on the 'Atlas of American Geology'.*

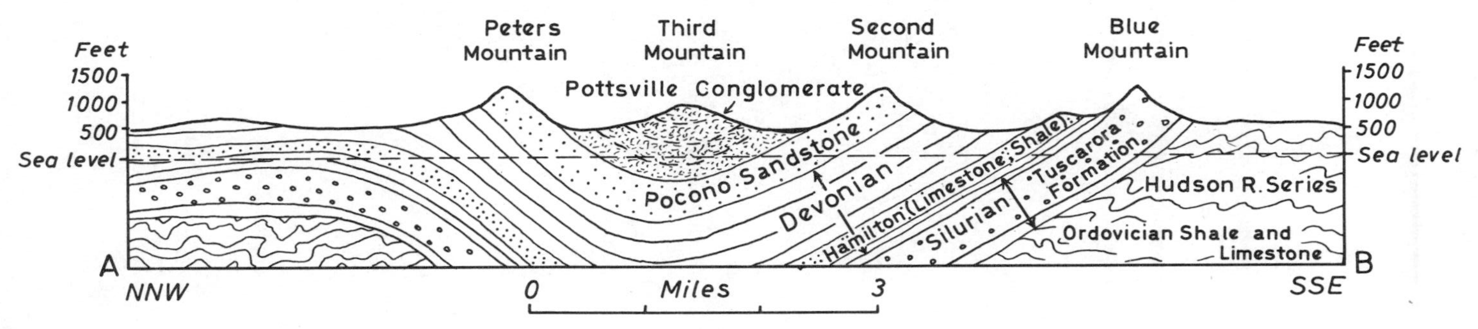

Fig. 34. A GEOLOGICAL SECTION EAST OF THE SUSQUEHANNA RIVER

This section, which runs east of the Susquehanna river on Fig. 35, shows that scarps sharper and higher than the Kent and Sussex Downs of South-east England, which there span 60 miles, are here condensed to 6 miles.

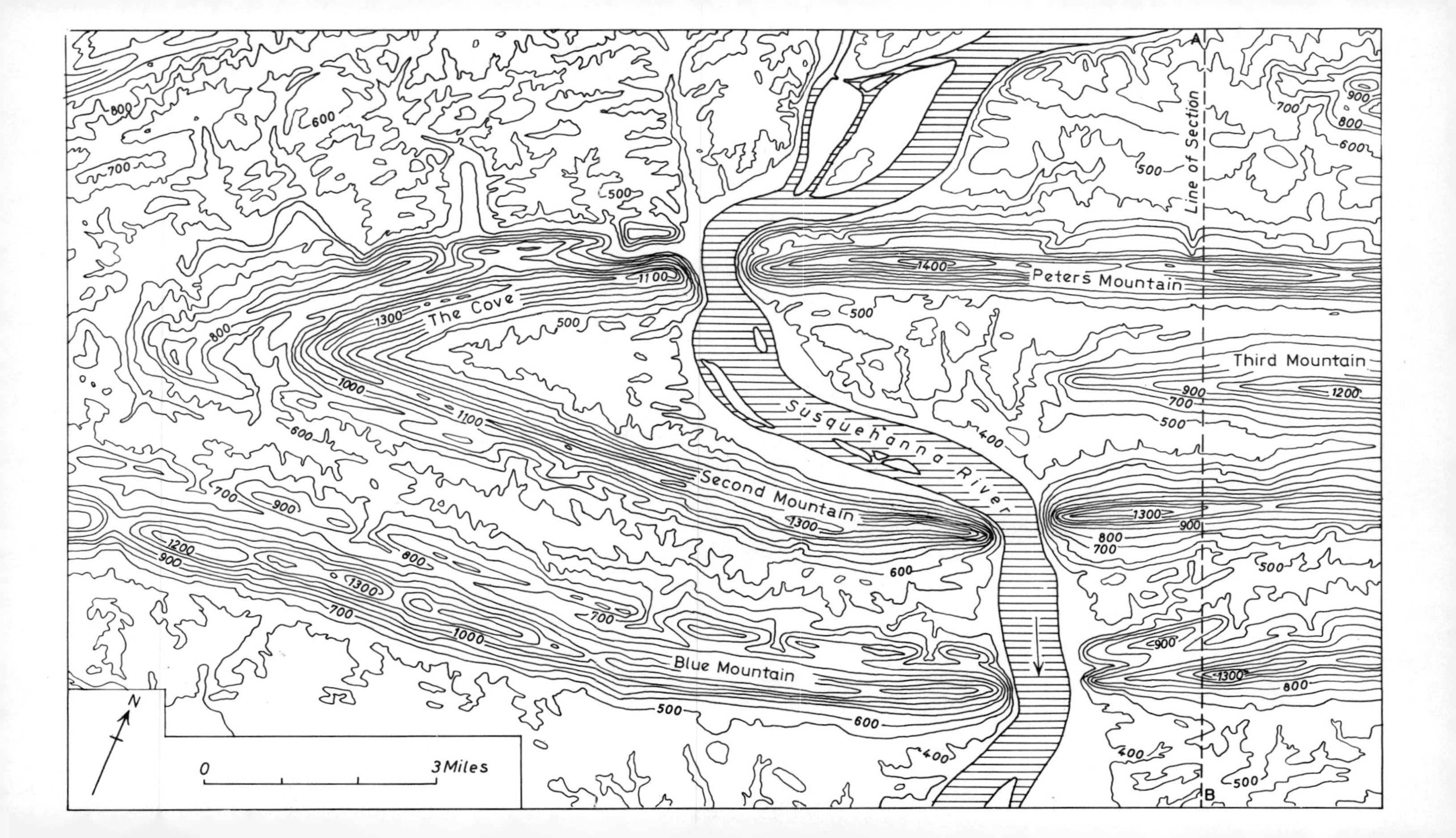

A
B
Line of Section
Peters Mountain
Third Mountain
Susquehanna River
The Cove
Second Mountain
Blue Mountain
N
0
3 Miles

relief, and here we find clear examples of a trellis type of drainage. The rocks range from Ordovician to Carboniferous in age, and among them the chief scarp-formers are the Tuscarora and Medina groups (Silurian), the Oriskany Sandstone (Devonian), and the Pocono group (Carboniferous) (Figs. 33, 34).

In the northern half of the Ridge and Valley Province the main streams drain south-eastward, and this is a relic of the past. Some controversy exists regarding the evolution of the landscape, but the views of A. K. Lobeck[1] may be summarized as follows: The existing rivers originated when the land rose from the Cretaceous and Tertiary seas and a slight arching directed the drainage to the north and the south. The rivers first entrenched themselves in the cover of younger rocks, and then stripped them off. Once their courses had been established they could not be changed, and the rivers began to cut across the more resistant bands of material below, while their side-streams etched out valleys in the weaker strata. So have arisen the deep river gaps, such as those of the Susquehanna north of Harrisburg, where the river has achieved the apparently impossible task of cutting through three parallel ridges: Peters Mountain (1400 feet), Second Mountain (1300 feet), and Blue Mountain (1200 feet), while the river itself flows at a little above 300 feet (Fig. 35).

The ridges have accordant summits, which reflect the peneplain of Tertiary times (the Schooley peneplain); at a much lower level the rivers pursue winding courses which indicate a later lowering in sea-level: this is the Harrisburg peneplain, at about 550 O.D. in its type area. The meanders, now incised, of the two 'forks' of the Shenandoah river are so symmetrical that they remind one of a text-book diagram rather than an actual river (Fig. 31).

The Ridge and Valley Province is by no means deserted. It is true that the ridges present formidable barriers: they are wooded to their summits, and there are few through routes across them. But every longitudinal valley has its road or railway, which serves a string of villages and farms (Plate 3).

The Ridge and Valley Province is largely rural, but in the north-east

[1] See, for example, *Atlas of American Geology* (Geographical Press, Columbia University, New York, 1932).

Fig. 35. THE LANDSCAPE OF THE RIDGE AND VALLEY PROVINCE

These transverse gaps cut by the Susquehanna river must have been initiated at a higher level. They have formed important routes to the interior, though for the sake of clarity communications are omitted from this map. The shape of The Cove is due to a pitching anticline. The area lies just north of Harrisburg, Pennsylvania, and its location is indicated on Fig. 32, p. 89, while its structure is shown in Fig. 34. The contour interval is 100 feet. *Based on the official 1:62,500 map, Harrisburg quadrangle, 1899, reprinted 1937.*

of Pennsylvania is the important anthracite coalfield. This is the largest producer in the United States, and accounts for about half the entire world output of this rather rare variety of coal. As the geological section (Fig. 36) indicates, the pressures of Carbo-Permian times have thrown the strata into tight folds. The district indicated is near Shenandoah, about 50 miles south-west of Scranton, and here there are three ridges and furrows in the space of only two miles.

It is clear that the mining conditions stand in complete contrast with those on the Cumberland Plateau: the seams dip at all angles, and mining is difficult. There is nothing to correspond with the famous Pittsburgh Seam farther west. It is true that the remarkable Mammoth Bed reaches the astonishing thickness of 50 feet; but it is restricted in area. The whole anthracite field extends over only 484 square miles; in contrast, the Pittsburgh Seam alone covers about 14,000 square miles, while the total area of the Appalachian bituminous fields is estimated at 70,000 square miles.

The chief producing valley in the anthracite field is that occupied by the Susquehanna below Pittston, and by its tributary the Lackawanna; but coal is raised also in the valleys of the headstreams of the Schuylkill and the Lehigh, tributaries of the Delaware. Scranton, on the Lackawanna, is the largest town of the district. With a population of 125,000, it is a university centre, and in addition to its mining activities manufactures silk and woollen goods. The valley, however, is almost completely built-up, from Carbondale in the north-east, through Scranton, Pittston, and Wilkes-Barre, to Nanticoke in the west. Essentially mining towns, they have in addition developed tobacco and textile industries, for these offer the opportunity of employment for the womenfolk.

Almost the whole of this coal is moved out by rail to the nearby cities for central heating, and it is indeed fortunate that the world's largest built-up area (Megalopolis) is close to the world's largest anthracite coalfield. These populous mining and manufacturing valleys are now linked to Philadelphia by a fast motor road, the north-eastern extension of the Pennsylvania Turnpike. But the future of the anthracite coalfield appears to be in some doubt, for the current production is less than a quarter of what it was 40 years ago.

Trans-Appalachian Routeways. The Mohawk–Hudson gap provides the only crossing of the Appalachian system entirely below 500 feet; but

---

Plate 3. A PORTION OF THE RIDGE AND VALLEY PROVINCE NEAR HUNTINGDON, PENNSYLVANIA

The lofty, straight, and barren ridges, of resistant limestone, stand in striking contrast to the watered and productive farm-lands of the valleys, which are floored by soft shales. Huntingdon lies about 70 miles west of Harrisburg, Pennsylvania.

Photo by courtesy of the Commonwealth of Pennsylvania Department of Internal Affairs

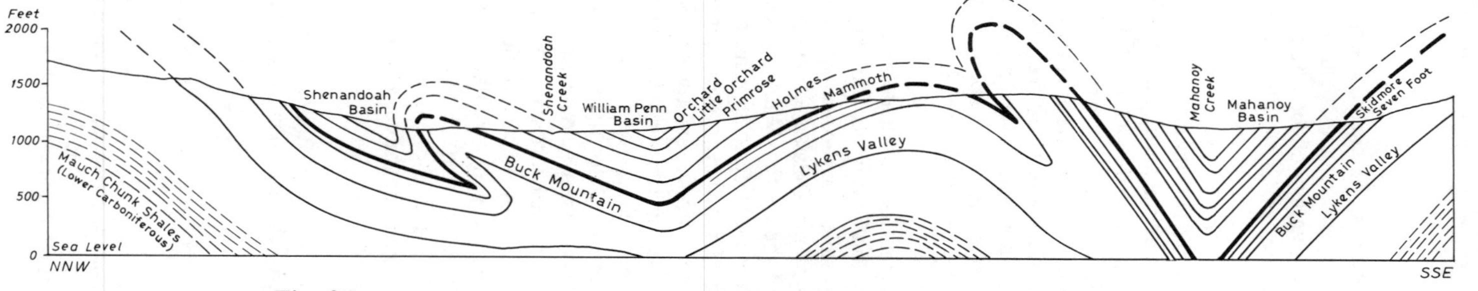

Fig. 36. A GEOLOGICAL SECTION ACROSS PART OF THE ANTHRACITE COALFIELD

The continuous black lines represent coal seams, which are named. The thicker line represents the Mammoth Bed, which reaches 50 feet in thickness. The length of the section is little more than two miles, yet in this there are three folds. Modified after W. J. Miller, 1925, quoting the U.S. Geological Survey.

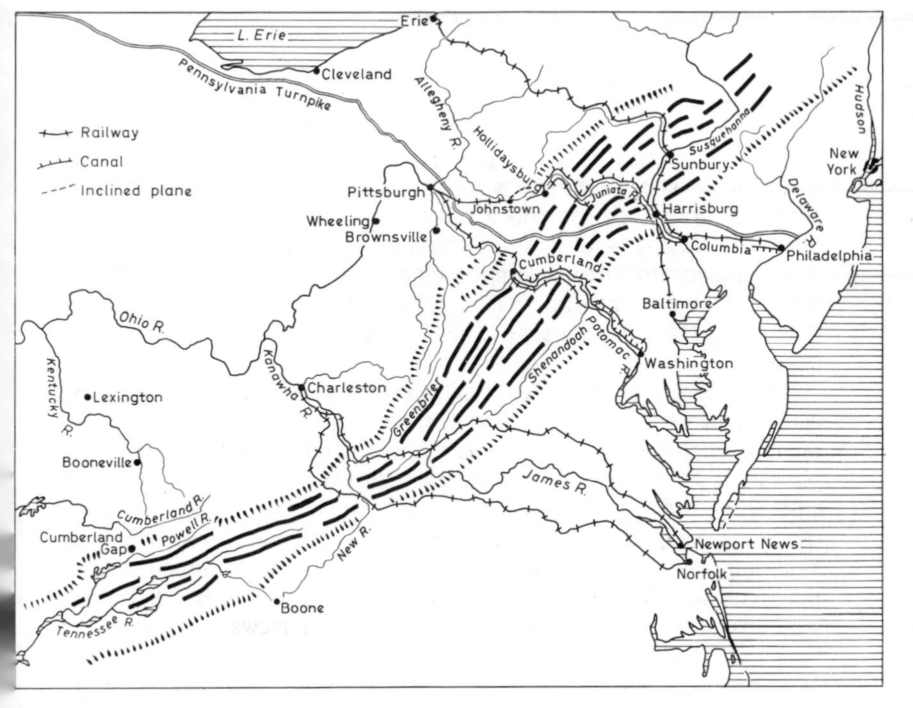

Fig. 37. TRANS-APPALACHIAN ROUTES

The diagram illustrates the main routes across the Appalachian ridges. The edges of the Cumberland and Piedmont plateaux are shown by hachures; the ridges are diagrammatic, and for clarity only the main rivers are inserted.

the maps reveal that almost every river, as it zigzags its way through the ridges, is followed by roads and railways. Some of these routes have had greater significance than others. Here we notice five of them: they are, from north to south, the Susquehanna route, the Potomac valley (the 'Cumberland Road'), the James-Greenbrier valleys, the New River gorge, and the Cumberland gap route ('Boone's Road') (Fig. 37).

The Susquehanna has long formed an important routeway through the ridges. There are rapids in its lower reaches, so that no large town has grown up at its mouth, and roads, railways, and canal connections have made the Susquehanna traffic tributary to Philadelphia. But above the rapids the river was navigable for small craft right into New York state. For part of its course the river was paralleled in the nineteenth century by a canal: this linked Philadelphia to the river at Columbia, followed the main-stream as far as its right-bank tributary, the Juniata, and continued up-stream along that river until at Hollidaysburg it reached the formidable scarp of the Cumberland Plateau. This could be surmounted only with the aid of a series of inclined planes, which led boats to the navigable Conemaugh river at Johnstown, and so to Pittsburgh.

Essentially the same route is followed today by the Pennsylvania railroad, busy with the carriage of coal from the Pittsburgh district to Philadelphia and Baltimore. The produce of more easterly mines is gathered up by railways which follow the valley of the west branch of the Susquehanna and join the main-stream traffic at Sunbury. The latest addition to this route is the modern toll-road – the Pennsylvania Turnpike. It uses the same major water gaps of the Susquehanna, near Harrisburg, but then pursues a more southerly path to Pittsburgh and beyond.

The Potomac too has been used at least since the eighteenth century, when pioneers followed the 'Cumberland Road' into the interior. It led them through the ridges, past the town of Cumberland, and on to the plateau near Unionstown. If their destination was Pittsburgh they would embark at Brownsville, below which the Monongahela was navigable; those travellers aiming farther west would continue to the Ohio at Wheeling, and could then make their way by boat to within 60 miles of the fertile and famous Blue Grass district of Lexington. By 1818 there was a regular mail-coach service between Baltimore and Wheeling.

A canal – the so-called Chesapeake and Ohio Canal – was built from Washington, following the Potomac for well over a hundred miles; but it stopped short at Cumberland, and never actually reached the Ohio. The American canals, in fact, were later than their English counterparts, and they were followed so soon by the railways that they proved to be costly failures. The line of the middle and lower Potomac is continued by the Youghiogheny, and a busy railway links the two valleys and carries Pittsburgh coal and steel to Washington.

Farther to the south-west there is no easy crossing of the ridges for over a hundred miles, until the extreme south of West Virginia is reached. Here are two passages, which were not utilized until the railway age. Headstreams of the easterly-flowing James river have cut back close to the Greenbrier, an affluent of the Kanawha river, and the Chesapeake and Ohio railroad uses these valleys to carry coal from the pits of West Virginia eastward to Newport News. Farther south, a parallel railway uses the great gorge cut by the New river to carry its coal to Norfolk, on the opposite (south) shore of Hampton Roads. These are among the busiest railways in the United States, and this stretch of water, shipping over 20 million tons annually, forms the greatest exporter of coal in the world.

Still farther south is the famous route pioneered in the 1770's by Daniel Boone, and now followed by a railway. Boone led his party south-westward, following the Appalachian ridges for 300 miles or more. Striking westward, he crossed the plateau scarp at Cumberland gap, where Virginia meets Kentucky and Tennessee. Here he followed an Indian trail northward, and this took his party to the Lexington Blue Grass district. His name is commemorated in Boone, in the Blue Ridge, and Booneville, in the Blue Grass district.

The Tennessee Valley Authority. In the south-central parts of the Ridge and Valley Province – in the 'panhandle' of Virginia and in eastern Tennessee – the land is drained by tributaries of the Tennessee river. Those tributaries which rise in Virginia pursue parallel longitudinal courses towards the south-west: they include the Powell, Clinch, and Holston rivers. Others, rising in North Carolina, have cut transverse valleys, and perhaps represent superimposed streams similar to those we have seen farther north: they include the Hiwassee, the Little Tennessee and the French Broad river (Fig. 38). Since 1933 all have been brought within the sphere of a single planning agency, the Tennessee Valley Authority (T.V.A.).

We may illustrate the need for such an agency by quoting an example from eastern Tennessee. About 50 years ago copper was discovered in the mountains of eastern Tennessee. In order to smelt the local ores a plant was established at Ducktown; for fuel it used the local hardwood timber, and the forests were felled for this purpose within a radius of seven miles. The remaining vegetation was killed by the sulphurous fumes from the smelter. Then came the heavy rains which are characteristic of the Appalachian ridges. Without its protective cover of grass and trees the land was soon cut into great gullies 20 feet deep or more, while the loosened soil clogged the rivers and began to silt up the reservoir of a power company downstream.[1]

This is a particularly notorious example of the evils of soil erosion, but it has occurred over large areas of Appalachia, wherever trees have been cut down on moderately sloping land without replanting, and wherever soils have been impoverished severely through bad farming.

T.V.A. is a multi-purpose organization which aims to improve the social and economic life over the entire basin of the Tennessee river. The region has an area four-fifths the size of England, and a population of about 4½ million. T.V.A. seeks to improve the methods of agriculture by establishing experimental plots and by the production cheaply of phosphate fertilizers; it tries to repair the ravages of soil erosion by afforestation and other methods; it controls the flow of the river and its tributaries by ponding back the water in a series of barrages, so that the Tennessee has now become a great stairway of artificial lakes (Fig. 39). At each barrier the falling water is harnessed to produce electricity,

[1] The example is quoted by David E. Lilienthal, *T.V.A.* (Penguin Books, 1944). A photograph of the eroded land in question appears in the current edition of *Encyclopædia Britannica* under the heading 'Tennessee'.

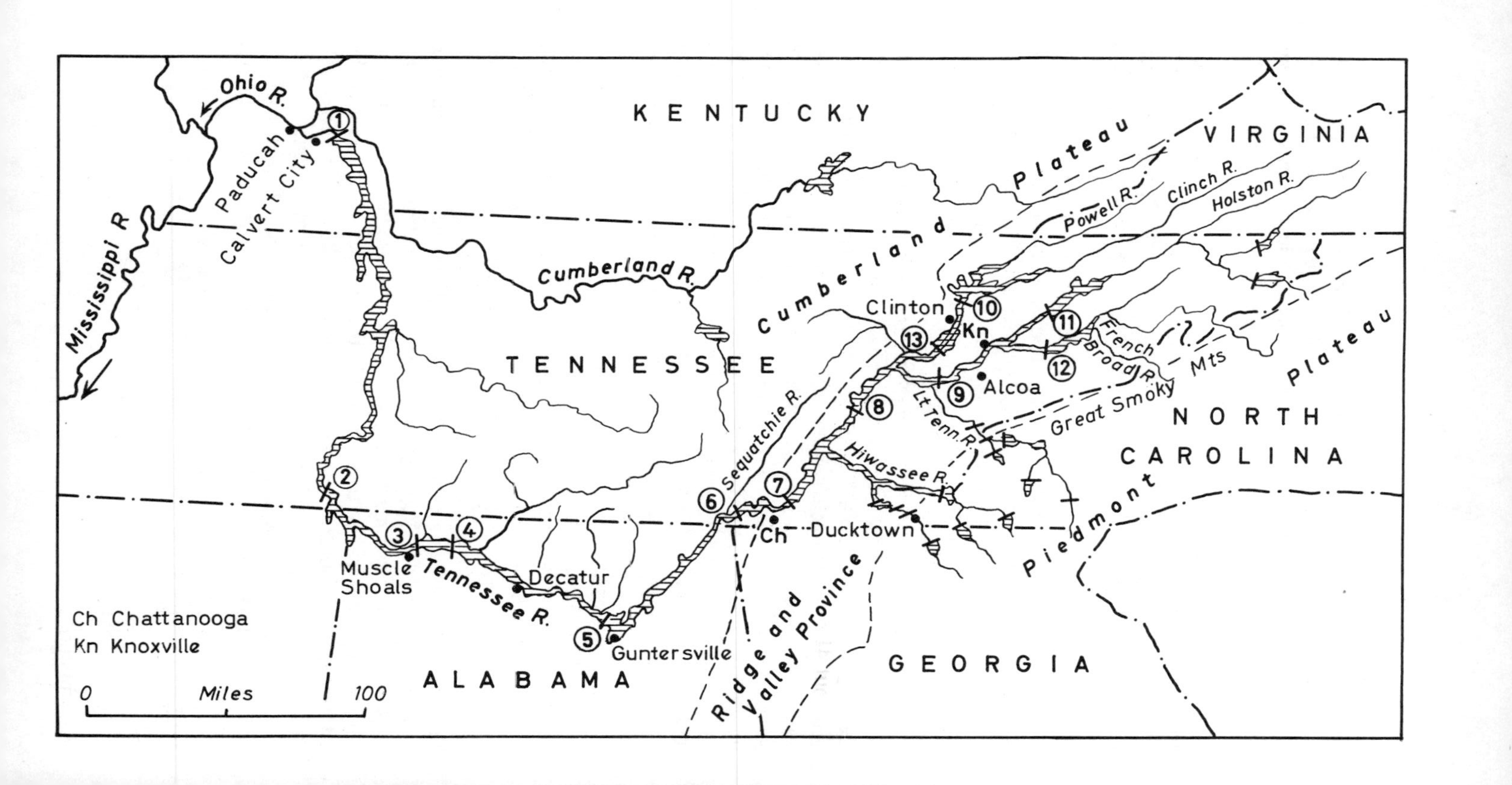
KENTUCKY
VIRGINIA
TENNESSEE
NORTH CAROLINA
GEORGIA
ALABAMA
Ohio R.
Mississippi R
Paducah
Calvert City
Cumberland R.
Cumberland Plateau
Powell R.
Clinch R.
Holston R.
Clinton
Kn
Alcoa
French Broad R.
Great Smoky Mts
Plateau
Lt Tenn. R.
Hiwassee R.
Sequatchie R.
Ch
Ducktown
Piedmont
Ridge and Valley Province
Muscle Shoals
Tennessee R.
Decatur
Guntersville
1
2
3
4
5
6
7
8
9
10
11
12
13
Ch Chattanooga
Kn Knoxville
0
Miles
100

and locks are inserted to allow navigation. While navigation and water-power are important aspects of the work of T.V.A., one of its primary objectives is flood-control. This we may illustrate from a single example in 1964.

During March 14th and 15th, 2 to 3 inches of rain fell over the eastern half of the valley. Without regulation this would have produced a crest of 31·9 feet of water at Chattanooga, and since the flood-level is 30 feet, serious damage would have been caused. T.V.A. cut off the flow of water from the tributary storage dams and allowed several feet of additional water to accumulate in the main-stream reservoirs. This reduced the crest by 8·6 feet, so that there was no flooding.

T.V.A. has a creditable list of achievements. In 1963 it opened its twenty-first dam – Melton Hill Dam on the Clinch river. Before 1933 there were dangerous shallows on the Tennessee at Muscle Shoals, and for long periods in the year there was only 4 feet of water to Chattanooga and only 1½ feet beyond. Now the shoals have been submerged and a 9-foot navigable channel has been provided as far up-stream as Knoxville, in the heart of the Ridge and Valley Province, and extended as a result of the new dam by a further 38 miles up the Clinch river, to the neighbourhood of Clinton. This waterway links with the Mississippi system, so that 30 states now have water connection with the Tennessee valley.

'Tow' boats push trains of 5–18 or even 24 barges through the locks and along the reservoirs: they carry coal and coke to the riverside power stations, stone, sand and gravel, petroleum products, and grain, to the extent of over 10 million tons annually. A new record of traffic was set up in 1963, when 14·4 million tons of cargo were handled.

In 1933 only three per cent. of the farms in the valley were supplied with electricity. Now virtually every farm is so served. The consumption of electricity in the valley per head of population is now more than twice the national average, while its cost to the consumer is only half the average price. So great has been the expansion in the use of electricity that it could be met only by the construction of new steam plants, and in 1964 77 per cent. of the total power produced was thermo-electricity, from nine T.V.A. steam-generating stations. The coal required for this purpose amounted to 22·9 million tons, so that T.V.A. is the largest single consumer of coal in the United States. More than half of it is derived from western Kentucky. The total installed capacity of all the

Fig. 38. THE TENNESSEE BASIN

The map shows the physiographic and state boundaries and the positions of the dams. The major dams are numbered as follows: 1: Kentucky; 2: Pickwick; 3: Wilson; 4: Wheeler; 5: Guntersville; 6: Hales Bar; 7: Chickamauga; 8: Watts Bar; 9: Fort Loudoun; 10: Norris; 11: Cherokee; 12: Douglas; 13: Melton Hill.

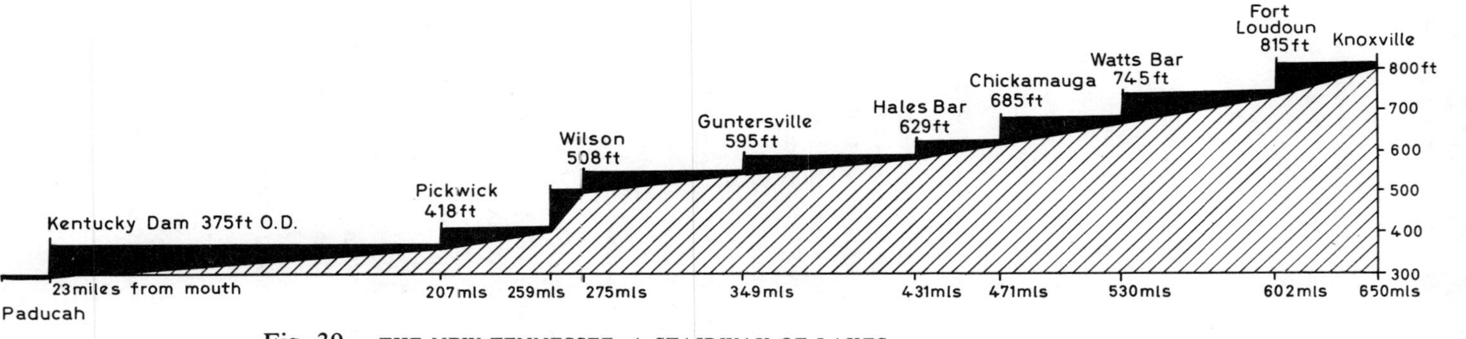

Fig. 39. THE NEW TENNESSEE: A STAIRWAY OF LAKES

At each dam there are lock gates and a power-plant, and the waterway has a minimum depth of 9 feet for 650 miles. The heights refer to the tops of the lock gates.

power-plants in 1964 was 13·4 million kW, and of this only 4 million consisted of hydro-electric capacity. It was therefore with some dismay that the coal-producers learned in the summer of 1966 that the next major T.V.A. generating station is to be an immense nuclear plant. Its capacity will be 2200 MW, and it is scheduled for completion in 1970.

Farming has greatly benefited since the establishment of T.V.A. During the First World War a plant was built at Muscle Shoals for the production of nitrates; this has been converted to the production of phosphate fertilizers, which are supplied cheaply to the farms. Now the farmers of the region use five times as much fertilizer per head as does the average farmer in the nation as a whole. Between 1934 and 1960 the quantity of milk produced in the valley trebled; the value of all the crops sold increased by $3\frac{1}{2}$ times, and the value of all the livestock produce increased by 6 times.

Industry too has expanded as a result of the activities of T.V.A. The cheap electricity has fostered the growth of many branches. The Tennessee valley is now a major producer of aluminium, at Thorpe and other centres. Alcoa, in the upper Tennessee valley, has the world's largest aluminium rolling mill. Towns such as Chattanooga, Knoxville, and Decatur have developed ferro-alloy, chemical, and petro-chemical industries, and the processing of wheat, maize, sugar, and oilseeds. Guntersville, formerly a mile from the river, now has navigable water at its doorstep, and new industries have appeared there: they include the assembly of motor-cars, the processing of soya beans, and the manufacture of animal food. Calvert City grew from a mere village of 300 people in 1948 to a town of nearly 20,000 by 1958: its inhabitants work in more than 20 chemical and metallurgical plants.

These are remarkable achievements. Finally, we may mention the control of malaria. In 1933 40 per cent. of the people in the valley were commonly infected with malaria; and in places the proportion rose to 76 per cent. It has been found, however, that an oscillation of the level of the water in the reservoirs by about two feet during the breeding season will effectively kill the larvae of the malaria mosquito, and now the valley is free from the disease.

The Cumberland Plateau

A bold east-facing scarp forms the western limit of the Ridge and Valley Province. Beyond it the landscape is in complete contrast to that farther east: in place of the steep-sided ridges we see a plateau of almost horizontal Carboniferous strata, whose summit level lies at about 2500 feet at the scarp in southern Pennsylvania and about 2100 feet in south-eastern Tennessee, decreasing westward.

Into this plateau surface the main rivers have cut deep trenches, in whose sides the more resistant bands stand out to form terraces. Wide

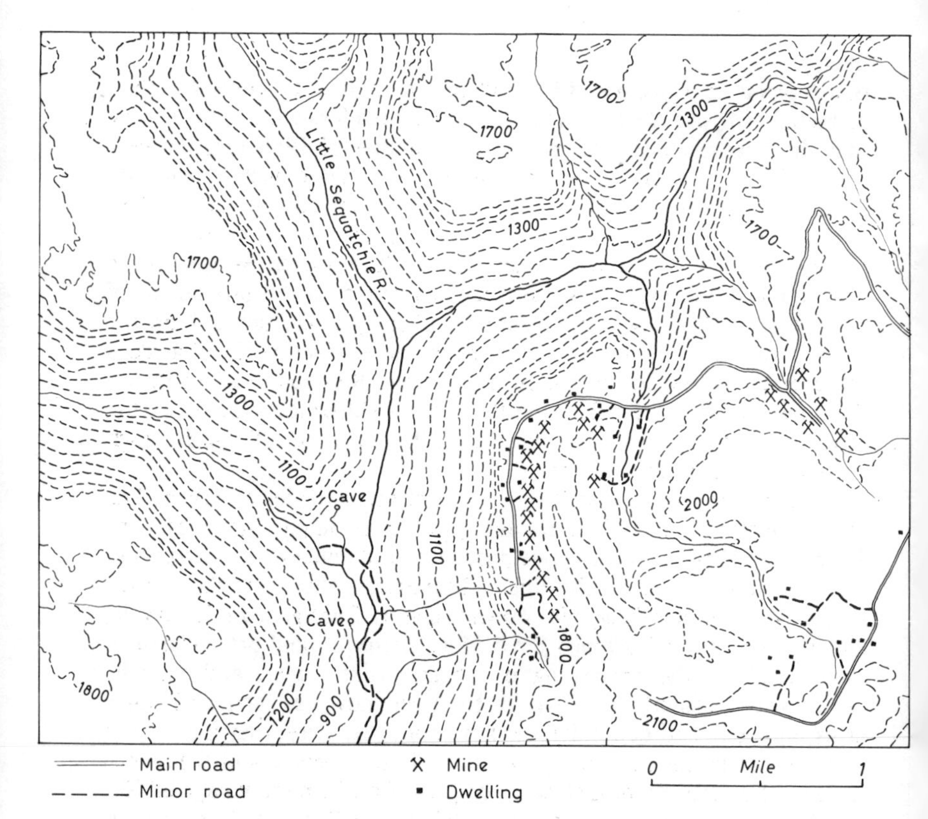

Fig. 40. COAL-MINES IN THE CUMBERLAND PLATEAU

The map illustrates a portion of the Cumberland Plateau in Tennessee. The row of coalpits in the valley side suggests that a coal seam outcrops at about 1750 feet above sea-level. The contour interval is 100 feet. *Based on the official 1 : 24,000 map, Whitwell quadrangle, Marion county, 1950.*

areas of the plateau are underlain by coal seams, and these are sufficiently near the surface to be exposed in the sides of the valleys. Here we find populous mining valleys, and in two localities – Pittsburgh and Birmingham – steel industries. Thus in eastern Tennessee rows of coalpits can be seen above a bench high up at about 1750 feet on the side of the Sequatchie river valley. A road links the mines together, and the coal evidently reaches the market by lorry. In one area four miles square there are no fewer than 74 pits (Fig. 40).

The Birmingham District

We have already discussed the Pittsburgh area (p. 57): for though physiographically it falls within the Cumberland Plateau, from the point of view of economic geography its affinities are with the Great

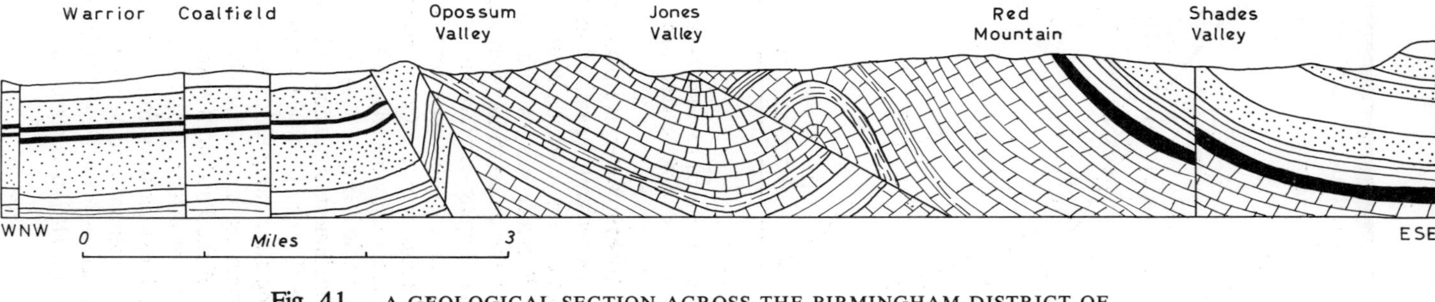

Fig. 41. A GEOLOGICAL SECTION ACROSS THE BIRMINGHAM DISTRICT OF ALABAMA

Eastward of Opossum valley the strata are of Cambrian to Silurian age, and illustrate the sharp folding of the Ridge and Valley Province; west of Opossum valley the strata are of Carboniferous age and the structure reflects the Cumberland Plateau. The ore outcrops in Red Mountain and the fluxing dolomite in Opossum valley. *After C. F. Jones and G. G. Darkenwald.*

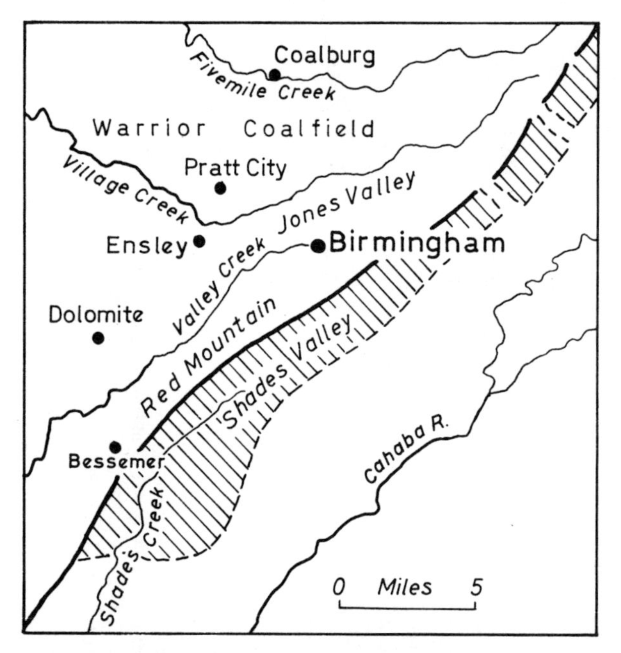

Fig. 42. THE BIRMINGHAM DISTRICT

The dark line marks the outcrop of Clinton ore and the lined area its underground extent. Pratt City is named after the main coal seam, four feet thick, and Dolomite from the fluxing limestone.

Lakes. The Birmingham district, however, is isolated and self-sufficient in its raw materials, and is conveniently examined here. We can hardly assign it to any one sub-region, for it stands close to all of them; and here the Ridge and Valley Province merges with the coast plain. The highly disturbed Silurian and Devonian strata pitch south-westward and disappear below the gently dipping Cretaceous and younger rocks. Twenty miles to the east is the southern terminus of the Great Appalachian Valley, here occupied by the Coosa river; to the west the Cumberland Plateau is represented by the almost horizontal Carboniferous strata of the Warrior Coalfield (Figs. 41, 42).

Here is a remote but flourishing steel district, with a capacity of about 3½ million tons a year. The Warrior Coalfield a few miles to the west yields a good-quality coking fuel, though it cannot quite compare with that of Connellsville. The main seam, the Pratt, is about four feet thick, compared with the six feet of the Pittsburgh seam.

The iron for the Birmingham district is mined in Red Mountain – a long and narrow ridge that flanks the town from the east; it is worked in shallow pits, and supplies are estimated to be ample for a century or so. A suitable fluxing limestone occurs in the local Silurian rocks, so that the three major raw materials are all found within a radius of about five miles, and the cost of steel-making here is lower than anywhere else in the continent.

Birmingham, however, is far from the traditional markets for steel, and the South uses less machinery in its farming than other regions. Nevertheless, local steel-using industries are developing in the district. At Bessemer, 15 miles to the south-west, are the works of the Pullman-Standard Company, the world's largest manufacturers of railway trucks: they are reputed to produce a railway wagon every ten minutes of each working day. Within reach of the district also are three important motor-car plants, all of them at Atlanta (Georgia), about 140 miles east of Birmingham. In the same state, at Newnan (about 115 miles east of Birmingham), is a large plant that manufactures elevated steel water-tanks. The oil industry of the Mid-Continent and Gulf fields is also an important consumer of Birmingham steel.

The largest single steel-producer is the Tennessee Coal, Iron and Railway Company, situated in Ensley, one of the Birmingham suburbs. It employs 32,000 people in the production of rails, billets, slabs, ingots, and pig iron. A speciality of the district is the production of pipes, and two other firms engage in this branch. The steel industry has been joined by non-ferrous metal producers: copper tubes are made at Decatur (Alabama, 75 miles north of Birmingham), and aluminium is produced near Florence, on the Tennessee river, in the same state.

THE MAJOR CITIES: PHILADELPHIA, BALTIMORE, AND WASHINGTON

We have already referred to Megalopolis (p. 2), and must now briefly examine the origin and development of the three main centres in our region.

Philadelphia (population, 1960: city, 2,002,509; urban area, 3,635,228)

Philadelphia, 'city of brotherly love', originated as a Quaker settlement. It provides one of the clearest examples of deliberate planning and construction in a city that has prospered and grown into one of the largest on the continent. It is now the fourth in size in the United States.

In 1681 Charles II granted to William Penn the patent for the territory of Pennsylvania. In a letter dated September 30, 1681, to the commissioners for the new province, Penn instructs them as follows:

> Let the Rivers and Creeks be sounded on my side of Delaware River, especially Upland in order to settle a great towne, and be sure to make your choice where it is most navigable, high, dry and healthy. That is, where most ships may best ride, of deepest draught of water, if possible to Load or

unload on ye Bank or Key side. . . . Such a place being found out, for Navigation, healthy situation and good soyle, for Provision, lay out ten thousand acres contiguous to it in the best manners you can . . .[1]

The commissioners carried out their instructions faithfully. They chose a site between the Delaware and Schuylkill rivers, where the current sweeps along a concave bank of the Delaware and provides deep water. Here they laid out a rectangular grid of streets. At the centre of each quarter they left an open square, and where the four quarters met, a central, larger square (Fig. 43). Here was later built the city hall: covering $4\frac{1}{2}$ acres, it is one of the largest single buildings in the whole of the United States.

Within a generation the new city boasted 5000 inhabitants, and was shipping flour to the West Indies, as the first leg of a triangle of trade

[1] Quoted by Jean Gottmann, *Megalopolis*, 1961, p. 176.

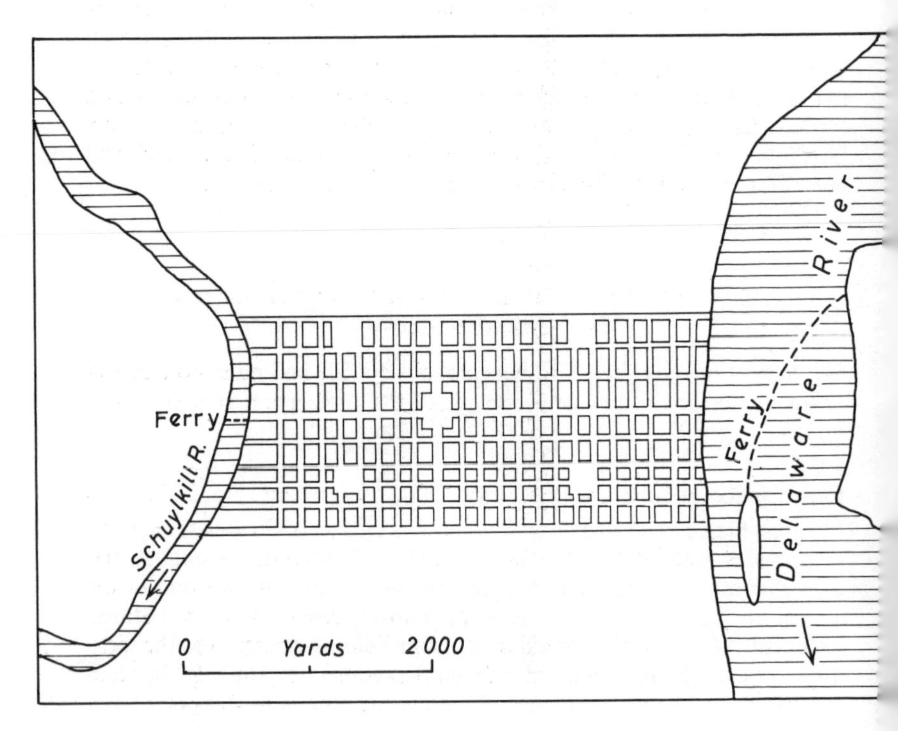

Fig. 43. EARLY PHILADELPHIA

The map shows the appearance of Philadelphia in 1777, nearly a century after its foundation. plan became the prototype for many American cities. *Based on a plan in the British Muse reproduced by Jean Gottman in 'Megalopolis', 1961.*

with England. As settlement extended westward into the Piedmont and southward along the Coast Plain, Philadelphia became a route-focus, and its expansion was rapid. By 1760 it had surpassed Boston in population, and in 1775 it claimed to be second only to London in the British Empire. Only when the Mohawk-Hudson route was opened up did Philadelphia yield in commercial importance to New York.

The prosperity of modern Philadelphia stems largely from its port activities, and in this connection the whole of the lower Delaware river ranks officially as a single port. Recent dredging has provided a 40-foot channel as far up-stream as Morrisville, where the river makes its right-angled bend. In the city itself is a whole row of general-cargo jetties, and both above and below are many important privately owned piers where bulk cargoes are handled to serve the adjoining industrial plants. A group of seven refineries accounts for the fact that more than half of all the nation's imported oil is handled in this river.

At Morrisville are the large integrated works of the United States Steel Corporation, and the Delaware river ports receive ore not only for these, but to supply steel-works farther inland. At Wilmington and at other points along the river are chemical works, and two large sugar-refineries import a million tons of raw sugar annually. In sum, the Delaware ports receive a greater tonnage of overseas cargo than any other port of the United States. They also form an important centre for shipbuilding, and carry out naval contracts. At Camden was built the world's first nuclear-powered merchant ship – the *Savannah.*[1]

Baltimore (population, 1960: city, 939,024; urban area, 1,418,948)

The city of Baltimore was founded (after two earlier attempts) in 1729 where waterfalls offered potential power for the grinding of wheat grown in the Piedmont Plateau. As at Philadelphia and New York, flour was a staple article of export to the West Indies. Annapolis, closer to the tide-water of Chesapeake bay, had been chosen as the state capital of Maryland (which it still is); but it was soon surpassed as a market and port by Baltimore. Farther inland, this city could collect more easily the tobacco and other produce from the plantations, and it lay on the direct land route southward from New York through Philadelphia.

By about 1800 Baltimore had established a flourishing commerce with Europe and the West Indies, and its shipbuilders had evolved a characteristic craft in the speedy, streamlined schooners known as Baltimore clippers.

An important industry of Baltimore is the manufacture of fertilizers: this began with the import of guano from Peru in the middle nineteenth century, and by the 1930's the city had become the greatest centre of the

[1] Port details are from Gunnar Alexandersson and Göran Norström, *World Shipping* (John Wiley, 1963).

fertilizer industry in the world, and its products played a great part in restoring the fertility of the cotton and tobacco lands of the South.

In 1887 a steel-plant was established at Sparrows Point, on a peninsula on the southern outskirts of the city. Several times enlarged, this now has an ingot capacity of $7\frac{1}{2}$ million tons, and is probably the world's largest integrated steel-works. It relies on imported ore, to the extent of over 9 million tons annually, so that in the United States Baltimore is second only to Chicago as an ore-receiving port. Some of these imports are passed on to inland steel centres. The Sparrows Point steel-works supply the important local canning industry with tinplate, and the shipbuilding industry with structural steel; in addition they are well placed to supply steel products to the west coast.

In a state of nature the northward connections of the port were hampered by the 150-mile-long southward-pointing peninsula to the east. A canal was cut across its neck as early as 1829; this, the Chesapeake and Delaware Canal, has been deepened to 35 feet, and results in the saving of a day's sailing to and from Europe and the American ports to the north.

Washington, D.C. (population of metropolitan area, estimated, 1965: 2·4 million)

Washington, like Canberra and Brasilia, is one of the few towns deliberately planned as capital cities on virgin sites.

During the War of Independence Philadelphia had been the usual centre of government for the emerging nation, until mutinies of 1783 made this a dangerous centre. When the Constitution was drafted in 1787 Congress was authorized to administer a suitable district of up to 10 square miles as a seat of government, and the states of Maryland and Virginia indicated that they were ready to cede land for the purpose. President Washington favoured a site on the Potomac river; and in 1790 Congress passed a bill enabling him to appoint three commissioners to select and plan a site on that river, ready for Congress to enter in 1800.

A site was chosen at the junction of the Anacostia river with the Potomac; the land was surveyed, a magnificent plan was drawn up, and building began. But in 1800, when Congress moved in, only one wing of the Capitol was ready; Washington was a city of marsh and unpaved streets without houses, and members of Congress had to be housed in nearby Georgetown (now part of Washington). It was not until the Civil War (1861–65) that Washington was fully accepted as the national capital.

The original plan of Major Pierre Charles L'Enfant has in general been followed. There are two foci – the Capitol (Parliament building) and the White House (official home of the President). These are joined

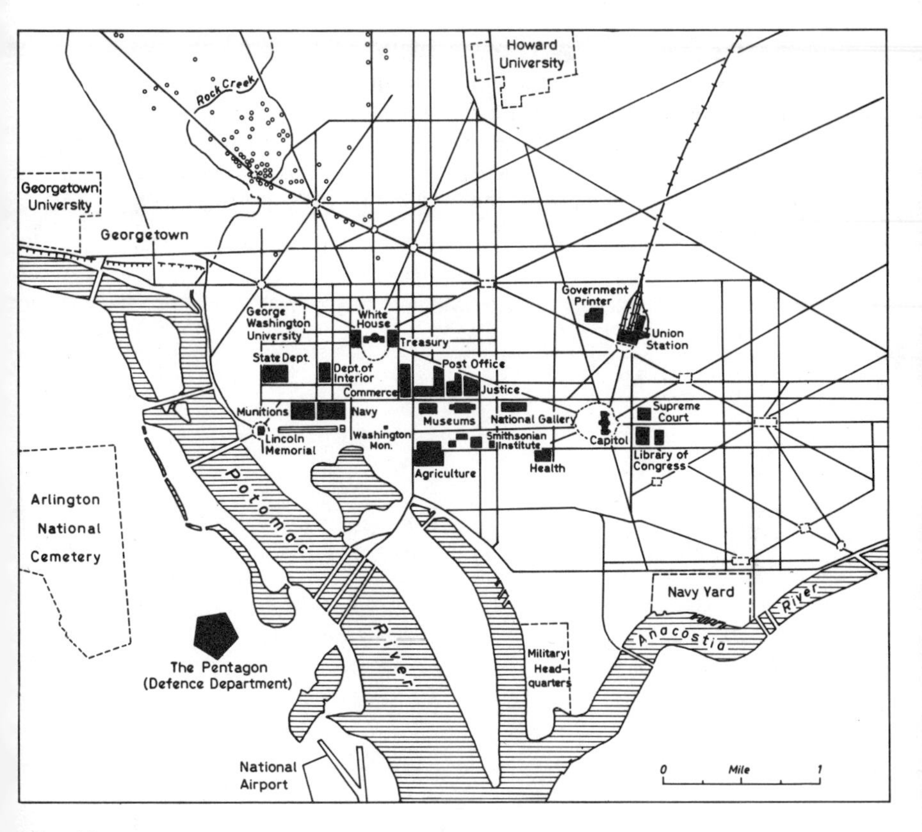

Fig. 44. WASHINGTON, D.C.: THE CENTRAL AREA

The map indicates some of the more important buildings and institutions, together with the framework of the street plan. The small circles represent the locations of foreign embassies and legations.

by a belt of parks and landscaped gardens, which extends also westward, past the Washington Monument to the Lincoln Memorial, overlooking the Potomac. In this belt are the departments of Government and the principal museums and art galleries (Fig. 44).

The naval and military headquarters are to the south, with river frontages; west of the Potomac are the Pentagon (Defence Department), the airport, and the national cemetery. Theatres, shops, and hotels are mainly to the north and east of the White House, while the embassies and legations are grouped within a bend of Rock creek, a small left-bank tributary of the Potomac.

Washington is a major centre of learning: the Library of Congress and the Smithsonian Institution are among the world's largest of their kind, and there are many other cultural institutes. The city houses two cathedrals and no fewer than five universities! It has long outgrown the original 10 square miles authorized in the Constitution, and the 69 square miles of the District of Columbia: metropolitan Washington now spreads over 1500 square miles, and its inhabitants number more than 2 million. Like other planned capitals, it has few industries apart from printing and publishing, the preparation of foodstuffs, and the care of tourists.

CHAPTER FOUR

THE SOUTH

Introduction

The name of this region is misleading: geographically it would be more accurately described as the South-east; but it received its name during the period before the Civil War, when the lands west of Texas were little known, and not part of the Union.

While the region has a measure of physical unity, its 'personality' stems essentially from its culture. As Carl Sauer once wrote, 'The South is one of the greatest cultural units of the U.S.A.'

One of the characteristics of the Southern way of life was the plantation system, which was introduced from Barbados. It was characteristic of an agriculture that depended on a single cash crop, invariably a tropical plant, and one that required considerable labour for its successful cultivation. The system had its beginnings in the early tobacco plantations of Virginia, where indentured white labour was employed; but it reached its greatest development in the cotton plantations, using the labour of imported Negro slaves. The earliest examples were established in the Sea Island district of Georgia and South Carolina, particularly at Charleston and Savannah. In addition to cotton and tobacco the plantations produced rice, indigo, and sugar-cane in a region which stretched from Virginia to Louisiana, and from the Carolinas to beyond the Mississippi.

Southern institutions held sway throughout the Piedmont Plateau, whose broad valleys could support a flourishing agriculture. But the populations of the less congenial uplands to the west were too poor to own slaves, and had little sympathy with the Southern way of life. During the Civil War period West Virginia in fact broke away from the rest of the state and joined the Northern cause, and there were strains in Kentucky, though no real break. Farther west, the Mississippi lowlands formed an extension of the region to the north. Beyond it the South terminated at the beginning of the prairies of Texas: this region was as yet thinly peopled, for the Southern farmer was suspicious of these treeless plains, which were apparently unsuited to farming.

The Historical Background

The present-day activities in the South can be properly appreciated only in the light of their historical development. We have mentioned the early plantations of Charleston and Savannah: the long-stapled Sea Island cotton was introduced here as early as 1786. At first the arduous process of separating the lint from the seed could be carried out only by hand; but in 1793 Eli Whitney's cotton gin mechanized this stage of production and formed a milestone in the growth of the cotton trade. Exports to North-west Europe now began to expand.

Politically the western limit was formed by the Mississippi river, for beyond it lay French territory. But in 1803 the United States purchased 'Louisiana' from France; this included not only the area of the present state of Louisiana, but also a vast region bounded to the south by Texas and extending as far as the Rockies. Only the southern fringe was potential cotton land; but plantations could now be established beyond the Mississippi into what are now the states of Louisiana, Arkansas, and Oklahoma. In 1845 Texas was incorporated into the United States, and settlers were enabled to spread westward as far as the environment appeared favourable.

The Civil War had profound effects on the region. Exports to Europe ceased, and other countries took advantage and captured part of the trade. The defeat of the South was followed by the abolition of slavery. Plantations that were not abandoned were subdivided and share-cropped by former slaves, or subjected to other forms of tenancy. Cotton cultivation declined in the south-east in favour of extensions westward into Texas.

In 1892 the boll weevil was first noticed, at Brownsville in Texas: this was to become a scourge of the Cotton Belt. Yearly it advanced eastward. By 1910 it had crossed the Mississippi, and in 1921 had spread over the whole region. Its ravages have varied from year to year, but have been most serious in the more humid east, in spite of attempts to control it by the use of poison sprays and by the practice of burning the stubble. A general effect of the weevil has thus been to encourage the spread of cotton-growing into the drier districts of the West.

The inter-war years were a period of fluctuation and transition, during which the modern cotton belt took shape. In 1933 the Government introduced price control and acreage limits, and the Soil Conservation Service encouraged improved methods of farming by making payments to those who followed the official advice. There was an increased use of irrigation in the West, and of machinery generally.

The general result has been a redistribution of cotton-production within the belt. In the east the Sea Island district and the Black Belt of Alabama have declined, and there has been some reduction too in the Piedmont Plateau. Currently the chief producing districts are the Inner coast plain and north-eastern Alabama. In the centre of the belt the Mississippi bottom lands remain important; in the west the chief producers are the Black Prairie of Texas and the Grand Prairie of Texas and Oklahoma, a small district on the coast of southern Texas, and, farther inland, the Texas High Plains. In the last, cotton is grown with the aid of irrigation.

Physical Basis

Having sketched the historical background of cotton-growing, we may now discuss its physical basis. The South includes the Gulf coast plain and most of the Atlantic coast plain, the Piedmont Plateau, the Mississippi lowlands, and the interior plains of Texas and Oklahoma, and we may examine these in turn (Fig. 45).

The coastal plains are built up on sands, clay, and limestones of Cretaceous and Tertiary age, which dip seaward. Since the strata are of differing resistance, erosion has resulted in a series of scarps that face north-west along the Atlantic shore and north along the Gulf shore. The soils are varied, but much of the area is covered by red and yellow earths which are easily tilled and agriculturally useful, provided they are kept in good heart; but they are light in texture, and if neglected are prone to gullying and sheet erosion. They range from the thin sandy soils of the pine barrens of Georgia and the Carolinas to the rich soils, derived from limestones, of the 'black belts' of Texas and Alabama.

Florida forms a distinct unit, and separates the Atlantic and Gulf coast plains. It forms a block of limestone irregularly covered by sands. A sandy ridge about 200 feet high extends from the north-west through the northern third of the peninsula; to the south the land surface is only a few feet above sea-level. The limestone displays solution features, and there is much underground drainage. Along the east coast a narrow belt of sandspits and dunes yields light soils that are suitable for agriculture.

In the Piedmont Plateau our region overlaps with Appalachia (Chapter Four), and its structure is noticed there. Its surface consists of a rolling, deeply dissected plateau, rising from about 100 feet in the east to over 1500 feet in the west, and culminating in the Blue Ridge. Several distinct ranges combine to form the Blue Ridge: among them are the Unakas and the Great Smoky mountains. The Piedmont soils vary in fertility: the thin grey soils of the upper slopes are of little value, but in the valley bottoms and lower slopes are deeper and comparatively productive brown soils.

The Mississippi lowlands comprise a broad belt of level land extending about 600 miles from Cairo (at the junction of the Mississippi and the Ohio) to the Gulf of Mexico. In the lower reaches there is a constant struggle to prevent flooding, and some of the more fertile soils are denied to agriculture through waterlogging. But the land needs to be only a few feet above the mudflats to be valuable: there are rich loam-covered ridges in the old meander cores, and on the east bank between Memphis

High Plains
Break of the Plains
Low Plains
Grand Prairie
Eastern Cross Timbers
Black Prairie
Dallas
Waco
Rockdale
Austin
Beaumont
Houston
Port Arthur
Texas City
Corpus Christi
Lake Charles
Cairo
Memphis
Natchez
Baton Rouge
New Orleans
Black Belt
Unalsa Mts
Great Smoky Mts
Blue Ridge
Atlanta
Inner Coast Plain
Charleston
Savannah
Flatwoods
Flatwoods
Tampa
Miami

0 Miles 300

Alluvium
Tertiary
Cretaceous
Older rocks
Archaean and associated rocks of the Piedmont Plateau

ELEMENTS IN ITS STRUCTURE AND GEOLOGY

and Natchez the wind has redeposited the silts of the flats to form a ridge of inherently fertile loess.

West of the Mississippi lowlands lie the plains of Texas and the neighbouring parts of Oklahoma, separated into the Low Plains (to the east) and the High Plains (to the west) by the dissected scarp known as the Break of the Plains. At a lower level are two 'prairies' – the Black and Grand prairies – which in their turn are separated by a thin sandy formation, the Eastern Cross Timbers. Both prairies are famous for their fertile marly soils, and have been extensively cultivated.

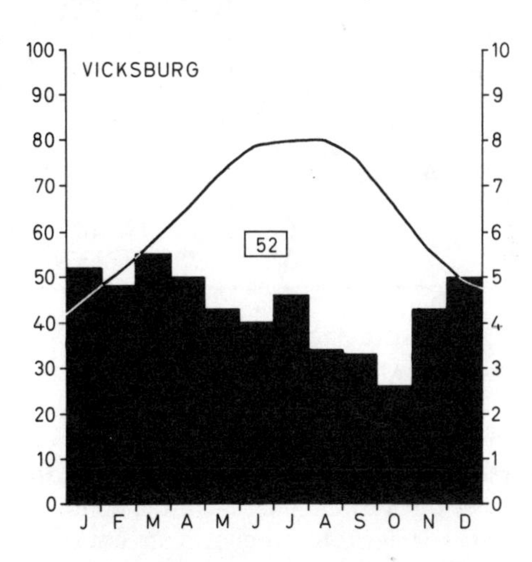

Fig. 46. VICKSBURG: TEMPERATURE AND PRECIPITATION

The graphs in this and similar figures are all drawn on the same scale for easy comparison. The initials along the base are those of the months. Mean monthly temperatures are plotted as a line graph, whose scale, in degrees Fahrenheit, is shown on the left-hand axis; mean monthly precipitation is indicated by column graphs, whose scale, in inches, is shown on the right-hand axis. The number enclosed by a rectangle represents the total precipitation for the year.

The South possesses a characteristic climate which may be summarized as humid and sub-tropical. No area experiences prolonged cold. The growing season is everywhere long, ranging between six months in the north and eight to nine months in the south. In most parts the mean annual rainfall is over 40 inches (Fig. 46); on the exposed slopes of the Appalachians it reaches 80 inches, and in the eastern portion of the Gulf coast 60 inches. The lowest totals of precipitation are found in eastern Texas, where the mean annual rainfall is between 20 and 30 inches.

Such a climate is broadly favourable for agriculture, but it has its hazards. Temperatures are high for long periods, and the effectiveness of the rainfall is then reduced by evaporation. The rainfall commonly

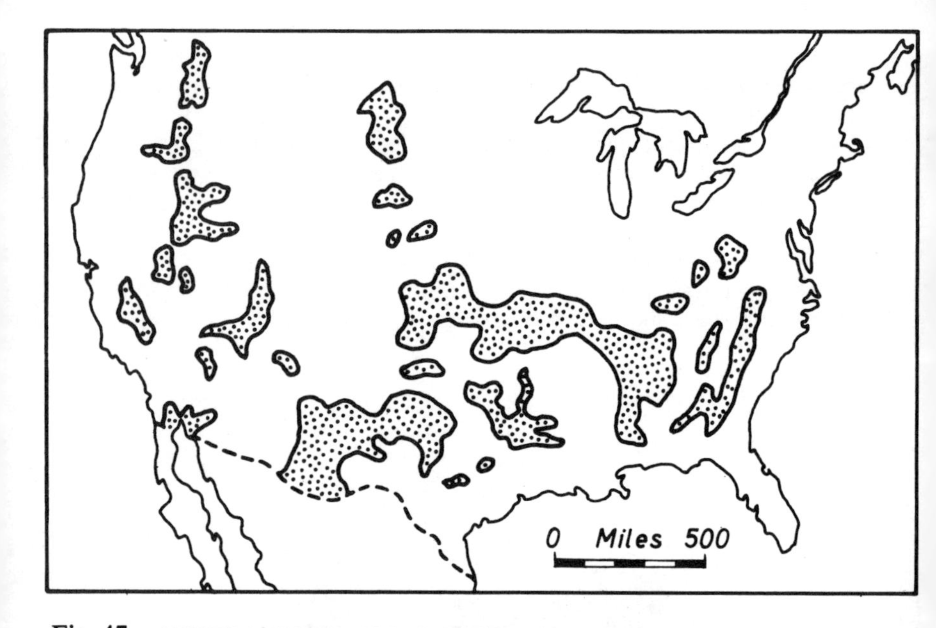

Fig. 47. NORTH AMERICA: SOIL-EROSION

The map indicates the areas within which soil-erosion is a serious problem.

arrives in the form of sudden torrential storms, which hasten soil-erosion. Conversely on occasions there are serious droughts. Furthermore, the South lies open to the interior of the continent: a winter high pressure in this area is likely to produce a stream of cold air down the Mississippi valley. Tropical hurricanes are more restricted in their influence, but locally they may be very destructive. They are more likely to affect the south-eastern half than other parts of the region.

Perhaps the most serious physical problem of the South is soil-erosion. Several elements combine to make the region especially vulnerable. Many of its soils are light, porous and easily moved, and at no time of the year is the ground frozen, when the soils would be anchored. Although the region forms mainly a lowland, it contains within it many districts with some quite steep slopes. We have already referred to the nature of the rainfall. All these are physical factors; but there would have been little soil-erosion without man's interference with the course of nature.

The early settlers stripped the forests from slopes which were too steep for effective cropping. The three major crops of the South – cotton, maize, and tobacco – are planted in rows several feet apart, so that the soil in between has nothing to keep it in place. Much land is left fallow in the winter, and is at the mercy of the agents of erosion. The attitudes of many farmers did not help: in the nineteenth century land was cheap and appeared plentiful; and after the Civil War tenant systems of farming reduced the incentive to conservation.

Soil-erosion has been most serious in the Piedmont Plateau, in parts of the Inner coast plain, the Black Belt of Alabama, and the loess ridge on the east bank of the Mississippi (Fig. 47). Marginal to the South are the eroded lands of eastern Oklahoma and the interior plateau of Tennessee. Since 1935 the Soil Conservation Service has made great efforts to combat the evil of erosion. Improved rotations, terracing, contour ploughing, and the introduction of new plants, such as the vine 'kudzu' and the deep-rooted leguminous perennial 'lespedoza', have all helped to rehabilitate the land. In some cases the landscape has been changed completely, and former cotton-land has become the home of stock-rearing and mixed farming.

The South is still mainly a rural region. Industry has never become closely integrated with the economy; but it is growing in importance, and much of it is quite recent. We first discuss the agriculture of the South, and distinguish two regions. These are the Cotton Belt and the sub-tropical coastlands (Fig. 48).

The Cotton Belt

For long cotton was 'king' of this wide stretch of land; but the recent introduction of more balanced rotations together with pasture and livestock has given many former cotton areas a totally different regime. In its old form the belt has ceased to exist, and many parts of it no longer rank as important producers. There has been a movement towards the drier lands of the West, where with the aid of irrigation improved strains flourish in the High Plains of Texas and beyond in Arizona and California. These newer regions enjoy certain advantages: they have not suffered from long cultivation of the three major crops – cotton, corn (*i.e.*, maize), and tobacco – all of which are exhausting to the soil; neither are they faced with the human problems associated with the Southern tenant and share-crop system.

Within the South cotton is now produced only on the more suitable soils, and throughout the region a wide range of other crops is grown, including wheat, oats, soya beans, peanuts, and many types of vegetables, together with typically sub-tropical crops such as the sweet potato. Animals have long been associated with the South; but the former horses, mules, and poor strains of cattle have given way to high-grade beef and dairy cattle, poultry, and hogs. Yet something of the old South lingers on, for, despite recent diversification, a few crops still dominate, and among them cotton and corn still share the chief place.

The limits of cotton-growing are set by climate. The plant is susceptible to frost, and demanding in the amount and distribution of the rainfall. The northern boundary of cotton-growing closely follows the 77°

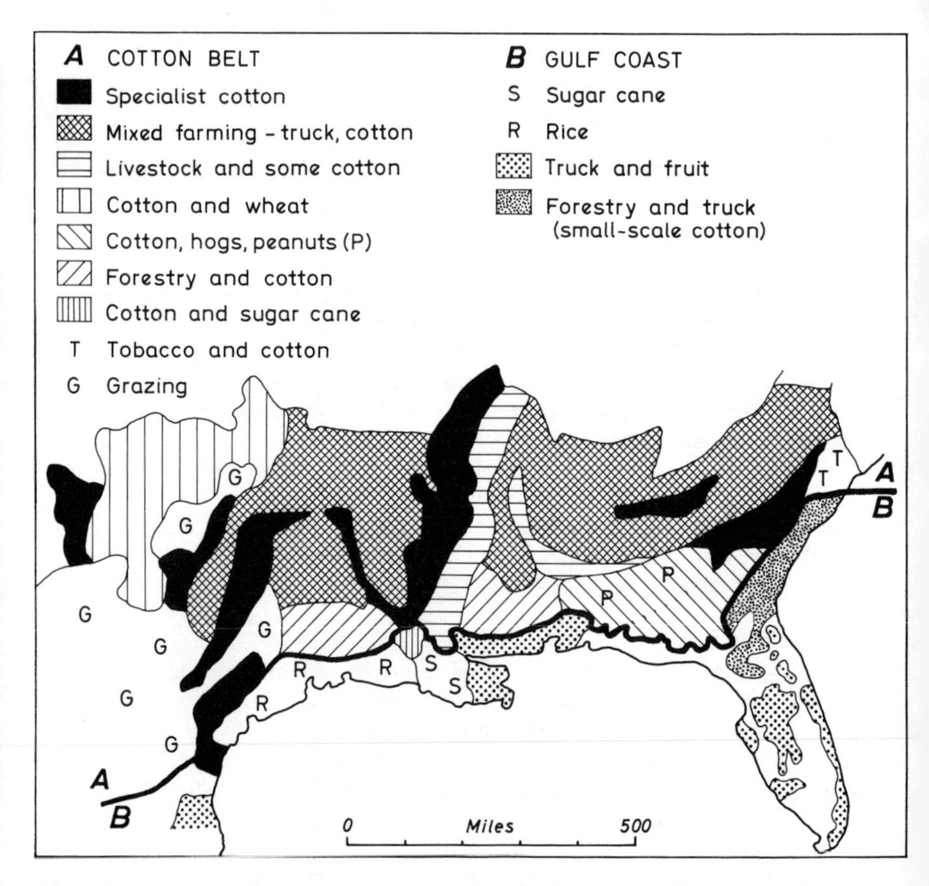

Fig. 48. THE SOUTH: AGRICULTURAL SUB-REGIONS AND LAND USE

July isotherm, and this corresponds broadly with a growing season of 200 days: killing frosts must not occur between the second week in April and the third or fourth week in October. The southern limit occurs where the autumn rainfall exceeds 10 inches. In the east cotton was formerly grown on the coast plains of Georgia and the Carolinas: this was the famous Sea Island district, but this area no longer ranks as the major producer, and a more realistic boundary now is the eastern limit of the Inner coast plain.

Cotton is grown on nearly all the soil types of the region, but yields are noticeably higher on the darker soils of the Mississippi bottom lands and the Black Prairie of Texas. The Black Belt of Alabama, formerly famous as a cotton area, has suffered severely from soil-erosion: in places the limestone subsoil shows at the surface, so that it has become a 'white belt'! – and it no longer ranks as an important producer.

We have already mentioned the location of the chief producing districts (p. 114). The eastern districts have a measure of advantage in that they are close to the textile towns of the Piedmont Plateau; but as a cotton-grower the Piedmont suffers in that it cannot produce cotton of long staple. The central districts, comprising the valleys of the Mississippi and its chief tributaries, the Yazoo, Red, and Arkansas rivers, have the asset of well-drained soils that are rich in lime, and here long-staple grades will flourish. In the western districts the soils of Black Prairie are more fertile than those of Grand Prairie, and the climate of the latter is more marginal. In Black Prairie, however, cotton has to compete with corn, wheat, and livestock-rearing. The only really coastal production takes place in a small area near Corpus Christi, where cotton is grown in conjunction with fruit and vegetables. The High Plains of Texas, as we have seen, form the only district of the South where cotton is grown under irrigation.

It is not surprising that the cotton output of Texas amounts to more than three times as much as that of any other state in the South. There follow in order Mississippi and Arkansas, both in the central district; and no other state approaches these three in production.

Outside the specialist regions cotton is still grown, but nowhere is it dominant: it is subservient to other crops, or to livestock, or to both. The increasing use of pasture and leguminous crops has entailed a striking increase in the number of livestock. The Black Belt of Alabama and Mississippi is an outstanding example: in Dallas county, formerly in the heart of a major producing district, the acreage under cotton fell from 108,100 in 1930 to 34,800 in 1950, and cotton has been almost ousted by the rearing of beef cattle. Livestock have become important too in the Mississippi valley and in the northern part of the Black Prairie of Texas. In south-east Texas and Georgia the specialization is on poultry: Georgia records an almost fantastic increase in the production of broilers to 261 million head in 1957, and leads all states in the South. Dairy farming is widespread: there are concentrations of dairy cattle in the Mississippi valley and Texas, and the three leading states of the South, in terms of dairy cattle, are Texas, Tennessee, and Mississippi. Dairying is also important round the large cities.

In the new Cotton Belt many other crops are grown. Recently introduced fodder crops, together with the sweet potato and the peanut, are widespread. There are concentrations of peanut-production in southern Alabama and Georgia and in central Texas: the crop is used mainly in the fattening of pigs. The sweet potato is produced both as a food crop and a fodder crop: it is also a source of starch, and a factory established in Laurel (Mississippi) manufactures adhesives and starch for textiles from the sweet potato.

Corn for long has been the twin of cotton, and it remains important in the more humid eastern half of the belt, but in the drier parts, such as in Oklahoma and the northern part of the Black Prairie, its place is taken by wheat. Farther west wheat itself is replaced by grain sorghums, such as kaffir corn, feterita, and milo maize.

Vegetables and tree fruits have spread widely. Peaches lead all other fruits. Georgia is acclaimed as the 'Peach State', but is in fact far outstripped by South Carolina. Tomatoes are a feature of north-eastern Texas, onions of the Black Prairie, and melons of central Texas on the western Cross Timber belt. The rise of the frozen-food industry has encouraged these specializations, and many new food factories have been established in the South.

Rice and sugar are long-established Southern crops, and still flourish. They are concentrated mainly along the Gulf coast, but the area under rice is increasing in south-eastern Arkansas.

Forestry too is a major source of wealth in the Cotton Belt. Originally most of the area was timbered country; but, in the south-eastern section particularly, drastic clearing for agriculture depleted the forests. More recently, the improvement of farming has been accompanied by an enlightened campaign to re-establish the forests.

The South in fact contains about half the nation's reserves of saw timber, much of which consists of southern yellow pine. The paper mills exert a brisk demand for pulpwood; over large areas the forests are young, and the future of the industry seems assured. The states with the largest areas under woodland are Alabama, North Carolina, and Georgia, with South Carolina only a little behind.

We illustrate farming in the Cotton Belt by three specimen farms.[1] The first lies in the Black Belt of Alabama (Fig. 49). It was formerly a cotton plantation, but suffered badly from erosion. Now the whole of the land is under either forest or grass, and the farm specializes in the rearing of beef cattle. It covers 540 acres: about 20 per cent. of this is timbered and the remainder grass, a small proportion of which is reserved for hay for the winter.

The second farm is situated in the Mississippi delta (Fig. 50), and comprises 718 acres. Apart from the very small woodland area, it is divided into leguminous meadows, which cover rather less than half, and crop-land, which covers rather more than half, the land. The meadows fatten a herd of beef cattle, and the arable land is almost entirely devoted to cotton, with only 15 acres under soya beans and the same area under corn.

The third is a smaller farm, of 118 acres, and is situated on the sandy soils of the coast plain in Virginia, in the far north-east of the Cotton Belt. A little more than half the area is under woodland (Fig. 51), much

[1] These are based on Edward Higbee, *American Agriculture* (John Wiley, 1958).

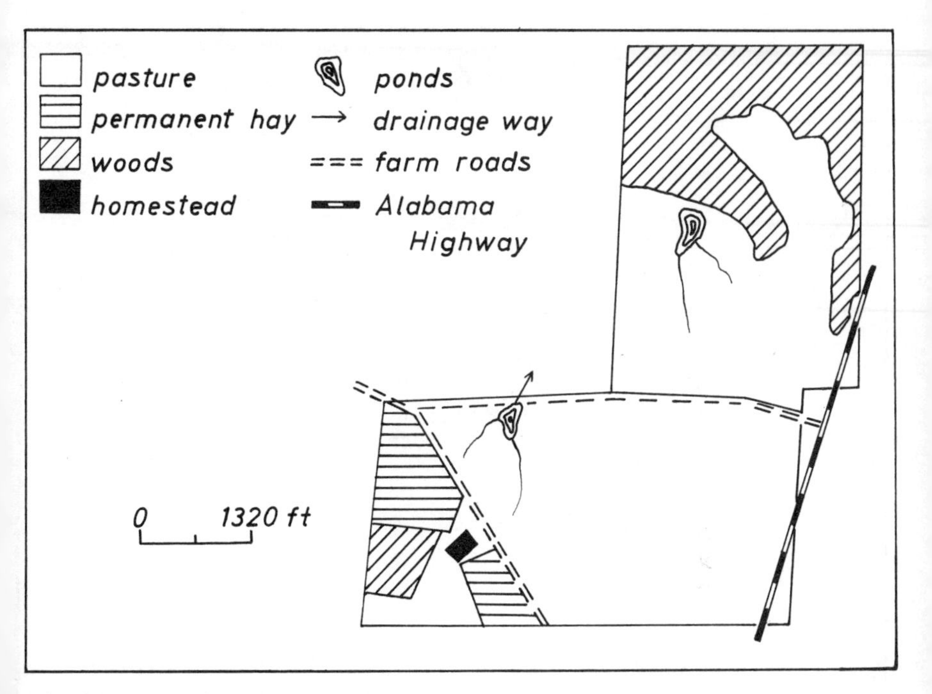

Fig. 49. A FARM IN THE BLACK BELT OF ALABAMA

This and the following two figures, together with Fig. 57 (p. 000), are based on Edward Higbee, *American Agriculture* (John Wiley, 1958). Lines bearing arrows represent drainage ditches, and these do not necessarily form field boundaries: the latter are indicated by thin black lines (without arrows).

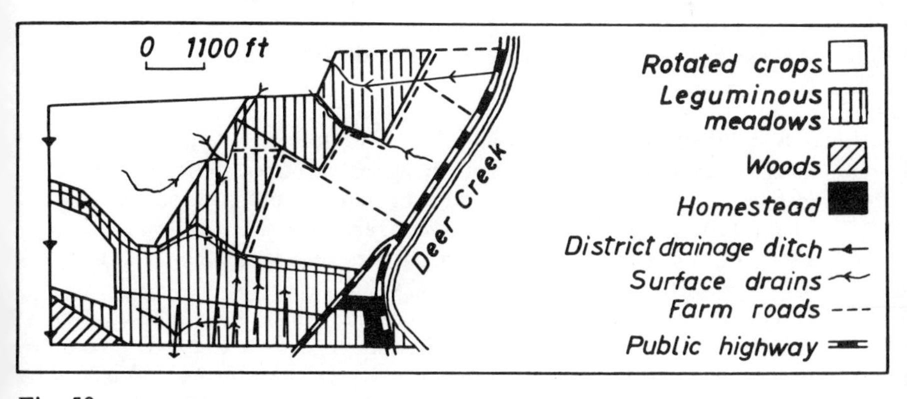

Fig. 50. A FARM IN THE MISSISSIPPI DELTA

See note to Fig. 49.

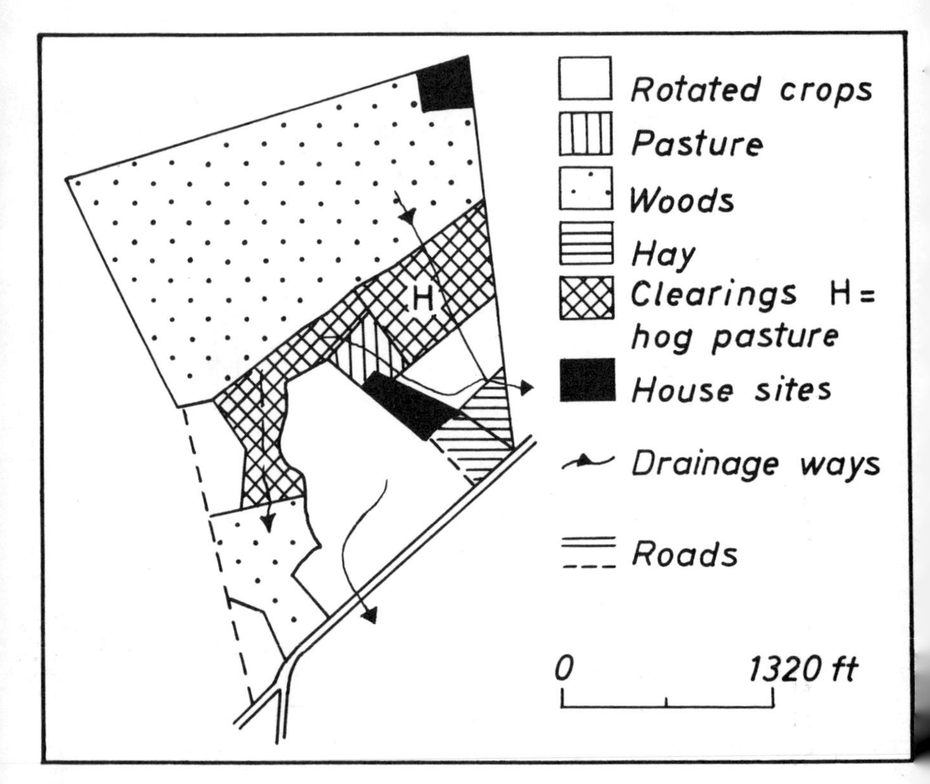

Fig. 51. A FARM IN THE COAST PLAIN OF VIRGINIA
See note to Fig. 49.

of which occupies the poorly drained land. As the land becomes progressively drained, more is set free for crops. The farmer specializes in the growing of peanuts, with which he fattens pigs. Peanut-production makes heavy demands on labour, so that the farm units tend to be small but intensively operated.

The Sub-tropical Coastlands

This, the outer coast plain, is a low-lying region, poorly drained and with large areas of swamp. Its soils tend to be thin, except for the alluvial land of the Mississippi delta. In south-west Texas and the southern third of Florida are coastal prairies and mangroves; elsewhere the light sandy soils support a forest of southern pine – the flatwoods.

The region has a characteristic climate. Mean July temperatures exceed 80°F., while in January they average 50°. Rainfall is comparatively high, for the most part ranging between 40 and 50 inches per annum, but approaching 80 inches east of New Orleans. There is a summer maximum, with a tendency for heavy falls in summer and late autumn. Much of the rainfall, however, is ineffective owing to high rates of evaporation, so that even here drought is a danger, and dry spells are widespread and destructive.

The Gulf coast presents some unique opportunities for agriculture, but suffers also from liabilities. Impeded drainage in the swamp and delta lands makes reclamation schemes a necessity; but when the land is drained the climate permits the growth of a wide range of crops, many of which are suited only to this small part of the country. Neither of the two traditional Southern crops makes much headway here, for the prolonged summer heat is unfavourable to corn, while the autumn rains restrict the growth of cotton. The region is rather a long distance from the north-eastern markets, but not so far away as its great rival, California; and good roads and the growth of a regional market in the South have encouraged the production of specialist crops.

Farming is confined to favoured districts, and the crops consist especially of citrus fruits, vegetables and small fruits, sugar-cane, and rice. In addition there is some livestock farming. Individual areas, however, have their own character.

The citrus fruits are mainly confined to Florida: they are grown in a narrow strip along the east coast, on the low sandhills in the centre of the peninsula, and in a district in the west around Tampa. Oranges and grapefruit constitute the main types, and they are grown in approximately equal proportions. Limes and pineapples cannot stand frost at all, and are confined to the southern tip of the east coast, beyond Miami. The collecting centre for fruit is Orlando, 75 miles north-east of Tampa, and from here much of the fruit is transported by lorry to eastern markets.

Vegetables and small fruits are cultivated more widely, both within the areas already mentioned and farther north along the sandy ridges. Their extension has been made possible by the reclamation of the swampy black soils near Lake Okeechobee and farther south. The crops include tomatoes, celery, and strawberries, together with less familiar examples such as egg-fruit and peppers. In the south sugar-cane and green beans are grown. The tourist trade and expanding towns have encouraged dairy farming and poultry-keeping, while the introduction of improved pastures has led to an increase in the number of beef cattle.

The sugar plantations of the Deep South lie amid the forest-lands of southern Louisiana, and are maintained only through a heavy investment in drainage and equipment. Rice-lands extend westward to the border and far into Texas (Fig. 48). As in Florida, dairy cattle are kept on farms close to the cities, and dairying is important too on the Mississippi delta. The same farms usually rear pigs, for they can be fed on the skimmed milk.

In Texas citrus fruits and vegetables are grown in the far south of the state, on land irrigated from the Rio Grande; the commercial centre for industry is Brownsville. The expanding industrial towns of the region, such as Houston, have encouraged the spread of dairy farms.

Industry in the South

The South is rich in minerals, and many of these form the raw materials for manufacturing industries. Other manufactures are based on farm and forest products: they include textiles, furniture-making, tobacco-processing, and food industries. The aircraft industry of Texas has little geographical basis except for 'good flying weather'. In this section we discuss the industries of the South, and notice their comparatively recent growth. The oil industry, however, is no respecter of cultural boundaries, and stretches into the Great Plains, so that we meet it again in Chapter Six, and in California (pp. 161 and 205). In the north-east our region overlaps with Appalachia; and the industries of the fall-line towns, of the Piedmont and Atlantic coast towns, and of the Birmingham district of Alabama are discussed in Chapter Three (pp. 84–107).

Until the beginning of the Second World War manufacturing occupied only a small part in the economy of the South. Food-processing and cotton textiles, however, are old-established industries. Wartime needs resulted in important expansions in many factories; and in addition the policy of decentralization favoured the establishment here of other activities, such as aircraft-production, shipbuilding, and the manufacture of petro-chemicals. These have remained, and have given the South a more balanced structure.

The greatest single mineral resource of the region is its petroleum. The whole of the Gulf coast field and much of the Mid-Continent field lie within the South, and Texas and Louisiana are the first and second producing states in the U.S.A. The scale of the industry is vast: the comparatively small state of Louisiana produces nearly twice as much as the whole of Canada, and almost as much as any country of the Middle East. Since it is cheaper to move oil to the main centres of consumption in the North-east by tanker rather than by pipeline, most of the oil from the Gulf field is refined locally. A whole row of about 30 major refineries extends along the Gulf shore, and a constant stream of tankers uses their wharves and jetties, so that the shipping route between the Gulf coast and the north-eastern U.S.A. is one of the busiest in the world.

In order of export tonnage the chief ports are Houston (handling about 20 million tons annually), Port Arthur (about 15 million), and Beaumont (about 10 million). Other important oil ports are Corpus Christi, Texas City, Lake Charles, and Baton Rouge. In many instances chemical industries have developed in these ports, using as their raw materials the by-products of oil-refining. The output of these plants includes such varied materials as synthetic rubber, man-made fibres, plastics, and resins.

Associated with most oilfields is natural gas. Until recently much of this was wasted; but now gas pipelines, especially from the Louisiana fields, supply many communities and industries with a valuable fuel.

Apart from oil and gas, the South has several other important mineral deposits. The iron and coal of the Birmingham district we have already considered (p. 106). In Texas there are deposits of lignite (brown coal) in a broad belt that extends into Louisana and Arkansas. Commercial production has begun at Rockdale, about 50 miles north-east of Austin, in south-east Texas, by the Aluminium Company of America. Reserves are estimated to be 200 million tons in this area alone, and most of the lignite is workable by open-cast methods.

Florida is the nation's largest producer of rock-phosphate, and the district forms one of the world's chief sources of supply. The phosphate is worked in a belt 100 miles long and parallel to the west coast of the peninsula; the deposit is near the surface, and is worked by huge drag-line excavators. It is well known as a raw material for fertilizers; but the mineral has many other uses, such as in the manufacture of jellies and preserves, medicines and insecticides.

Other minerals are present, though they are not worked on a very extensive scale: they include sulphur and rock-salt in the coastal districts of Louisiana; and in Texas sulphur, magnesium, bromides, and gypsum.

Three other types of industry need to be mentioned: these are food-processing, timber and associated activities, and aircraft-manufacture. Food-processing was one of the earliest to be established: it includes the canning of fruit and vegetables, flour-milling, sugar-refining, and the processing of corn and rice. All the major ports engage in one or more branches of the industry.

Sawmilling and pulp- and paper-making form an important group of activities, which remind us of the wooded nature of much of the coast plain. We have already referred to paper-making (p. 82): many of the mills have tide-water sites, and among them is the giant Champion Paper and Fibre Company's plant on the Houston Ship Canal. It uses east Texas pine as a source of pulpwood and natural gas for power.

The dry and sunny weather of the South-west has encouraged the establishment both of aircraft test bases and of aircraft-manufacture in the region. Dallas and Fort Worth engage largely in this industry. The most important single unit is that of the Consolidated Vultee Aircraft Corporation at Fort Worth, but two other large plants are also situated in the district, together with several subsidiary producers of components.

Our study of the South concludes with the examination of the sites and functions of a few representative cities.

Atlanta, the state capital of Georgia, lies eight miles from the

Chattahoochee river in the foothills of the Blue Ridge. It stands at the junction between the inhospitable country of the Blue Ridge and the settled lands of the Piedmont Plateau and the coastal plain, and close to the zone where the Atlantic and Gulf coast plains meet.

The city owes its rise to the railways, which took advantage of its dominating site, so that after 1836 it became the hub of a rail system. The population reached 89,872 in 1900; and with the continued expansion of its transport and industrial functions the figure grew rapidly to 331,314 in 1950, and to 768,125 (in the urbanized area) in 1960. Atlanta is thus the largest city in the South outside Texas. Its major industries comprise the manufacture of transport equipment, the processing of food, and printing and publishing.

Memphis (population, urbanized area, 1960: 544,505) stands at the northern gateway to the South on the Chickasaw bluffs, about 50 feet above flood-level on the left bank of the Mississippi. An early bridging point, it grew as a market and transport centre, owing much to the traffic along the river. When this declined it was able to take advantage of the growing east-to-west trade. Set amid the rich alluvial lands of the Mississippi flood-plain, Memphis has become the world's largest cotton market. Its industries are served both by natural gas piped from Louisiana and by electric power from T.V.A. installations to the east. They include food-processing, the manufacture of chemicals, machinery and cotton goods, and industries based on timber.

New Orleans, situated 107 miles from the Mississippi river-mouth on the south side of Lake Pontchartrain, was founded by the French in 1718. It passed to Spain and back to France before becoming an American city following the Louisiana Purchase of 1803. Despite its unfavourable site among the swamps and bayous of the delta country, its position near the mouth of the great river gave it a vast hinterland. The river traffic reached its peak during the 1850's; since that time the city has become reorientated to the developing South-west, and it now serves as one of the ports for that region. About a hundred steamship lines use the port, which has a waterfront of seven miles. From 339,075 in 1910 its population grew to 845,237 (in the urbanized area) in 1960.

Farther west, in Texas, two cities of the 'new South' are of interest. Houston, situated 50 miles inland from the Gulf at the terminus of the Houston Ship Canal, is of much more recent growth than the cities so far discussed and is one of the most rapidly expanding centres in North America. Its functions are largely related to its situation amid the oil-fields of the Gulf coast. In the city and along the canal banks are oil-refineries, petro-chemical plants, foundries and cement works, factories producing transport equipment and processing sugar and rice, so that the city is one of the greatest industrial centres of the region. Its popula-

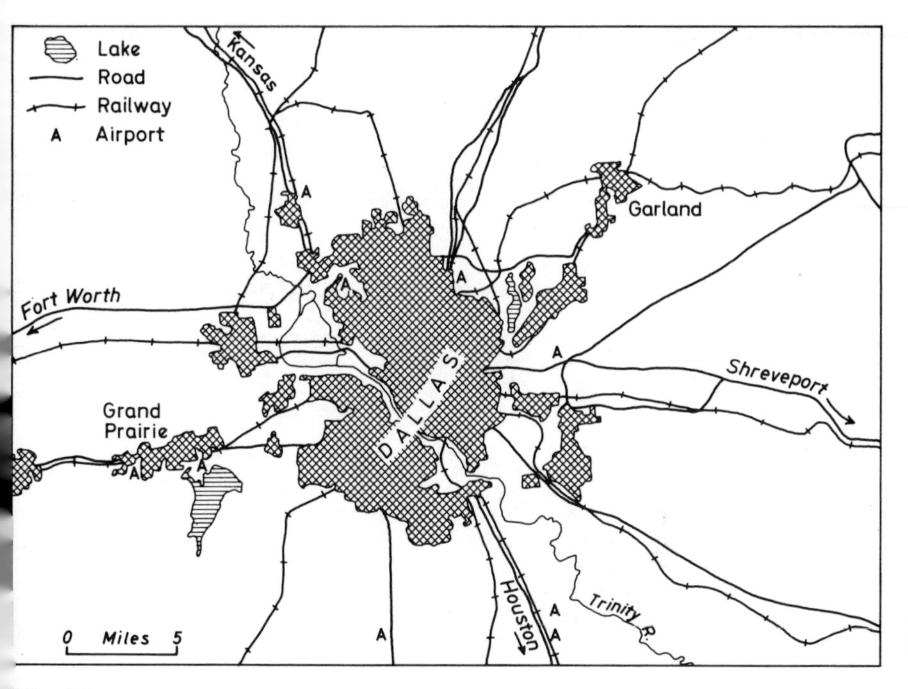

Fig. 52. THE SETTING OF DALLAS

tion, numbering 44,633 in 1900, has climbed steeply to reach 596,163 in 1950, and 1,139,678 (in the urbanized area) in 1960.

Dallas lies about 270 miles inland, in the north of the Black Prairie region of Texas – amid potentially rich corn and cotton land. The setting of the city is illustrated in Fig. 52. Like Houston, it has grown rapidly in the twentieth century, and its population, 932,349 (in the urbanized area) in 1960, is not far short of that of Houston. The city, together with its twin, Fort Worth (about 50 miles to the west), serves as a regional centre for agricultural lands and mineral industries of northern Texas. Its chief industrial establishments are accordingly related to the assembly of farm equipment and the manufacture of cotton gins and of machinery for the neighbouring oilfields. Its many industrial activities include food-processing and flour-milling, and the manufacture of clothing, cement, and iron and steel products.

Dallas has long been important as a transport centre for roads and railways; these have been followed by air transport as an acknowledgment of the city's status, not only as a regional centre but also as an important stage on the long-distance routes to the west. Since 1941 an important aircraft industry has been established in the city, and its leading industry according to the 1956 census was the production of

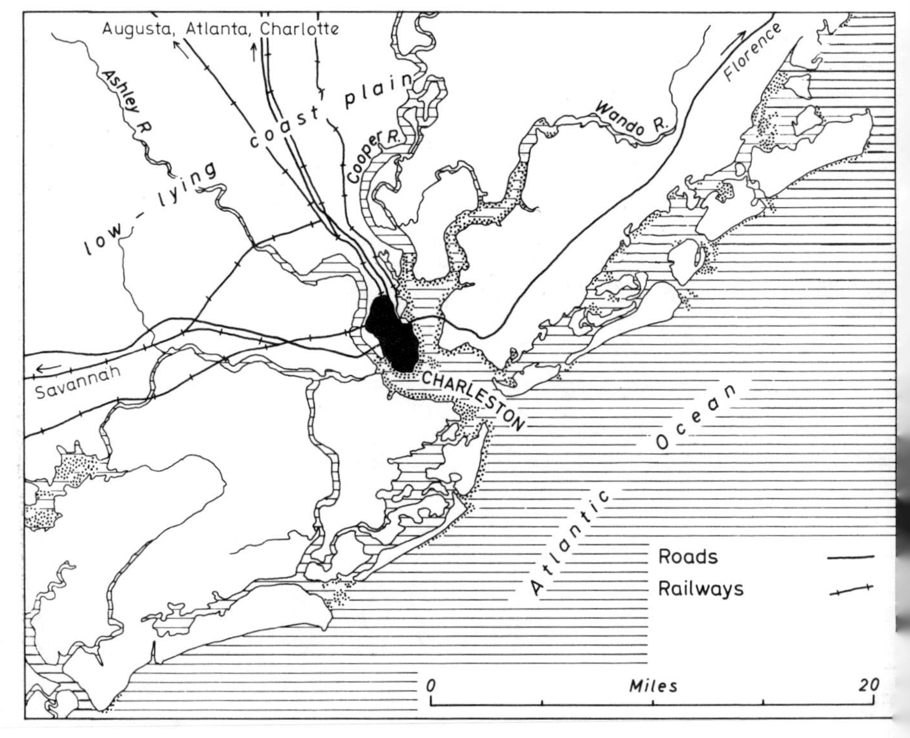

Fig. 53. THE SETTING OF CHARLESTON

'transport equipment'. Most of the 16,000 employees in this group were in fact making aircraft and components.

No discussion of Southern cities would be complete without a mention of Charleston and Savannah, two of the early ports of the old 'South'. Only 90 miles apart, they lie amid the creeks and mudflats of the southern part of the Atlantic coast plain. Charleston is centrally placed on the shore of South Carolina; Savannah lies to the south-west, just within the state of Georgia.

Savannah acts as a general port for the South-east, which has few other good harbours, but it receives nearly three times as much tonnage as it ships. Expansion in the west of the region has reacted unfavourably on the city: its industry is little developed and its population remains relatively small (urbanized area, 1960: 169,887).

Charleston, founded in 1670 on Albemarle Point, was rebuilt in 1683 on its present site on the peninsula between the Ashley and Cooper rivers (Fig. 53). It served as the commercial centre for the small Charleston settlement, and later, together with its rival, Savannah, became an outlet for the expanding production of the South. Charleston now functions as a regional centre for commerce and administration, and with its shipments of cotton, tobacco, timber, and coal it reflects many of the activities of the South. The estimated population of the metropolitan area in 1964 was 303,000 – a little larger than the state capital, Columbia.

CHAPTER FIVE

THE MIDDLE WEST

The Middle West lies in the very heart of North America. It includes both the rich agricultural area of the Corn Belt and the industrial region based on Chicago and Gary, while through it pass many of the great transcontinental routes. It presents something of a contradiction, for it is not only a region of movement, both north to south and east to west, but it is at the same time as balanced and self-sufficient a region as any in the continent.

The very place-names picture the westward spread of peoples across the country. Indian, French, English, Dutch, and German origins are suggested by names such as Oshkosh, La Salle, Plymouth, De Kalb, and Bismarck. Some show a distinct 'eastern' repetition; thus Quincy and Springfield occur in Massachusetts and Connecticut on the one hand and Illinois on the other. As for What Cheer in Iowa, we are not so sure!

Three phases may be discerned in the development of the Middle West. Until the opening of the nineteenth century it was a thinly peopled borderland, the scene of the struggles between English and French settlers and adventurers. During this period the War of Independence established the American state, of which the region was later to form part; the Louisiana Purchase put an end to French claims in the south; and the futile war of 1812 brought to a head the rivalry between the new American state and the English in Canada. After 1815 the Middle West was open for peaceful settlement, and the region as we know it was founded, and began to grow.

The next phase comprises the first half of the nineteenth century: it makes a fascinating study, for it illustrates the way in which physical geography exercises a guiding influence on the migration of peoples. The real beginnings of the Middle West may be traced back to the eighteenth century, with the first settlements in the Blue Grass country of Kentucky and the Nashville Basin of Tennessee. Farmers of eastern Pennsylvania had brought to these areas a long tradition of crop-rotation and animal husbandry that was well suited to the land. Here the Middle West had its roots, and here began the farming practice that characterizes its central core, the Corn Belt.

After 1815 settlement spread westward into Ohio, Indiana, and Illinois. The steel plough, developed during the 1830's and 1840's, made farming possible on the heavier soils of the prairies, while the opening of the Erie Canal between Buffalo and Albany in 1825 made eastern markets more accessible. Until about 1860 the great highway was the Mississippi–Ohio system: this was the era of the steamboat, which carried on most of the trade between the early Middle West and the South, and with its development grew the river towns, such as Cincinnati, Louisville, and Memphis.

The third development phase begins with the Civil War. Migration into the area increased rapidly, and was aided by the passing of the Homestead Act of 1862. This invited settlers to take up land, usually in 160-acre units (that is, in quarter-sections), with the promise of freedom from payment after five years' occupation. Much of the region was settled in accordance with this measure. To administer it, the land was divided into 'sections' of about 640 acres, which were subdivided into half- and quarter-sections. The landscape thus received its familiar impress of rectangular units that we see today.

The settlers came along three main routes: in the south they used the traditional Cumberland gap (p. 97); in the centre they penetrated along the western branch of the Susquehanna to reach Pittsburgh and the Ohio valley; while in the north settlers from New England used the Hudson and Mohawk valleys.

Commercial farming, however, awaited the improvement of transport to the growing urban markets of the eastern seaboard and Europe. In this connection the rivers were of little use, and there had been no improvement since the opening of the Erie Canal. All this was changed by the railways, which developed their network during the 1850's and 1860's. Thus in 1852 there was only a single railway in the Chicago area; but by 1865 there were 13, and Chicago had entered upon its role as one of the world's major railway centres. The Appalachians, which hitherto had cut off the Middle West from the tidewater cities, was now threaded by busy routeways (see pp. 95–99 and Fig. 37, p. 97).

The modern Middle West is thus little more than a century old. As in the South, there is a problem of definition. Like that region, much of the Middle West consists of lowland country; but whereas the South was basically forested, the Middle West was largely a grassland. The character of the region stems from a highly developed commercial agriculture based on livestock and crop-rotations, together with a complementary growth of urban and industrial activity. Nowhere else are rural and urban communities so intimately bound together.

The rural areas have been described as the 'seed-bags' of the towns, for many people reared in the country migrate to the towns in search of employment, sustaining and swelling industry and commerce. Agricultural produce feeds the cities and provides raw materials, while industrial products find a market in the rural areas. The Middle West is thus a region of prosperous farms and large cities, whose clearest examples are seen in the Corn Belt and the city of Chicago.

Physical Basis

In the Middle West we are concerned with two of the main physiographic regions of the continent. The greater portion is occupied by the Central Lowlands; but in the north these give way to the Laurentian Shield, here known as the Superior Upland (Fig. 54). Only in the southeast does the margin of the Middle West correspond with a physiographic boundary. To the west are the Great Plains, but, as we see below (p. 135), the precise position of the dividing line is a matter for debate

The Central Lowlands are formed of almost horizontally disposed strata of Palæozoic age (Ordovician to Carboniferous), and this, together with the smoothing action of the Pleistocene ice sheets, has resulted in the formation of a flat or gently undulating landscape. In pre-glacial times the land must have been rather similar to its present appearance, though river dissection would have been rather more in evidence. The ice sheets spread outward across the region in a great southward-pointing spur, carrying with them quantities of ground-up rock. They encountered little opposition from the soft shales and limestones of the plain, scouring the tops of the hills, but filling in the valleys with boulder clay ('till'). In the Middle West the ice sheets reached their most southerly limits, so that within the region they gradually lost their transporting power, and with the final melting deposited their load. The area is now blanketed with sheets of till up to 100 feet thick. The term 'Boulder clay' is hardly appropriate here, for the material is remarkably free from stones and boulders: unlike the igneous and metamorphic rocks of New England, the ice sheets in the Middle West encountered only soft sediments. In the western portion of the region a veneer of loess ranging from a few inches to several feet in thickness has contributed to the evolution of some of the richest soils in the continent.

The general disturbance of the surface rocks and the deposition of till, together with the sorting work of meltwaters and wind, has resulted in a surface mantle rich in mineral constituents. This formed an excellent foundation for the development of soils in post-glacial times. When the climate improved plant life returned, and part of the area may have been covered with forest. Later, man arrived on the scene; and early mid-Western explorers observed and commented on the Indian practice of burning timber to produce grazing-lands. In the heart of the area, from Illinois to Iowa and Missouri, the result was the development of a landscape dominated by tall and luxuriant grasses.

Under these prairie conditions a high humus content was added to the developing soils. While we cannot be certain of the sequence of events during post-glacial times, it is clear that these soils could not

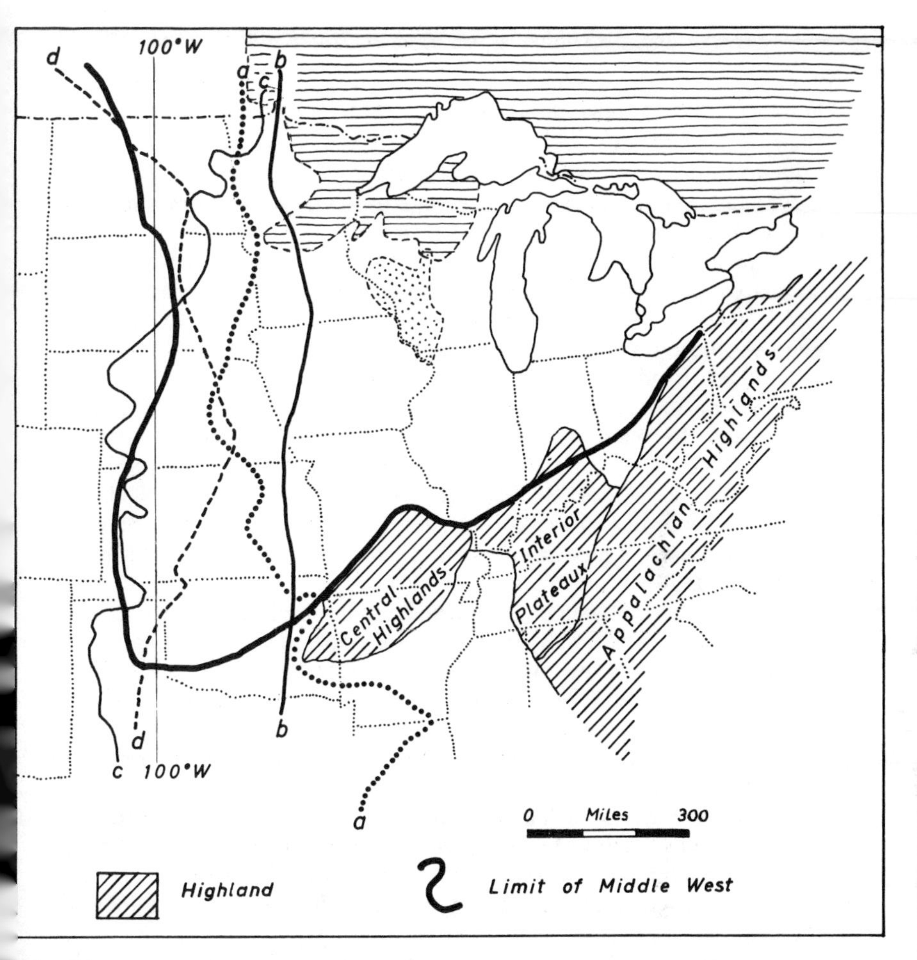

Fig. 54. THE MIDDLE WEST

The thick line marks the southern and western limits of the region. Other lines near the western border are as follows: *a:* the effective moisture line, west of which there is little or no surplus of water available for farming; *b:* the boundary separating the pedalfer soils in the east from the pedocals in the west; *c:* the 20-inch isohyet; *d:* the physiographic boundary between the Central Lowlands (to the east) and the Great Plains (to the west). The stippled area to the west of Lake Michigan represents the Driftless Area of south-west Wisconsin; the horizontal lines indicate the Laurentian Shield.

have evolved under forest conditions. With such an endowment it is not surprising that the Central Lowlands have become a rich farming area. Their only important drawback is the interrupted drainage system, which shows itself in waterlogging and flooding, particularly in the lower-lying districts near the rivers.

In the east the Central Lowlands merge into the more deeply dissected country of the Cumberland Plateau, where the soils are shallower and less valuable. In the south-east and south, the rims of the Interior Plateaux (the Ozarks and the Nashville Basin) present a more abrupt margin. In the west the boundary is climatic, and may be placed where decreasing rainfall limits plant growth to produce the short grass prairies of the Great Plains.

There is an interesting district in south-west Wisconsin which was missed by all the ice sheets: this is the Driftless Area (Fig. 54, p. 135), and it gives us an idea of what the whole region might have been like had there been no glaciation. Decidedly hilly in character, and with poor soils, it provoked the American geologist T. C. Chamberlin to observe that Wisconsin ought to have sued the ice sheets for neglect of duty.

Between the main mass of the Laurentian Shield and the Central Lowlands lie the Great Lakes. In the west a small salient of the Shield extends into the United States, and is known as the Superior Upland. Before noticing this, however, we need to refer again to the origin of the Great Lakes, which mean so much to the economy of the Middle West (see p. 30).

The maximum advance of the ice sheets lay well beyond the present Great Lakes, and probably reached as far south as Cincinnati. Between it and the lakes lies the low watershed between the Mississippi and the St Lawrence systems. As we have seen, the Great Lakes occupy a depression that is probably pre-glacial in origin. When the ice 'retreated' northward beyond this watershed the meltwaters began to be impounded between it and the ice front; in places the shapes of the new lakes were determined by moraines. The evolution of the Great Lakes is illustrated in Fig. 55, which shows also their overflow channels. These are not mere academic matters, for as the old lakes shrank they left behind them silts and gravels which play important parts today in the local geography of the lakeside districts.

The Superior Upland is very different from the Central Lowlands, in both character and economy. Its landscape is hummocky, and shows evidence of both glacial erosion and deposition. In this area of old, hard rocks glaciation has been a hindrance rather than a help. The low-lying districts are covered with the drift, but elsewhere there is much bare rock; the soils are thin and hungry, and nowhere do they equal in value those farther south. Yet the Upland has its own contribution to make, for within the igneous and metamorphic rocks from which it has been carved lie important mineral deposits, especially of copper and iron.

The Middle West has a humid continental climate with warm summers characterized by convectional rainfall, and rather long, cold winters. In the north the Great Lakes (which are frozen in winter) exert a cooling effect, and accentuate the difference due to latitude. The isotherms, broadly speaking, range east and west at all seasons, with the

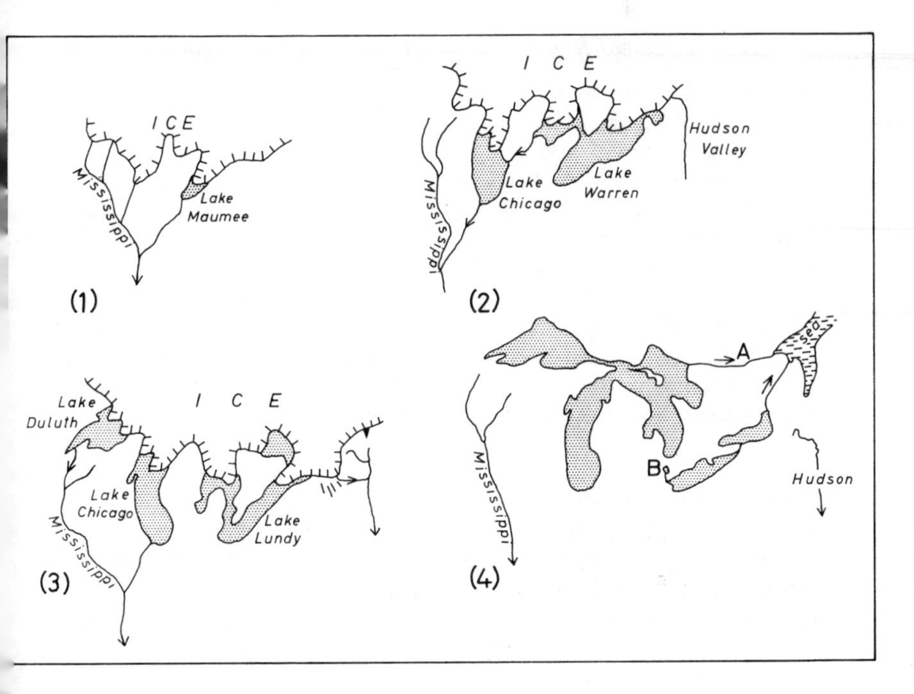

Fig. 55. THE EVOLUTION OF THE GREAT LAKES

Four stages are illustrated.

Stage 1: The entire discharge of meltwater is south-westward to the early Mississippi by way of the Wabash, Illinois, and other tributaries. Lake Erie begins to appear in the shape of Lake Maumee.

Stage 2: Further retreat of the ice exposes the southerly portions of the hollows of Lake Michigan (Lake Chicago) and Lake Huron. Glacial Lake Warren is an enlarged Lake Erie. Meltwater begins to find an outlet southward along the Champlain–Hudson valley.

Stage 3: Lake Superior begins its existence as Lake Duluth and drains southward to the Mississippi by way of the Ste Croix river. The retreating ice sheet exposes the Mohawk valley, and meltwaters spill through the Hudson–Mohawk valley.

Stage 4: The lakes assume almost their present shape. Southward drainage ceases, and the entire lake water passes eastward by way of the Ottawa river (A) and the St Lawrence. The Port Huron outlet (B) becomes closed. Later, A closes and B reopens and the present-day system is reached. The last changes are due to slight tilting of the land surface as a result of the removal of the load of ice.

The human importance of these events lies in the many easy routeways that now lead to and from the Great Lakes. They are followed by roads, railways, and canals.

normal southerly bulge in winter and northerly bulge in summer that are typical of the continental masses.

The growing season ranges in length from nearly 200 days in the south to about 140 days in Wisconsin and 120 at the Canadian border. The crop belts therefore range east and west, and although the climate may be critical for individual crops in the north the whole region is generally favourable for arable farming.

In contrast, the rainfall decreases from east to west. It reaches an annual total of 40 inches in the east, and at the western limit of the region has declined to about 20 inches. There is a distinct summer maximum, which is favourable to cereal crops.

Average figures, however, do not give a complete picture of the climate of a region, and here we must notice that on the drier western margin of the Middle West the rate of evaporation increases considerably as one moves southward, so that the rainfall becomes less effective. In North Dakota wheat is grown successfully with as little as 15 inches of rain annually, but in Kansas the same crop needs at least 20 inches because of the greater heat. Not only is a smaller proportion of the precipitation available, but in higher temperatures the plants themselves require more moisture for transpiration.

Farming in the Middle West

The core of the region consists of the Corn Belt (Fig. 56), and around it are regions with slightly different emphasis in farm policy. To the north-west it is bordered by the Spring Wheat Belt, and to the north-east by the Hay and Dairying Belt. Along the southern and south-eastern margin is the zone of general farming, and in the south-west the Winter Wheat Belt of Kansas.

Corn, which of course in North America means maize, is grown well beyond the limits of the Middle West; as we have already seen, it forms a major crop in the South. But in the Middle West it enjoys the optimum conditions for its growth, and here is the intense production that gives the Corn Belt its character. These optimum conditions include a deep and rich soil and a growing season of 150 to 160 days. From June to August the temperatures must be high both day and night: this implies 70°–80°F. during the day and not lower than 50° at night. The water requirements of the crop increase until July, the critical month, when four inches of rainfall are needed, and the convectional showers that occur in the Mid-Continent are ideal for its growth.

For those who are unfamiliar with the plant, it is perhaps worth mentioning that maize is the basis of corn-flakes, cornflour, and popcorn, though these uses account for only a very small proportion of the product. Corn grows very quickly, and very high – taller than a man – and its cob (or 'ear'), 8 or 10 inches long, is one of the largest among all cereals. The golden-yellow grain is rich in oil, and therefore will speedily fatten livestock; this is the prime purpose of its cultivation.

The optimum conditions for corn cease to obtain on the margins of the belt. In the north the summer temperatures are too low and the growing season too short, and, as we have seen, its place is taken by wheat and dairying. In the east the rich soils of the Middle West give way to the thin soils of Appalachia. Shallow soils occur again in the

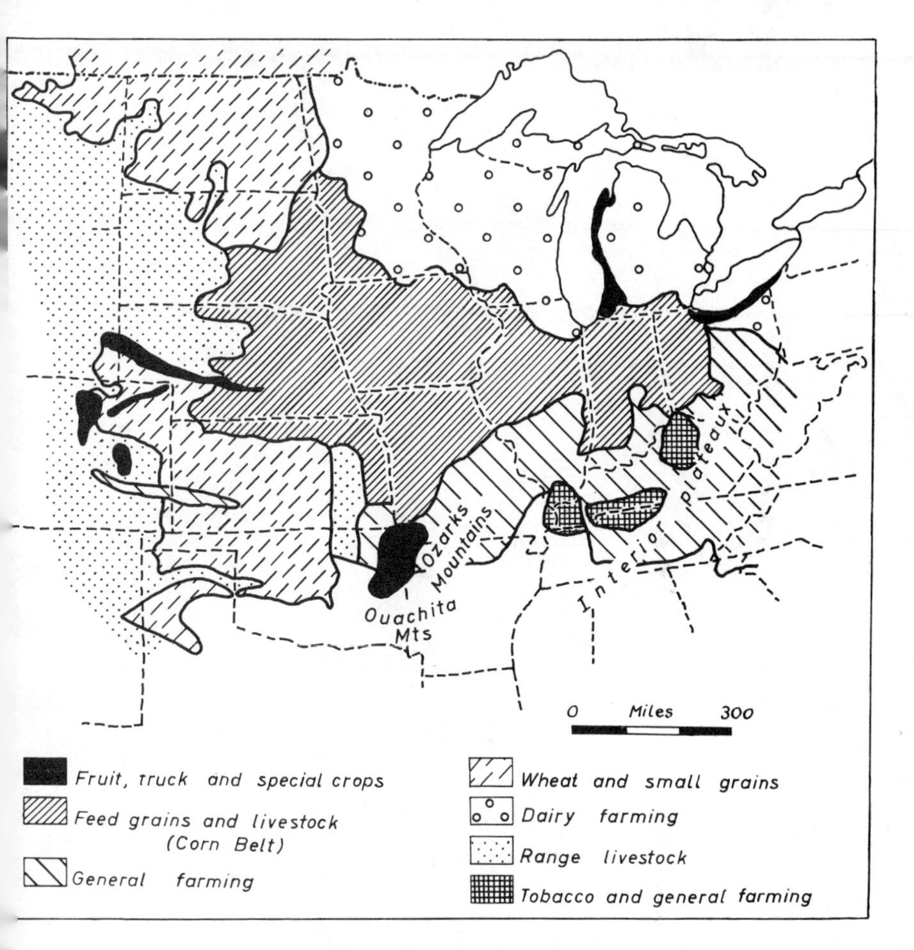

'ig. 56. THE MIDDLE WEST: MAJOR LAND-USE REGIONS

south; in the south-west the rate of evaporation is too high, and in the west there is insufficient rainfall.

The Corn Belt is characterized by the growing of maize for feeding to pigs and cattle. The crop is grown in rotation with oats and hay, usually forming a three-year rotation, in that order. The core of the belt consists of central Indiana, Illinois, Iowa (Plate 4), northern Missouri, and eastern Nebraska, and here the chief animal is the pig, with beef and dairy cattle in smaller numbers; to the north and south poultry and dairy cattle become more important, while in the west pigs give way to beef cattle.

In common with the prairies and Great Plains, the Middle West was hard hit by the Great Depression of the 1930's. The United States

Government established the Agricultural Adjustment Administration, whose object was conservation and research: it discouraged any increase of the area under corn, but developed improved varieties, and encouraged the introduction of other crops into the farming system. Hybrid types of corn now are dominant, and they have not only improved the yields within the belt but have allowed corn-production to extend northward into southern Wisconsin and Minnesota.

Corn, even more than other grain crops, depletes the humus content of the soil. The farmer now restores his soils by making an increased use of nitrogenous fertilizers; in addition he interplants his corn with winter rye, and then ploughs in the rye as a green manure. Corn Belt farming has also become more diversified: grasses, alfalfa, and sweet clover have been introduced for silage; and the soya bean has become popular: from about 3 million acres in 1933 it has been extended over about 10 million acres today.

Since the 1930's industrialization, the growth of cities, and the rise of motor transport have profoundly influenced the region. The lorry provides a far closer link between town and country than the railway ever did: many farmers near the bigger cities now grow tomatoes and vegetables for the urban markets, while dairy farming shows a corresponding development. Chicago, formerly the unique city of stockyards, meat-packing stations, and canneries, all based on rail transport, is losing this position with the rise of local centres fed by the lorry. Towns such as Omaha, St Louis, and Kansas City have become regional centres, and although Chicago remains the foremost city its functions have changed (p. 50). With the improvements in transport many farm-owners have become city-dwellers, who leave their farms in charge of a tenant or manager. But the family farm has by no means vanished: indeed, it still forms the backbone of the region.

We have seen that farms taken up under the Homestead Act of 1862 consisted usually of quarter-sections of about 160 acres. Experience has shown that a larger unit is more economic: the average size of farm in 1916 was about 200 acres, and it has since risen to about 300. This increase in size has been accompanied by an extension in the use of machinery and a reduction in the number of farm workers, so that the

---

'late 4. AN AREA IN THE CORN BELT NEAR CEDAR RAPIDS, IOWA

;edar Rapids is situated in east-central Iowa. With 16 farmsteads in the area shown, his is a district of relatively close rural settlement. There is an exceptionally high pro-ortion of arable land, but the crops are fed mainly to pigs and cattle. The rainfall, with mean annual total of about 31 inches, is normally adequate for arable farming; but oil erosion is a danger: notice the gulleys that have formed in the centre of the picture nd elsewhere. Wise farmers are contour ploughing their land (bottom, left, and top, entre).

Photo by courtesy of the U.S. Department of Agriculture, Agricultural Stabilization and Conservation Service

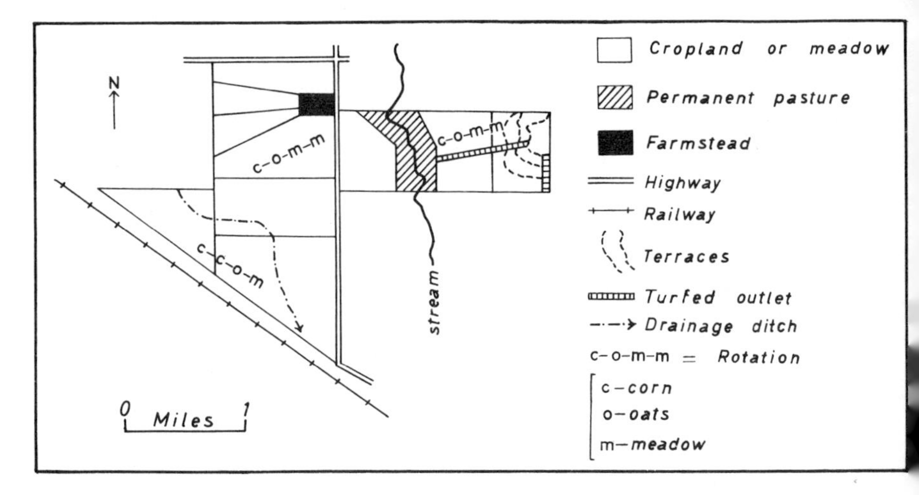

Fig. 57. A DIVERSIFIED STOCK FARM IN IOWA
See note to Fig. 49 (p. 123).

modern farm in the Corn Belt is a highly mechanized unit, efficiently organized, and making good use of science in both its livestock management and its crop rotations.

We illustrate from a farm on the prairies of eastern Iowa (Fig. 57). Part of the land to the west of the stream is flat, and was formerly liable to waterlogging: this has been carefully drained, and the course of the main ditch is shown. In contrast, the undulating land east of the river was liable to erosion, and this has been terraced for contour ploughing, and provided with a safe water outlet. On his flat land the farmer grows corn in two successive years, but on the slopes, with their greater risk of erosion, he leaves the land for two years under grass for hay. All his crops are fed to his animals: these comprise a dairy herd of 20 head, a beef-cattle herd of 40 Herefords, and what he must regard as his chief enterprise, his 300 pigs.

As we have mentioned, the boundary between the Corn Belt and the Spring Wheat Belt to the north-west has been blurred by the introduction of hybrid types of corn, so that the Wheat Belt has tended to recede northward. It has also retreated somewhat from its former western limits, for the great droughts of 1934–37 made it clear that wheat-growing beyond the 15-inch isohyet was fraught with danger. Within the existing belt, which consists essentially of North Dakota, wheat occupies a far more prominent position than does corn in the Corn Belt, since it is not linked with the rearing of animals.

We have already referred briefly to the Hay and Dairying Belt (p. 138). Only its western part falls within the Middle West, and this portion is physiographically divided into the Superior Upland of the north-west and the Central Lowland section of the south and east. In the Superior Upland farming shares the land with forestry, and in the rougher parts is of only minor importance. In the richer lands to the south and east grass is dominant, and is grown for both pasture and hay: but this is basically arable land, and the grass is grown in rotation with maize and small grains. The essential object of the farming is to provide food for dairy cattle. Maize, however, will not ripen properly in these cooler parts, and is converted into silage. Farms that are near large cities or are served by speedy transport concentrate on the production of fresh milk or butter; the more remote areas convert their milk into cheese, and the greatest reputation for cheese-making has been gained by southern Wisconsin.

The Winter Wheat Belt of the south-west, like its counterpart in the north-west, is transitional between the Middle West and the Great Plains. It is separated from the Corn Belt by a zone of hilly land of poor soils, the Flint hills of south-east Kansas; but in the remainder of that state enormous quantities of winter wheat are grown. In the east, with an annual rainfall of 33 inches, the wheat is combined with maize and pasture; farther west, wheat becomes dominant, and the size of farm increases. The western limit is set by rainfall, but, as we have seen, not by a single isohyet: in the north of Kansas the crop can manage with 17 or 18 inches, while in the south it requires about 20 inches of rain. Farther west, crops give way to ranching.

South and south-east of the Corn Belt is the general-farming sub-region, a belt of great variety of physique and agriculture, a transitional zone between the Corn and Cotton belts. Its mean annual rainfall is relatively high, ranging from 33 inches in the west to over 40 inches in the east. Its summers are warm, but the growing season – between 180 and 200 days – is not quite long enough for cotton to flourish.

Differences in relief, structure, and soils within the sub-region are reflected in farming. On the rugged slopes of the Ozarks and of the Appalachian plateaux there is much heath and woodland, with occasional subsistence farming. In the more favoured districts corn, wheat, and hay form the main crops, with livestock farming in the more accessible areas. Nowhere, however, is the agriculture as rich as in the Corn Belt, and this is, broadly speaking, a land of poor soils and low productivity, relieved only by the cultivation of tobacco in parts of western Kentucky, and by apple and peach orchards on the sunnier slopes of the Ozarks.

Industry and Towns

Industry was slow to develop in the Middle West. It had no cities at the outset, which might have supplied capital; it was far from the sea, by which it might have imported raw materials or supplied foreign markets; and it had few hill farms, which might have supplied it with labour. Industries developed as the region was settled during the nineteenth century: they leaned heavily on agriculture, and comprised such activities as milling, distilling, and the manufacture of textiles. As we have seen, apart from the Erie Canal the early trade routes led north and south, for they consisted chiefly of the navigable Ohio and Mississippi rivers. Moreover, the canals were tributary to these routes: they included the Ohio and Erie Canal, which aided the rise of Cleveland (p. 54), and the much longer Wabash and Erie Canal, opened in 1843, which connected Lake Erie with the lower Ohio at Evansville.

The first industrial centres were thus the river towns such as Cincinnati and Louisville, and they developed flour-mills, tan-yards, woollen factories, and blacksmiths' workshops.

The region is not without mineral wealth, but for the most part the deposits are peripheral. The Keweenaw copper ores were discovered in 1844 (p. 36), and soon the district had a virtual monopoly of copper-production in the United States. The iron ranges of Lake Superior were developed during the second half of the century; their exploitation was accompanied by the development of the Great Lakes traffic and the growth of the railway network. The Middle West now gained commercial links with the markets of the North-east, and with the coking coal of Pennsylvania. The details, however, together with the rise of Chicago, are closely linked with the emergence of the Great Lakes routeway, and we have examined them in Chapter Three.

The commercial and cultural needs of the Middle West are served by many bustling cities, and we now examine briefly the sites and functions of four of these – namely, St Louis, Kansas City, Omaha, and Des Moines.

St Louis, with a population in the metropolitan area of 2,060,103 (1960), is the commercial centre for a large part of the Mississippi valley. The site has great natural advantages, for on it converge routes following three of the great rivers of North America – the Ohio, the Mississippi, and the Missouri.

The first permanent settlement, close to the junction of the last-named rivers, originated in 1764 as a fur-trading post, and was named after the medieval French king Louis IX. An era of expansion was heralded by the arrival of the first Mississippi steamboat in 1817, and this traffic prospered for more than 50 years, until it was superseded by the railways.

St Louis functioned during much of the nineteenth century as a gateway to the west, fitting out exploring and trading expeditions, and pioneers in search of gold in California. Today it remains one of the world's largest fur markets, and handles great quantities of grain and tobacco. It benefits from local supplies of natural gas, and coal from Illinois. Among its varied industries are oil-refining and the assembly of motor-cars.

About 230 miles west of St Louis, at the junction of the Kansas river with the Missouri, is Kansas City (population of metropolitan area, 1960: 1,092,545). Administratively here are two distinct cities, separated by the Kansas–Missouri state border; geographically, however, they form a single urban area that provides one of the greatest grain and cattle markets of the United States.

Permanent settlement in the area dates only from 1821, and until the middle of the century the town functioned as the starting-point of the Santa Fé trail (p. 186), forwarding supplies westward and receiving in return wool, buffalo hides and meat, and precious metals and ores. In 1865 the railway reached the city from the east, and it now grew rapidly, with the development of the maize and wheat lands to the north and east and the cattle lands to the west. From 4418 in 1860 its population expanded to reach 55,785 in 1880. Its present-day industries include meat-packing, flour-milling, food-processing, and oil-refining.

Omaha, Nebraska (population of metropolitan area, 1960: 457,873), lies upstream of Kansas City on the Missouri river, about 170 miles to the north-north-west as the crow flies. Originally sited on a terrace overlooking the west bank of the river, it has now extended on to the hills to the west.

There had been a sporadic occupation of the area earlier, but the city was not founded till 1854. Its future was assured when a few years later the railway-builders chose it as the springboard for the first transcontinental railway. Though it lies within the rich Corn Belt, Omaha has close links with the ranching lands to the west. The Platte river, whose valley is followed by rail and roads, joins the Missouri only 15 miles below the city. Omaha is a great cattle market: its stockyards are second only to those of Chicago. It refines petroleum and manufactures farm machinery; it is the commercial and financial centre for an extensive region to the west, and has developed a wide range of insurance services.

Des Moines (population of metropolitan area, 1960: 266,315) lies 120 miles east of Omaha, on the Des Moines river, which flows south-eastward to join the Mississippi. The derivation of the rather strange name is uncertain, but it appears to be a corruption of an Indian name, Moingana (there are several variant spellings). Essentially the city, which is the state capital of Iowa, has grown as a commercial centre for the rich Corn Belt. It has in addition benefited from nearby supplies of coal. Among its activities are meat-packing and the manufacture of farm machinery, and, like Omaha, it is an important centre for insurance.

It will be seen that the Mid-West cities are closely concerned with the needs of the farming population around and to the west of them. To the east, Milwaukee and Chicago act as ports for the region: these cities we have discussed in connection with the Great Lakes (pp. 50–51).

CHAPTER SIX

THE GREAT PLAINS

Between the Corn and Cotton belts on the east and the Rocky Mountains on the west lies an extensive plateau known as the Great Plains. It has considerable diversity of climate and land use, but almost everywhere its surface is composed of relatively soft and almost horizontal Cretaceous and Tertiary rocks that provide a sharp contrast to the complex landforms on either side. Some writers extend the region northward to include the prairies of Canada; and they have indeed some justification, for the structure, landforms, and climate do not change suddenly beyond the international boundary. But the 49th parallel has great human importance: it is crossed by few roads or railways, and it forms a real economic divide. We recognize that there are some problems common to both, but feel the need in a regional treatment to separate the prairies from the Great Plains.

To modern minds it seems strange that until the 1840's this region was usually described as the Great Desert. The term stemmed in part from the reports of travellers, who exaggerated the extent of sandy areas that certainly existed; in part, however, it seems to have been due to a series of dry years that misled some observers. Thus in the *Carte du Missouri* of 1802 what is now west-central Nebraska bore the description, 'Great Desert of drifting sand without trees, soil, rocks, water or animals . . .'[1] In the 1820's contemporary maps marked the Great Desert or Great American Desert on the region now occupied by north Texas, western Oklahoma, north-central Kansas, and eastern Colorado; even then, however, some writers expressed the view that this was potentially a pastoral region.

That the 'Great Desert' was a myth was demonstrated during the 50's and 60's. Cattle were driven westward to the goldfields of California and Colorado, and northward from Texas to the railheads leading to eastern markets: they flourished on the natural pastures; and those that by chance were left behind in the autumn not only survived but fattened during the winter. Gold-mining in Colorado provided a stimulus to the production of food in the former 'desert', and it was seen that, with the aid of irrigation, fruit and vegetables could be grown. Nature

[1] G. M. Lewis, 'Regional Ideas and Reality in the Cis-Rocky Mountain West' (*Transactions, Institute of British Geographers,* June 1966).

came to the aid of the farmers, and the former drought was replaced by a series of wet years.

The name 'Great Plains' first appeared in a map of 1848 and has never been displaced, though it means different things to different people, and its eastern boundary is uncertain. To the geologist it is a region of Cretaceous and Tertiary strata; to the student of vegetation, a treeless region of short and long grasses; to the climatologist, a region of continental climate. To the statesman or economist it is a problem area of marginal farming, where state aid is necessary: a region that includes the notorious dustbowl, whose existence was not suspected before the disastrous droughts of the 1930's.

Here we include in the Great Plains not only the ranch-lands of the west but also the grain-lands of the east, where the rainfall is adequate for crops without the need for dry farming or irrigation. Our boundaries are conventional: we include the states of Montana, North and South Dakota, Wyoming and Nebraska, Kansas and Oklahoma, eastern New Mexico and western Texas.

PHYSICAL BASIS

The Great Plains are not plains in the normal sense of the word. It is true that their general surface, sloping very gently down to the east, is level over wide areas; but it is in no sense a lowland. In western Oklahoma, Elk City stands at 2092 feet above sea-level; Kearney, in south-central Nebraska, is at 2136 feet; and Bismarck, down on the Missouri in central North Dakota, is at 1675 feet. All these are near the eastern margin of the Plains. At Lubbock, in the Staked Plains of Texas, the altitude is 3190 feet, and on the border of New Mexico, 3500 feet. Sites nearer the Rocky Mountain foothills in eastern Colorado are over 4000 feet. When we compare these heights with Snowdon summit (3560 feet) we realize that it is only in relation to the Rockies that the region may be regarded as a 'plain'.

Structurally the Great Plains form a broad and shallow syncline along a north-and-south axis, so that for the most part the strata are almost horizontal. On a Pre-Cambrian floor, the Lower Palæozoic rocks are succeeded by Carboniferous, Permian, Cretaceous, and Tertiary strata (Fig. 58). The older deposits outcrop in a broad zone to the east, and in narrow disconnected strips at the foot of the Rockies.

North of latitude 40°, with only minor interruptions, the Cretaceous and Tertiary rocks extend across the whole width of the Great Plains, and continue north of the international border to form the prairies of Canada. Farther south, erosion has stripped off the newer rocks from the eastern portion of the Plains to reveal the underlying Permian and Carboniferous material. Here we may recognize a lower, easterly

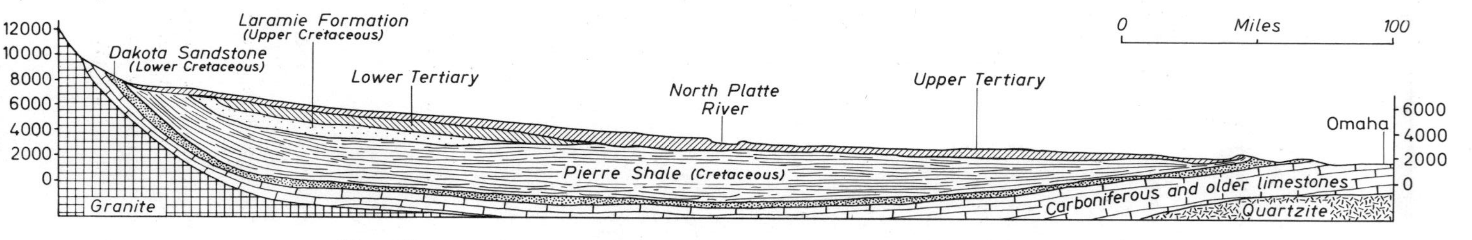

Fig. 58. A GEOLOGICAL SECTION FROM OMAHA TO THE ROCKIES

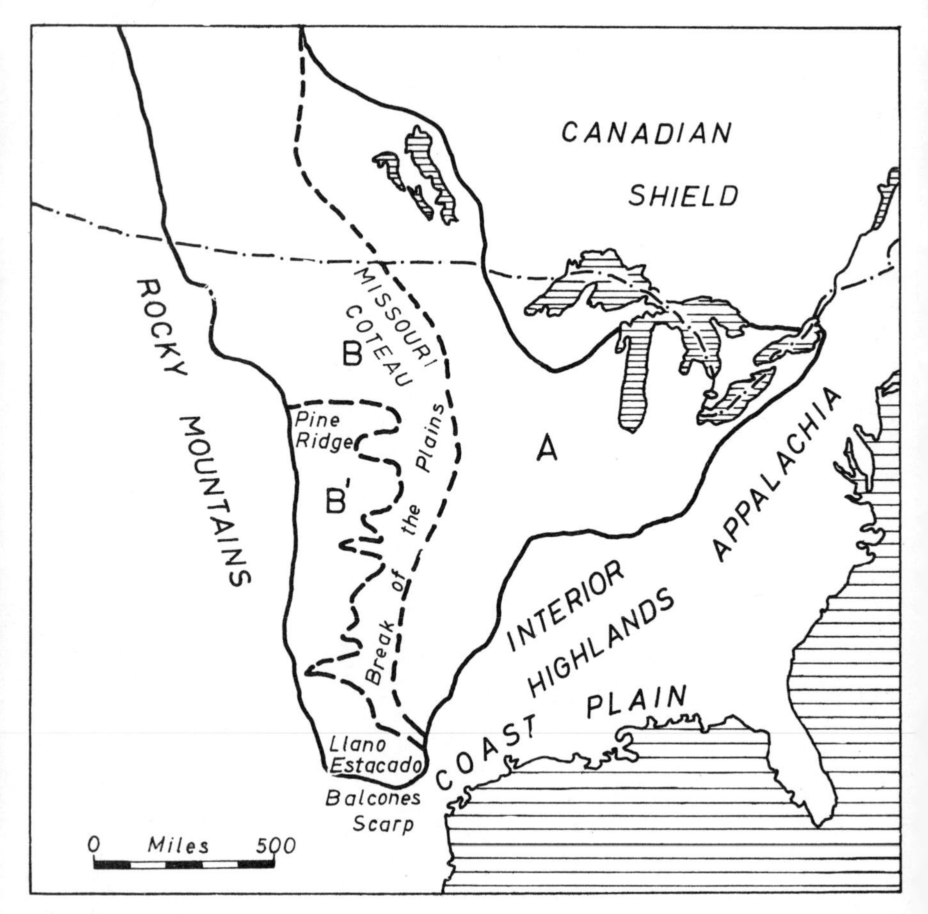

Fig. 59. SUB-REGIONS OF THE INTERIOR LOWLANDS

The map illustrates the rather complex portion of the United States where three 'plains' approach one another. Each is at a higher level as one progresses inland. They comprise the Gulf coast plain, the Low Plains (B), and the High Plains (B′). The Low and High Plains are separated by a Tertiary scarp, the Break of the Plains. It continues to form the southern edge of the High Plains, and is there known as the Balcones Scarp. A is the Central Lowlands, whose rocks are older than the Tertiary and Cretaceous strata that constitute the Great Plains.

sub-region (the Low Plains) and a higher, westerly sub-region (the High Plains). In places they are separated by a Tertiary scarp: this is prominent in west-central Texas and elsewhere, and is named the Break of the Plains (Fig. 59).

The most characteristic feature of the landscape of the Great Plains is its lack of a forest cover. This is a result partly of extreme temperatures (in particular, of cold winters) and high winds – themselves related to the level surface; but it is due mainly to a relatively low rainfall. The region is semi-arid: its eastern margins receive about 20 inches of precipitation per annum, and its western margins 15 inches or less. This rainfall is seasonal: as in other continental interiors, the greater portion occurs in the summer half of the year, and much of the moisture is lost by evaporation.

We may illustrate some of these generalizations from the panhandle of Oklahoma: this lies towards the western edge of the Great Plains, and formed the core of the dustbowl of the 1930's. The 'average' precipitation has little practical value since there are radical departures from it – more usually below than above the 'average'! Moreover, the experts do not agree on their computation of the average, since records are few and data incomplete. The Government yearbook of agriculture for 1941, for example, placed the 22-inch isohyet at about 100° W. long. in north-west Oklahoma; but in 1954 a local water-resources committee placed the 20-inch isohyet in that same place. Estimates of annual precipitation for Kenton, in the far west of the panhandle, have ranged between 15½ and 17 inches.

Wind velocities here are higher than in any other part of the mainland United States. The winds are bitterly cold in winter, and occasional blizzards do severe damage: temperatures below freezing are common. During summer the winds are searingly hot, and temperatures rise into the 90's. The rate of evaporation is computed at over 60 inches a year.[1]

As one proceeds westward into the Great Plains the rainfall becomes insufficient to keep the subsoil permanently moist, and at the downward limit of percolation a layer of salts is deposited. Farther west, with a diminishing rainfall, this layer approaches nearer to the surface, and the depth of soil available for the roots of plants correspondingly shrinks. In consequence we find that long grasses are typical of the eastern portions of the Plains and short grasses of the western portions. The change in the character of the pasture is accompanied by a change in soil character and colour: the long grasses grow normally in black (chernozem) prairie soils and the short grasses in dark-brown soils.

The line separating the short from the long grasses is rarely far from 100° W. long., which passes through the middle of Nebraska and the Dakotas. To the east of it precipitation is usually adequate for the successful cultivation of cereals; to the west are pastoral lands, where cereals are risky unless they are grown with the aid of irrigation or dry-farming techniques. This is one of the most important dividing-lines in the United States.

In the western Great Plains are extensive spreads of Tertiary material: they consist of unconsolidated gravelly material, and are interpreted as old alluvia rather than marine deposits. They were distributed by swift,

[1] Arthur H. Doerr and John W. Morris, 'The Oklahoma Panhandle – A Cross Section of the Southern High Plains', *Economic Geography*, Vol. 36, 1960, pp. 70–88.

debris-laden streams that descended from the newly raised Rocky Mountains. Material of this type covers the High Plains of western Kansas and the arid Llano Estacado (Staked – *i.e.*, fenced – Plains) of west-central Texas.

In a region of sparse vegetation, high wind, and erratic but occasionally torrential rainfall such soft, loose material is prone to destructive erosion. Here are the 'badland' districts, where one sees pinnacles and platforms, fantastic tall columns separated by vast deep gulleys – a landscape that is useless except for a limited tourist value. Badlands are extensive south and east of the Black Hills of South Dakota and along the Break of the Plains in Texas. About 40 miles east of the Black Hills is the Badlands National Monument.

South-east of the main badland area is the Sand Hills region of west-central Nebraska, which covers about 20,000 square miles of undulating land between the North Platte and Niobrara rivers (Fig. 60). This is a region of Quaternary dunes whose 'ripples' of sand are usually 25 to 50 feet high, but in places rise to 200 or even 300 feet. There are still patches liable to wind erosion, but in general the Sand Hills are now well grassed. Rather surprisingly, the soils are retentive of moisture and fertile, and here is a westward extension of long-grass territory into the short-grass country. The Sand Hills are accordingly famous for their cattle pastures.

The relatively young, horizontal strata that constitute the Great Plains are broken in a few districts by local upfolds where erosion has stripped off the surface layers to reveal some of the underlying older rocks. The most symmetrical of these upfolds is seen in the Black Hills of South Dakota. Whether the traveller approaches eastward from Wyoming or from any other direction, he meets the same succession. The Black Hills are surrounded by Cretaceous material whose more resistant members form a series of concentric inward-facing scarps. These are succeeded by weaker and more low-lying Jurassic strata, and these in their turn by more elevated Carboniferous Limestone in the central district. Finally, in the eastern portion of the centre, the limestone itself has been eroded to expose a rugged core of ancient schists.

At their summit in Harney Peak the Black Hills reach 7242 feet, while the surrounding 'plains' stand at between 4000 and 5000 feet. The greater elevation induces the winds to release sufficient moisture for the growth of forest: this delighted the eyes of travellers from the east who had traversed 400 miles of grassland, where trees were to be seen only fringing the watercourses. The woodlands are now preserved for the nation in the Black Hills National Forest.

The structural accident that produced the Black Hills dome has been of profound importance to the region, for these ancient metamorphic rocks contain gold. The precious metal was discovered in 1874 by a

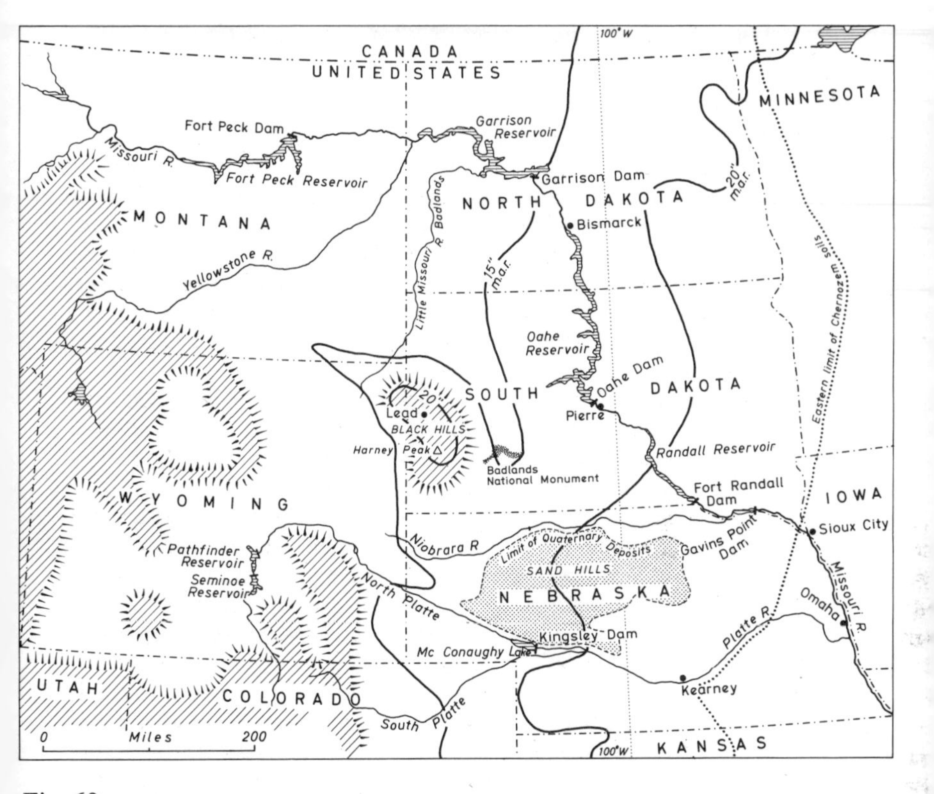

Fig. 60. THE NORTHERN GREAT PLAINS

The map indicates the dams, reservoirs, and other features mentioned in the text. The mountain areas are lined obliquely. The two isohyets are inserted from the *U.S. Year Book of Agriculture, 1941.*

scientific and military reconnaissance party, a thousand strong, led by General George A. Custer. The resulting gold-rush had the permanent effect of peopling this part of the Great Plains and linking it with the settled regions to the east. In 1876 two prospectors discovered gold where is now the town of Lead, and from this beginning has developed the large and important Homestake mine, the greatest producer of gold in the Americas.

In the Low Plains of western Oklahoma a similar local doming is responsible for the Wichita hills, and, farther east in the same state, the Arbuckle mountains. The latter are famed for their rich pastures. Well to the south, in Texas, is yet another dome. Here subsequent erosion has exposed a core of ancient metamorphic rocks bounded by a ring of Cambrian strata: this broken country constitutes the central mineral district of Texas.

Cereal Farming

As here defined, the Great Plains include the major Wheat Belt of the United States, and produce over half the national output of wheat. In addition they include important corn (maize) growing lands which lie beyond the boundaries of the conventional Corn Belt. The chief wheat-producing state is Kansas, with North Dakota ranking second; and together these two yield nearly one-third of the national total. From North Dakota the wheat-lands spread west into Montana and south into South Dakota; and from Kansas they spread north into Nebraska and south into Oklahoma and the Texan panhandle.

Though most of Wyoming falls within the Great Plains, this state produces little wheat: nor do the Plains portions of Texas or New Mexico. All these lands lie well within the short-grass territory, where the rainfall is insufficient for successful wheat-growing.

The occupation of the Great Plains is little more than a century old. The first settlers were soldiers returning in 1865 from the Civil War. Land was cheap; farm machinery was being improved; the railway network was spreading westward; and native-born Americans were being reinforced by a host of immigrants. Some of the latter were responsible for a major advance in 1874: this was the introduction of a hard winter wheat known as Turkey Red. Its seeds were brought in by a group of Germans – the Mennonites – who had earlier migrated eastward into southern Russia. Turkey Red is a hardy grain: it can survive severe winters and is resistant to drought, and it has become the basis of Great Plains wheat farming, just as Red Fife did in the Canadian prairies (p. 259). Turkey Red is sown in the autumn, and cattle are allowed to graze on the young growth until the winter sets in. The harvest is early: beginning in June, the huge combines move northward, and are at work in central Kansas early in July.

The story of Great Plains farming has been one of alternate advance and retreat. The 1860's were unusually wet years, and the farmers pushed westward; but the 90's were dry, and farmers in western Kansas were forced to retreat. In an attempt to come to terms with an erratic rainfall, the techniques of dry farming were evolved: essentially it consists of conserving the soil moisture by cropping the land only in alternate years. In any one year the farmer cultivates only half of his arable land: the other half lies fallow, and is worked only as much as is necessary to keep down the weeds. It has been found that by these means 20–25 per cent. of the year's rainfall can be stored for the following year.

Dry farming works! For more than a generation alternate cropping of wheat has been compared with annual cropping at the Colby Experimental Station in Kansas, and the resulting yields are most illuminating

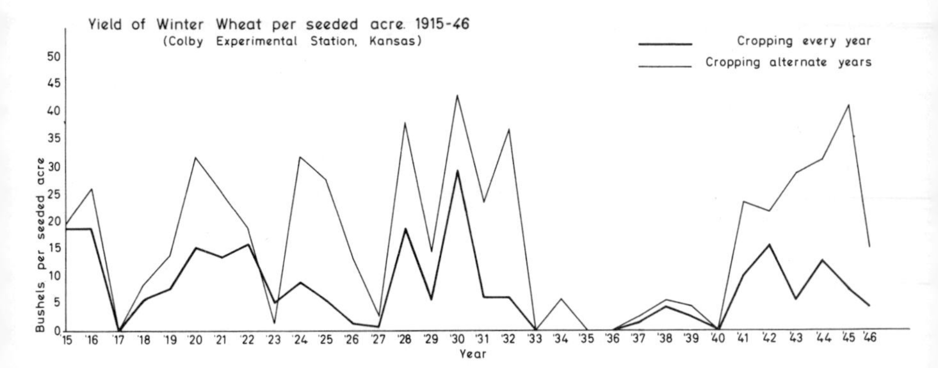

Fig. 61. WHEAT YIELDS BY DRY FARMING

The graphs illustrate a period of 31 years' experimental cropping in Kansas. It will be seen that in most cases cropping in alternate years results in more than double the yield of annual cropping.

(Fig. 61). The following table lists the five dry years 1936–40 and the five good years that followed [1]:

Year	*Yield in bushels per acre*	
	Cropped in alternate years	*Cropped every year*
1936	0·0	0·0
1937	2·5	1·7
1938	5·2	4·7
1939	4·2	2·5
1940	0·0	0·0
1941	23·2	10·0
1942	22·0	15·5
1943	28·7	5·5
1944	31·0	12·7
1945	41·0	7·8

If we consider only the short-term financial reward, the farmer will benefit if the yield from alternate cropping is more than double that from annual cropping (the double yield is necessary to compensate him for the loss of half of his crop area). In the very dry years he would not have benefited; but in the moister years that followed he would have suffered slightly in one year (1942), gained slightly in one year (1941), and gained greatly in the remaining years. If we average the returns over the 30 years 1919–48 we find that by dry farming he would have made a gain of 12 per cent. in the shape of increased yields (*cf.* Fig. 62).

Even dry farming, however, could not stand up to the terrible

[1] Barber, E. L., *Meeting Weather Risks in Kansas Wheat Farming* (Kansas Agricultural Experiment Station, 1950).

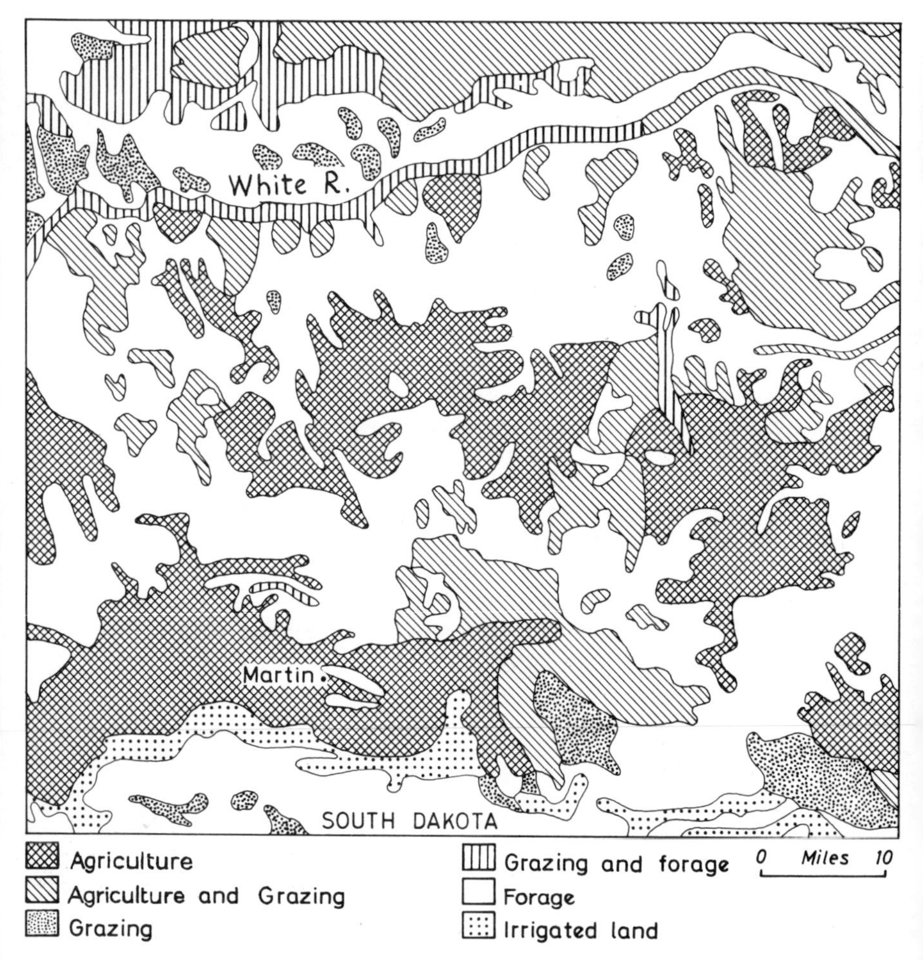

Fig. 62. LAND USE IN A PORTION OF THE NORTHERN GREAT PLAINS

The area illustrated lies south-east of the Badlands National Monument (see Fig. 60 – the Northern Great Plains), and the southern limit of the figure represents the border between South Dakota and Nebraska. The land lies west of long. 100° W., and its mean annual precipitation amounts to only 15–20 inches. Arable farming by normal methods is therefore risky, and the land is more efficiently utilized by dry-farming techniques. Of the six grades of land distinguished, about half the surface falls within the lowest grade (forage land). The distribution of farming (*i.e.*, arable) land is patchy. The influence of water supply is seen in the strips of better-quality land (including irrigated land) that follow the watercourses. The belt of irrigated land near the southern margin of the map follows the course of the Little White river, a tributary of the White river. Their combined waters join the Missouri. Part of the Badlands National Monument appears in the north-west.

droughts of the 1930's (p. 264), which corresponded, unfortunately, with a period of exceptionally low farm prices. The dry soil became powdery, and hot, dry winds raised it into clouds of dust, ruining the land not only where it was raised but also where it settled. So was coined the dramatic name 'dustbowl'. It covered the panhandle of Oklahoma and extended into the neighbouring portions of Colorado, Kansas, New Mexico, and Texas. It was feared that a new American desert had appeared, and was rapidly spreading.

But, sure enough, the dry years came to an end, and in the 1940's were replaced by a series of wet years. The land proved to be capable of recovery, and a survey of the Oklahoma panhandle in 1951 showed that 90 per cent. of the formerly eroded land was once more under cultivation.[1]

An important innovation of 1957 was the introduction of Conservation Reserve land: this is marginal land, liable to erosion in time of drought, which the Government is willing to hold on lease for a number of years. It is replanted to grass and, so long as it is on lease, may not be grazed, ploughed, or cut for hay. The latest policy during 1967 was to release some of this reserve land for ploughing, as stocks of grain were falling below the required level. As an example of the proportion of land on conservation reserve in the western Great Plains we may quote a traverse along one of the easternmost counties of Colorado. Carried out in 1962, this showed 46 per cent. of the land under wheat and 9 per cent. under other crops; 34 per cent. was under pasture, 8 per cent. under conservation, and only 2 per cent. was abandoned.

Two other recent tendencies may be mentioned. These are the increasing size of farms and the appearance of the 'suitcase farmer'. It is clear that dry farming will require a larger farm to be an economic unit compared with one in which conventional methods are employed. Thus in the Oklahoma panhandle the average farm increases from 900 acres in the east to about 2350 acres in the west. The 1950 census showed that the size of the average farm in North Dakota was 629 acres, while farther west in Montana it was 1688 acres. Moreover, the size of farms has been increasing quite rapidly in recent decades in every state in the Great Plains: this is largely a reflection of increased mechanization.

The 'suitcase farmer' was a product of the post-War shortage of grain, which sent its price soaring. Land suited only to grazing was bought cheaply by city investors and planted to grain: two years' harvests, even if poor, could more than repay this outlay, and the 'suitcase farmer' disappeared, without a care for the land he had ruined. Unfortunately, in the United States there is, it seems, no law which can prevent this sort of action.

As in the Canadian prairies, we can recognize the grain areas by their close network of railways. The point is well illustrated in Fig. 63, which covers Nebraska east of long. 102° W. While the south-eastern parts of the state comprise closely settled farm-lands, the north-central areas

[1] Doerr and Morris, *op. cit.*

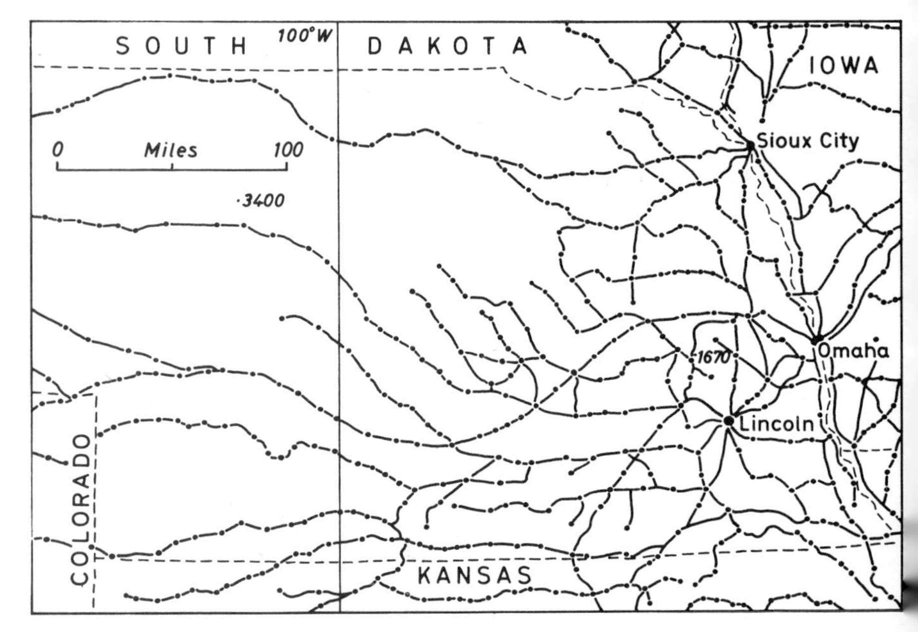

Fig. 63. NEBRASKA: RAILWAYS

Each spot marks a halt. There is a clear contrast between the corn and wheat lands in the damper south-east of the state, with their close rail network, and the sparsely served pastoral areas of the drier north-west, which largely comprises the Sand Hills region. The two spot heights suggest the increase in the altitude of the land surface as one moves west. A small portion of the western part of the state is omitted.

consist of the Sand Hills: these are pastoral in character, and are threaded by a single railway. The leading cereal, however, is maize and not wheat in this, the 'cornhusker' state, for its climatic conditions place it intermediate between the spring wheat of the Dakotas and the winter wheat of Kansas. The bulk of this corn is fed to animals, and Omaha, one of the few cities of the Great Plains, on the eastern border of the state, is second only to Chicago as a livestock market. Its pens for cattle, sheep, and pigs cover 160 acres, and the town has 13 meat-packing plants.

In South Dakota, Nebraska's northern neighbour, corn too is the leading cereal, and again it is the eastern section of the state that is closely settled. Here Sioux Falls corresponds with Omaha, in Nebraska: it contains one of the nation's largest meat-packers, which can handle up to 6000 pigs, 2000 sheep, and 900 head of cattle each day.

Pastoral Farming

Early trappers in the territory that is now Wyoming were struck by the healthy condition of the native buffalo and deer: even in winter the animals would scrape away the snow and browse on the previous season's grass, which seemed dead but was still nutritious. Before the advance of settlement the Great Plains were the natural home of vast herds of bison (buffalo). In 1871 Colonel R. I. Dodge recorded travelling for 25 miles through a single immense herd.

The slaughter and virtual extinction of the bison is one of the less creditable achievements of the white man. For the most part only the skin was held to be of value, and the carcase was left to rot. It is said that 'Brick' Bond during November and December of 1874 shot more than a hundred buffalo a day, and employed five skinners to remove their hides. William Cody ('Buffalo Bill') was employed by the railway-builders to provide the workers with meat, and during 18 months is said to have killed 4280 animals.

Even the vast herds of the 70's could not survive such slaughter. By 1890 the buffalo was a rare sight, and the Indian had lost his main source of livelihood. It was soon realized, however, that the pastures which could support the deer and the bison could also form the basis of a beef-cattle industry; and in the 1880's this was demonstrated when millions of cattle were driven northward from Texas into the rest of the Great Plains.

All the Plains states have extensive tracts that are mainly devoted to ranching. In the 1880's these were unfenced, and each covered a vast area: the cattle were expected to fend for themselves in winter. But the winter of 1886–87 was exceptionally severe, and proved fatal to many thousands of animals. Ranchers reduced the size of their holdings, set about fencing them, and grew hay or brought in feed for the winter months. A typical ranch in South Dakota now runs about 2000 cattle in place of the 15,000 to 20,000 head of the 1880's. Though the individual ranch is smaller, there are more of them, and there has been a considerable increase in the total number of cattle in the Great Plains.

Wyoming is *par excellence* a cattle state. Over a million cattle browse on its blue grama, bluestems, and other forage grasses, and the pastures here have successfully survived over 50 years of ranching. The state Brand Book lists 20,000 different brands. In Nebraska the Sand Hills are famous for their pastures, and one county here – Cherry county – bears the nickname 'Home of a Million Cattle'. The figure, however, should not be taken literally.

Western Oklahoma and Kansas likewise are important ranching regions. Not all the ranches are large by Western standards. One example in the Oklahoma panhandle covers 10,500 acres and runs about 370 head of cattle. As in many parts of the Plains, water is a problem, for though the ranch straddles the Cimarron river, this river carries little water, and it is supplemented by four wind pumps. In winter the animals' diet is aided by soya bean or cottonseed cake, together with alfalfa pellets. The ranch home is modern and well equipped, with running water and mains electricity, telephone, radio and television, and fitted carpets.

Farther east another renowned cattle area runs across the Kansas–Oklahoma border: it comprises the Flint hills of Kansas and the Osage plains of Oklahoma. In a structural dome here is an area of unusually nutritious bluestem pastures, on soils derived from a limestone of Lower Carboniferous age. Osage county in Oklahoma, with over 100,000 head of cattle, is one of the leading cattle counties in the United States. There is a similar bluestem district in the south-centre of the state, comprising the rolling limestone country of the Arbuckle mountains. Its nickname, 'Hereford Heaven', is a reminder of the chief cattle breed of the Great Plains.

To the south-west is Texas, with more beef cattle than any other state in the nation. Not all of the cattle lie within the Great Plains province, for there are important ranching lands as far south as the Gulf of Mexico. But spreading westward from central Texas into New Mexico are some of the greatest range lands in the whole of the United States. The rainfall, however, is low, the rivers are erratic in flow, and the pastures are scanty, so that the ranches must be very large. West of the Pecos river a typical ranch covers between 15,000 and 20,000 acres. Even these do not match the King Ranch, which is the largest in the nation. Lying in the south-east of the state, south of Corpus Christi on the Gulf coast, it is beyond the confines of the Great Plains, but we refer to it for the sake of completeness. It covers 900,000 acres, extends into eight counties, and with the aid of 3000 horses rears 85,000 head of cattle.

Irrigation

Irrigation is an important aid to cropping in the drier parts of the Great Plains. A series of wet years tends to slow down its progress; but in the following dry years the need to irrigate reasserts itself. Thus in western Oklahoma the real move towards irrigation did not begin till about 1937, after the droughts of the 1930's. Even in 'normal' years here irrigation will more than double the yield of wheat, while in dry years it converts what would have been certain failure into an excellent crop. Irrigated lands are scattered throughout the Oklahoma panhandle. A farmer drills a well 300–400 feet deep; he installs a pump and constructs a reservoir. He then digs a series of channels which lead the water by gravity to his crops or he sets up a sprinkler system. Irrigation may cost him 12,000 dollars (say, £5000) but he is now independent of the erratic rainfall. He grows sorghum, wheat, alfalfa, and maize, and will hope to cover the cost of irrigation in about seven years. In the small district of the Oklahoma panhandle there are over 350 irrigation wells; in the whole of Nebraska there are about 10,000.

One of the largest irrigation districts of the Great Plains centres on

Lubbock, in the panhandle of Texas. Here the limestone plateaux of the Llano Estacado are devoid of surface water, but the water table can be reached by means of deep wells. In this district there are over $3\frac{1}{4}$ million acres of irrigated farms, and this has become one of the world's greatest cotton-producing areas. Lubbock county, indeed, contains more cotton-land than any other county in the United States.

More spectacular than the single irrigation well of the private farmer is the large dam and reservoir constructed by state or Federal agency. Some of the largest of these form part of the Missouri Basin Project, and are multi-purpose schemes similar to that of the Tennessee Valley Authority (p. 99). On the Missouri above Sioux City five major dams have been constructed, and vast reservoirs are spreading in Nebraska, the Dakotas, and Montana. The longest of these, the Oahe reservoir, will stretch from Pierre in South Dakota to Bismarck in North Dakota – a distance of about 200 miles. About 60 miles up-stream of Bismarck is Garrison Dam, which ponds back the Missouri river in a vast reservoir in the west of North Dakota. Still higher up-stream, in Montana, are the Fort Peck reservoir and dam. The latter, when it was built in 1940, was the largest earth-filled dam in the world. The Missouri is becoming, like the Tennessee, a staircase of lakes. These are likely to form important sources of irrigation water, for they are situated in lands of marginal rainfall.

Smaller schemes too have their value, and the farmers of central Kansas benefit from two 'Missouri Basin' dams on the Smoky Hill river. The Platte is a silt-laden river of erratic flow, and in its natural state was of little use for irrigation. Now two dams impound the upper North Platte in central Wyoming to form the Seminoe and Pathfinder reservoirs, each of which is more than 25 miles long; and there are other smaller reservoirs in the same basin. Lower down-stream, in western Nebraska, is the Kingsley Dam, the second largest earth-filled dam in the world. This impounds the 28-mile-long Lake McConaughy, and supplies water to hundreds of farmers in the Ogallala district.

Irrigation on the Great Plains cannot compare with the extensive schemes of the Colorado or Columbia rivers, but it makes for a more stable agriculture in a region which in the past has suffered tragically from its uncertain rainfall.

The Oil Industry

No appraisal of the Great Plains would be complete without reference to the oil industry. Conditions for the accumulation and preservation of oil and natural gas are favourable in regions of sedimentary rocks that have been subject to only slight deformation. The structure of the Great Plains, as we have seen, conforms to this pattern, and together with the Canadian prairies contributes substantially to the American output of oil and natural gas. This is not to imply that the industry is confined to the Great Plains, for Louisiana on the Gulf coast and California in the west are important producers, and probably the greater part of the Texan production comes from that part of the state beyond the Great Plains.

The following table indicates the recent production figures for both Great Plains and other states.

State	*Production of petroleum, 1967 (million metric tons)*
Texas	142
Louisiana	92
California	48
Oklahoma	30
Wyoming	19
New Mexico	16
Kansas	13
United States total (including smaller producers)	409

In the Great Plains there are extensive oilfields in west-central Texas and the adjoining corner of New Mexico, and the oil-bearing lands stretch north-east in a broad belt through Oklahoma and curve northward and westward across Kansas. Oilfields are also widespread in Wyoming, and present in northern and eastern Montana and western North Dakota (Fig. 64).

Oklahoma occupies a unique position in the American oil industry. This was the chief producing state during the 1920's, when the industry was becoming established. Tulsa became the commercial centre, and the companies set up their headquarters there; and so it remains today. The output of Oklahoma reached a maximum of 37 million tons in 1927; it has since declined somewhat, and at the same time the state has been overtaken by three others. Its prosperity, however, is still largely dependent on the oil industry. It contains a dozen refineries, which are linked by a maze of pipelines to the oilfields and to other parts of the United States (Fig. 65).

The United States is by far the world's largest producer of petroleum, and her output is still expanding, though the proportion of the world

Fig. 64. THE UNITED STATES: OILFIELDS AND GASFIELDS

The Appalachian oilfields, where oil was first produced, now yield less than 2 million tons annually. Texas and Louisiana together produce more than half the total output. Notice the off-shore extensions of the oilfields in Louisiana and California. In recent years the production of natural gas has greatly increased, and it now supplies more energy than oil in the United States. More than two-thirds of the gas is raised in Texas and Louisiana. For the location of oil shales see Fig. 66.

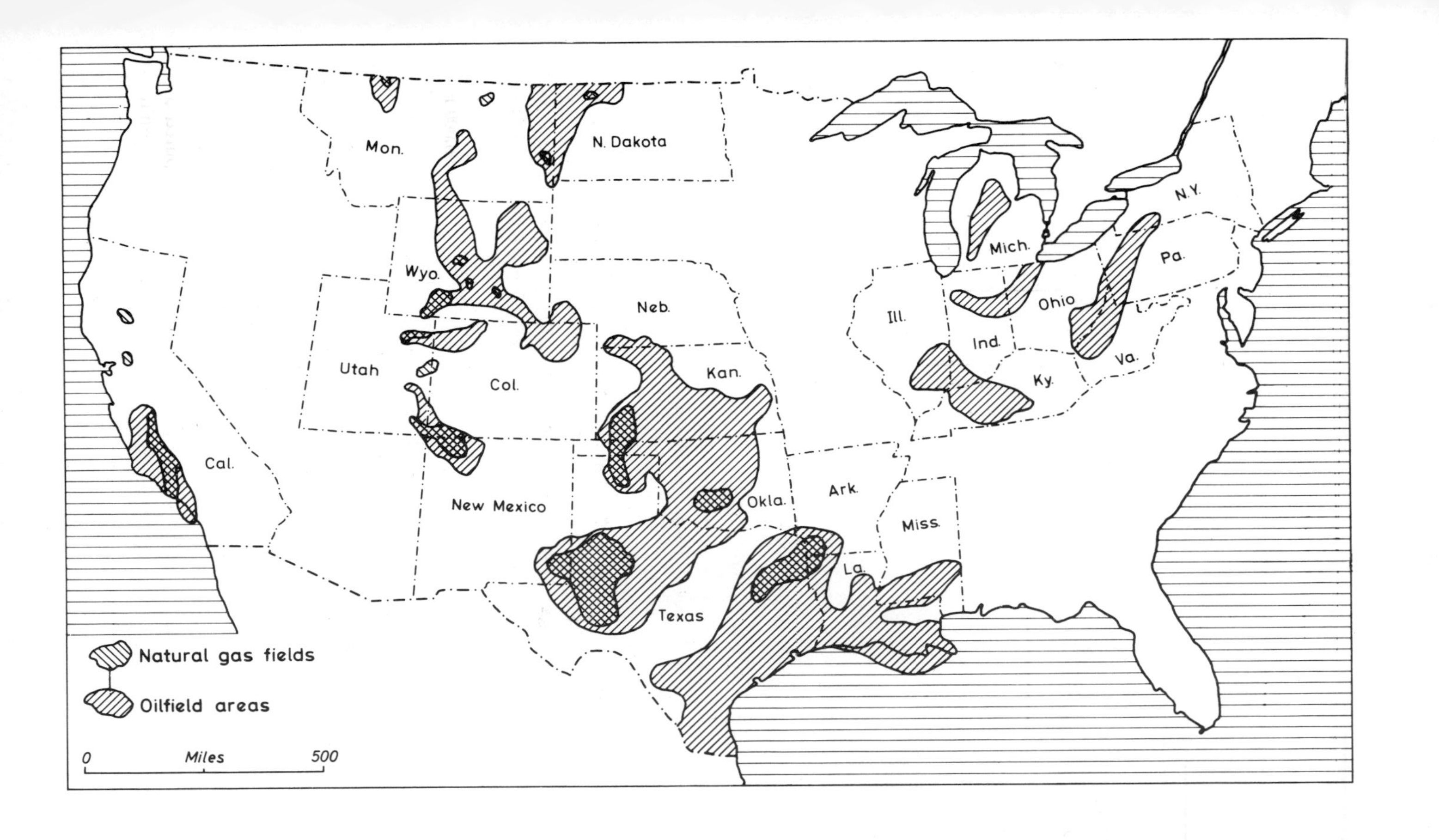
Mon.
N. Dakota
Wyo.
Utah
Col.
Neb.
Kan.
Cal.
New Mexico
Okla.
Texas
Ark.
Miss.
La.
Ill.
Ind.
Ohio
Ky.
Va.
Mich.
Pa.
N.Y.
Natural gas fields
Oilfield areas
0
Miles
500

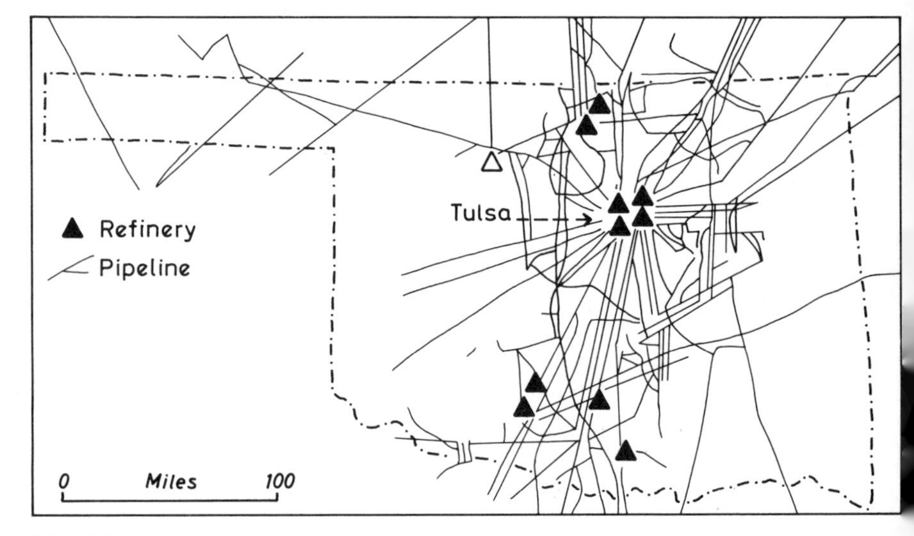

Fig. 65. OKLAHOMA: OIL PIPELINES

The map illustrates the complex system of pipelines that has been developed in this state, formerly the largest producer of oil. In the whole of the United States there are about 200,000 miles of oil pipeline and a further 260,000 miles of gas pipeline.

total that this output represents is declining. The United States raised 64 per cent. of the total in 1920; 52 per cent. in 1950; 35 per cent. in 1960; and 29 per cent. in 1964. The U.S.A. is also the world's greatest consumer of oil, and her demand is increasing. In 1964 it amounted to more than 500 million metric tons – considerably more than she produced. The difference was made up by imports of crude oil, mainly from Venezuela and Canada. In case of need the United States domestic production could be considerably increased, for at present it is being held in check, partly as a measure of conservation, and partly to prevent an undue reduction of price.

The known reserves of oil in the United States are computed to be sufficient for only 11 years. The position, however, is not quite so alarming as it might seem, for new fields are being discovered, and much potential oil-bearing country has still to be explored. Moreover, vast deposits of oil shale are known to exist in the interior, and a real shortage of conventional petroleum would encourage the exploitation of shales.

Oil shale occurs in most of the states of the U.S.A., but the largest deposits are found near the margin of the Great Plains, within a radius of about 125 miles of the meeting-point of Wyoming, Colorado, and Utah (Fig. 66). The oil is contained in a marlstone of Eocene age named the Green River formation; this extends over 16,500 square miles, and constitutes the world's largest-known deposit of oil. Commercial production of oil from the Green River shales is imminent.

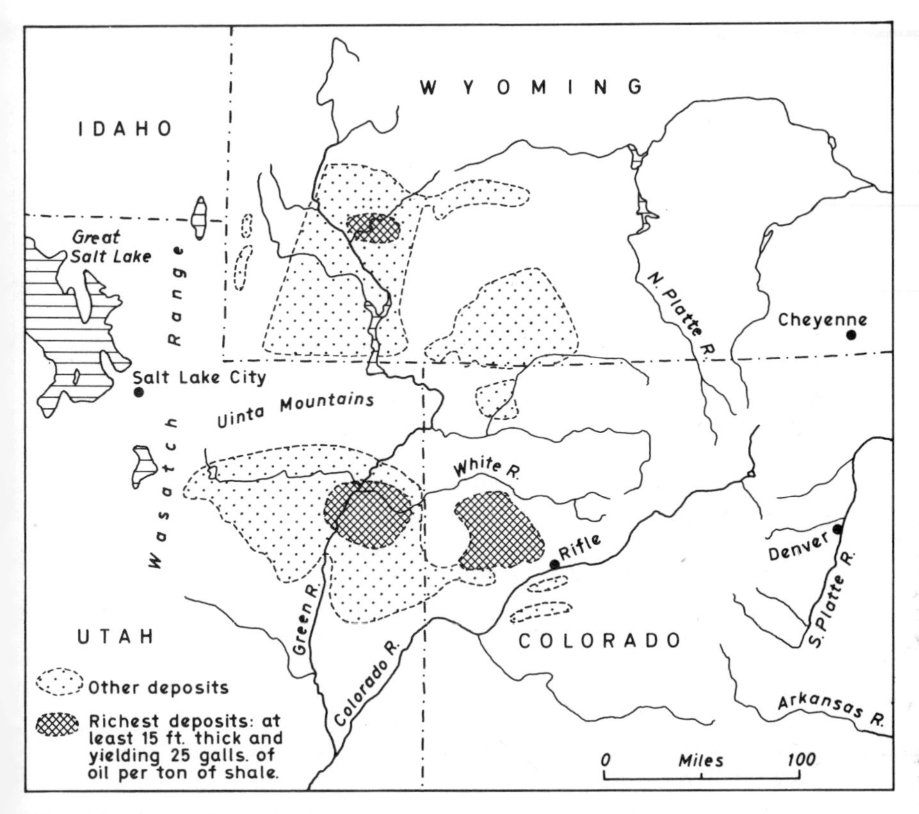

Fig. 66. THE GREEN RIVER OIL SHALES

They occur in a rather remote region near the headwaters of the Colorado and Platte, and form the greatest known reserves of oil in the world.

The oil industry may seem to have little or no connection with farming in the Great Plains. But oil men often engage in ranching, and usually farm very well: they are noted in Oklahoma for their enthusiastic cultivation of bluestem pasture and hay-lands, and for their alertness against prairie fires.

CHAPTER SEVEN

THE WEST

The West is the largest major region of the United States. Its limits are clear: to the north and south there are international frontiers, and to the west the Pacific. To the east the boundary is the Front Range of the Rockies, and for the most part this is a sharp line that separates the horizontal and relatively young (Cretaceous and Tertiary) strata of the Great Plains from the older, contorted material of the Rocky Mountains. Only in one district – the Wyoming Basin – is there a breach in the rampart of the Rockies. Here the structure of the Great Plains thrusts itself far to the west, and important trails made use of this gateway to the goldfields and to the Pacific coastlands.

The West has its own character. Much of it is deficient in rainfall; and here are both the largest deserts and the greatest areas of irrigation. In the West are the highest mountains and plateaux, and associated with structural upheavals are mineral riches: here are flourishing mining-camps based on the production of copper, silver, lead, and zinc, and many more 'ghost' towns. There are salmon fisheries and resources of timber, and two great rivers – the Columbia and the Colorado – that have been harnessed for both power and irrigation water. The West has also many fantastic sights: natural arches, pinnacles, and immense canyons; giant cacti and the tallest trees in the world; hot springs and geysers, volcanic craters and lava flows.

There are strange contrasts in the distribution of population. San Francisco and Los Angeles are as busy and congested as any metropolitan areas in the nation, while not far away are wide tracts of unproductive and uninhabited desert. Yet where water can be applied these soils are among the most fruitful on earth. Finally, the West contains the largest surviving remnants of the native Indian tribes. Some have become corporately rich through the possession of oil or minerals; but as individuals they continue largely as their forefathers did, living in primitive huts, hunting and fishing, and growing their precarious crops of corn.

PHYSICAL BASIS

Physically we may distinguish five sub-regions in the West. From east to west these are the Rocky Mountains, the Colorado Plateau, the Great

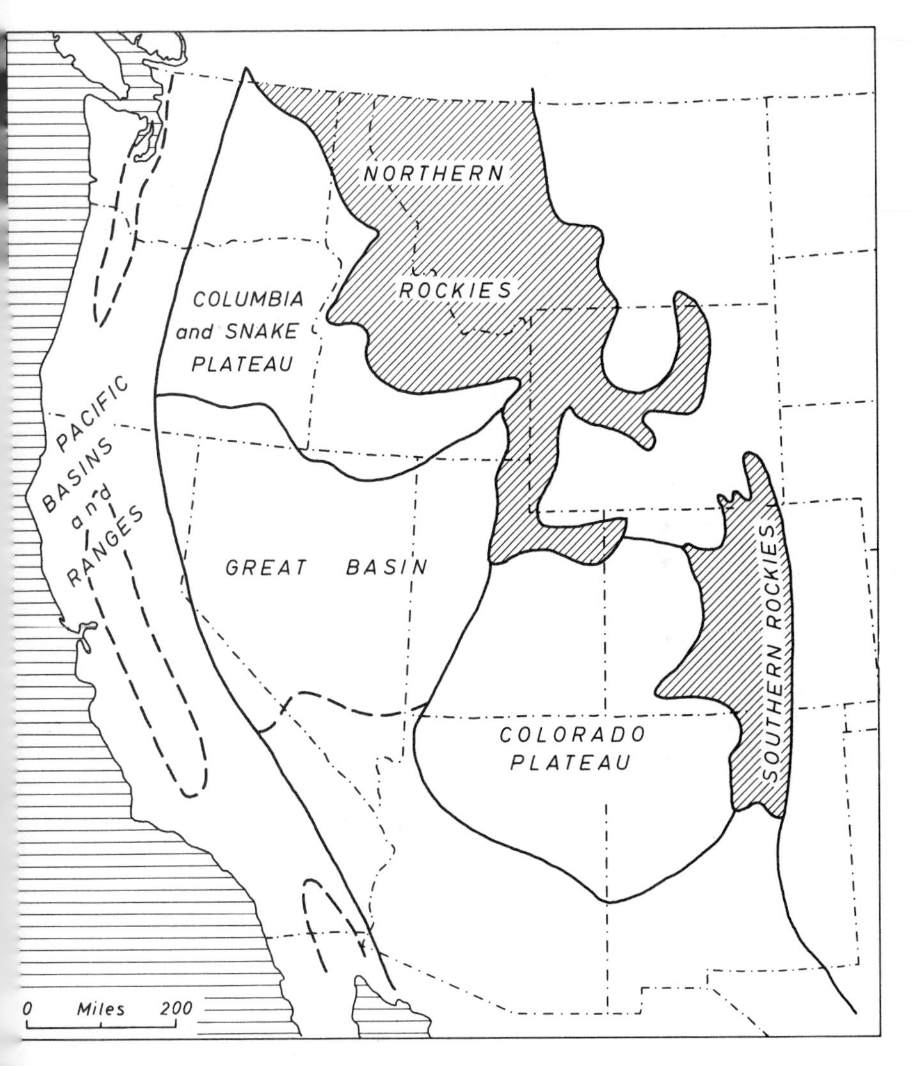

Fig. 67. PHYSIOGRAPHIC REGIONS OF THE WEST

Basin, the Columbia–Snake Plateau, and the Pacific Basins and Ranges (Fig. 67).

The Rocky Mountains

In the United States the Rockies form the high eastern edge of the broad upland that constitutes the western third of the country, and to the traveller approaching from the east they rise abruptly like a wall overlooking the Great Plains. Structurally, however, they are to be regarded as an interruption – a zone of uplift – in the generally horizontal strata which lie to either side.

This is most easily demonstrated in the southern Rockies. They display a variety of material, but their cores are usually of Archæan material, and their flanks include Carboniferous, Jurassic, and Cretaceous sediments, while they rise above plateaux to the east and west containing Cretaceous rocks.

The broad Wyoming Basin readily divides the Rockies into a northern and a southern section, each of which has a distinct character. It is in the northern Rockies that the mountain system attains its greatest width, of about 400 miles. Here, in central Idaho, it appears as a tangled knot of high masses, without any clear shape or direction. Farther north the Rockies develop a linear arrangement of lofty ridges separated by deep glaciated valleys. Prominent among the latter is the Rocky Mountain Trench, which extends northward from the Snake river plains up to the international border and far into Canada (p. 286). It is mainly in these trenches that the scattered population of the Rockies is to be found, and the valleys have been utilized by trails, roads, and railways in their zigzag courses westward, across the structural grain of the country.

Lewis Range, in the north-east, displays magnificent glacial scenery, which has been incorporated in both a national and international park; and in a similar fashion the hot springs and geysers in the north-west have been enshrined in Yellowstone Park.

The southern Rockies are narrower but higher, and in Colorado there are 46 summits exceeding 14,000 feet. Two great parallel ridges range north and south: these are the Front Range to the east and the Sawatch to the west. Both are anticlinal in structure (Fig. 68), and are so persistent that transverse routes have been developed only with difficulty. The Oregon Trail rounded them to the north, passing through Laramie, and to the south of them passed the Santa Fé Trail.

The Colorado Plateau

Immediately west of the Rockies is the Colorado Plateau. It consists of a relatively uniform block of horizontal strata, which range in age from Carboniferous to Jurassic. This block has been raised to the extent of 5000 feet or more, and its summits now are over 8000 feet above sea-level. During this persistent rise in the land surface the rivers gained fresh energy, maintained their courses, and excavated their beds more and more deeply into the plateau. The arid climate arrested the development of normal valley profiles, and the Colorado and its tributaries now flow at the bottom of immensely deep canyons.

The Grand Canyon is 217 miles long, on the average 10 miles wide, and a mile deep. The river has cut through 2000 feet of Carboniferous limestones, sandstones, and shales, and a further 1000 feet of Cambrian strata. All these are exposed in the sides of the outer canyon, whose character is determined by their varying resistance and colour. The inner gorge has been excavated in Pre-Cambrian sedimentary and metamorphic rocks, which are traversed by igneous masses, so that in the Grand Canyon we have a veritable museum of geology.

The Great Basin

Very different is the physiographic province beyond – the Great Basin. Its framework consists of a whole series of parallel tilted blocks whose scarp slopes face west: a landscape of corrugations on the grand scale. At its widest the basin includes a score or more of these parallel ridges, which are formed of a variety of material. Cambrian rocks are seen near the Nevada–Utah border, and Carboniferous to the south-west of Great Salt Lake. In north-west Nevada the ridges are of Jurassic age, and in central Nevada are composed of Tertiary volcanic material. Presumably the block faulting took place in Tertiary times. Wind and water erosion have attacked the ridges and distributed their waste in almost level tracts which surround the ridges; and above these flats their summits rise to about 7000 feet.

A few of these detrital areas drain northward to the Snake river, but most of them have no outlet, and their intermittent streams lose themselves in the deserts. The largest of the watercourses is that of the Humboldt, which empties itself into Carson Sink.

During the Ice Age two large lakes spread over wide areas of the Great Basin. The former Lake Bonneville in the east is now represented by the shallow, residual Great Salt Lake; Lake Lahontan in the west partly survives in Pyramid and other lakes, and its name has been preserved in a dam and reservoir. Where irrigation is possible the old lake floors and terraces can provide valuable agricultural land.

Two lofty inward-facing scarps enclose the Great Basin (Fig. 68 (*b*)). To the east the Wasatch mountains overlook Great Salt Lake, rise to summits of 12,000 feet, and from their snows provide irrigation water for a fruitful zone at their base. To the west are the Sierra Nevada, which culminate in Mt Whitney (14,495 feet) – the highest peak in the United States outside Alaska. Geologically the two ranges do not match exactly; nevertheless, they are believed to have formed originally the two limbs of a single arch whose crest has been eroded, and is in part represented by the intervening ridges.

To the south the Great Basin narrows, the ridges terminate, aridity and mean temperatures increase, and one reaches the American deserts, including the Mojave desert and Death valley. The latter lies about 270 feet below sea-level. The deserts imposed formidable hardships on the pioneers as they struggled westward along the Santa Fé Trail. After reaching Las Vegas they turned south-west to cross the Mojave desert

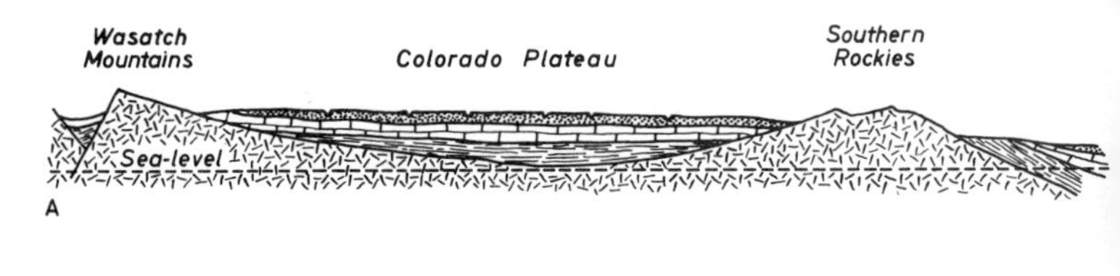

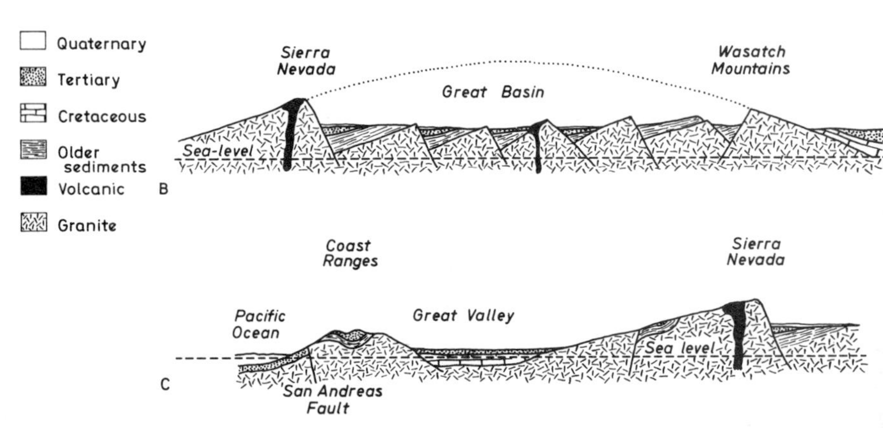

Fig. 68. THREE REPRESENTATIVE SECTIONS ACROSS THE WEST

The sections are diagrammatic and are not to scale: they illustrate (*a*) the Colorado Plateau; (*b*) the Great Basin; and (*c*) south-central California. Each is aligned east and west.

and traversed the San Bernardino mountains by way of the Cajon Pass (4301 feet) to reach the Pacific Ocean near Los Angeles.

The Columbia–Snake Plateau

To the north, beyond the northern boundary of Nevada, the tilted blocks of the Great Basin have been flooded by a sea of lava. Here, within the Columbia–Snake Basin, is one of the world's largest volcanic plateaux, which covers about 200,000 square miles. Time after time masses of lava issued from numerous fissures, burying the landscape below successive sheets, building up the land higher and higher until 5000 to 10,000 feet of basalt had accumulated. In places the contours of the older Tertiary land surface have been revealed, where the Snake has cut a stupendous 5000-foot canyon through the lavas. Only the Blue mountains and a few other isolated peaks escaped the floods of lava: they are now locally called steptoes after Steptoe Butte in eastern Washington.

The lava surfaces now exposed are not all of the same age. The earliest are of Eocene age, and are found in south-west Idaho and south-east Oregon. Those lying astride the Washington–Oregon border erupted in Miocene times; while the lavas of southern Oregon and south-eastern Idaho date from Pliocene times. In the latter area, south-west of Arco, are some of the most fantastic volcanic phenomena. They are associated with a series of fissures 16 miles long and clearly visible on the ground. Here are craters left by receding fluid lava and domes formed by slowly moving viscous lava; cinder cones built of ejected fragments, and congealed flows of black, pleated 'ropy' lava. Appropriately named, this is the Craters of the Moon National Monument.

The Pacific Basins and Ranges

Essentially the Pacific zone consists of two parallel series of ridges separated by long troughs. The outer ridges are the Coast Ranges, while the inner comprise the Cascades in the north and the Sierra Nevada in the south. The trough bordering the Cascades is the Willamette valley, and that bordering the Sierra Nevada the Great Valley of California (Fig. 68 (*c*)). Each of these physical elements has its own character.

In terms of relief the Cascades and the Sierra Nevada form a continuous feature; but structurally they are very different. The Sierra Nevada, 430 miles long and 40 to 80 miles wide, form one of the great tilted blocks of the earth's surface. They are composed mainly of Carboniferous sediments together with granitic intrusions of Jurassic age; and their eastern edge has been elevated to the order of two miles, so that here are some of the highest peaks in the continent. A row of short, parallel streams descends from glaciers and snowfields and supplies life-giving water to the Great Valley, whose floor is, indeed, composed of their sediments.

The steep descent from summits of 10,000–12,000 feet almost to sea-level in less than 100 miles has given to the rivers great erosive power, and they have excavated deep canyons. Most spectacular of these is the Yosemite valley, which includes among its many waterfalls four of the world's highest cascades. Three national parks testify to the scenic grandeur of the Sierra Nevada.

In modern times half a dozen roads cross the Sierra Nevada, though for a stretch of over 150 miles centred near Mt Whitney no passage is possible. The traditional pass was the Donner (7135), now followed by road and rail from Reno to Sacramento.

The Cascades to the north continue the direction of the Sierra Nevada, but their average elevation is lower. They are built of the same volcanic material that we have seen in the Columbia and Snake Plateau, and in fact form its western edge. The general level of the ridge, however, is dominated by a magnificent series of volcanic peaks, including Mts Baker, Rainier, Adams, Hood, Jefferson, and Shasta. Of these, Mts Rainier and Shasta are monarchs of over 14,000 feet. In the south, near to the point where the Cascades merge into the Sierra Nevada, is Lassen Peak, the only active American volcano outside Alaska.

Glacial and river erosion has deeply dissected the Cascades and has produced landscapes of great natural beauty. The superimposed Columbia river has cut a deep gash through the mountain system and forms the most important crossing. Beyond the Canadian border the Cascades continue as the Coast Range of British Columbia.

The Pacific Troughs. There is an almost continuous trough from the Strait of Georgia in the north (east of Vancouver Island) as far as the Gulf of California in the south. It is separated, however, into three sections by the compact block of the Klamath mountains astride the Oregon–California border and by the coast ranges of southern California. From north to south these are: the Puget lowland and Willamette–Cowlitz valley; the Great Valley of California; and the Imperial and Coachella valleys of the far south. All are important agricultural areas, though the need for irrigation increases as one moves southward.

The Puget lowland and the Willamette–Cowlitz valley have been eroded in a zone of relatively soft Tertiary material. In detail, however, the surface is varied, for it has been modified by the deposition of glacial drift and recent alluvium. Low platforms rising to between 250 and 500 feet border Puget Sound, whose shore is usually quite abrupt. The Sound itself represents a partial drowning of the lowland. In the north the soils are based on fairly heavy morainic clays; farther south they are derived from lighter outwash gravels and sands. Recent alluvium is confined to relatively narrow zones bordering the two main rivers. The bordering mountains receive some of the heaviest rainfall in the whole country: all the hilly tracts experience over 50 inches of rain during the year, and large areas receive more than 80 inches. During the winter half of the year great volumes of water pour from the hills, and the braided course of the Willamette in the southern part of its trough is a sign that wide areas are subject to flood.

On a far larger scale is the Great Valley of California. Nearly 500 miles long and 40 miles wide, its area is over half that of England. This is a structural trough, formed when the rocks on each side were folded, faulted, and tilted to produce the Coast Ranges and the Sierra Nevada; and its floor has been built from their wastage in the same manner as in the Great Basin. The northern half is drained by the Sacramento river, and the southern half by the San Joaquin. Little

---

Fig. 69. THE SAN ANDREAS FAULT

In this area, 35 miles north-west of San Francisco, the straight and deep valley which marks th course of the San Andreas fault is partially submerged. The fault continues north-westward an influences the shape of the coast for a further 60 miles. As the contours indicate, the land surfac at the scarp descends from summits of over 1200 feet to below sea-level within the space of 2 miles It was a movement along this fault that resulted in the disastrous San Francisco earthquake of 1906 *Based on the official 1:62,500 map, 1954.*

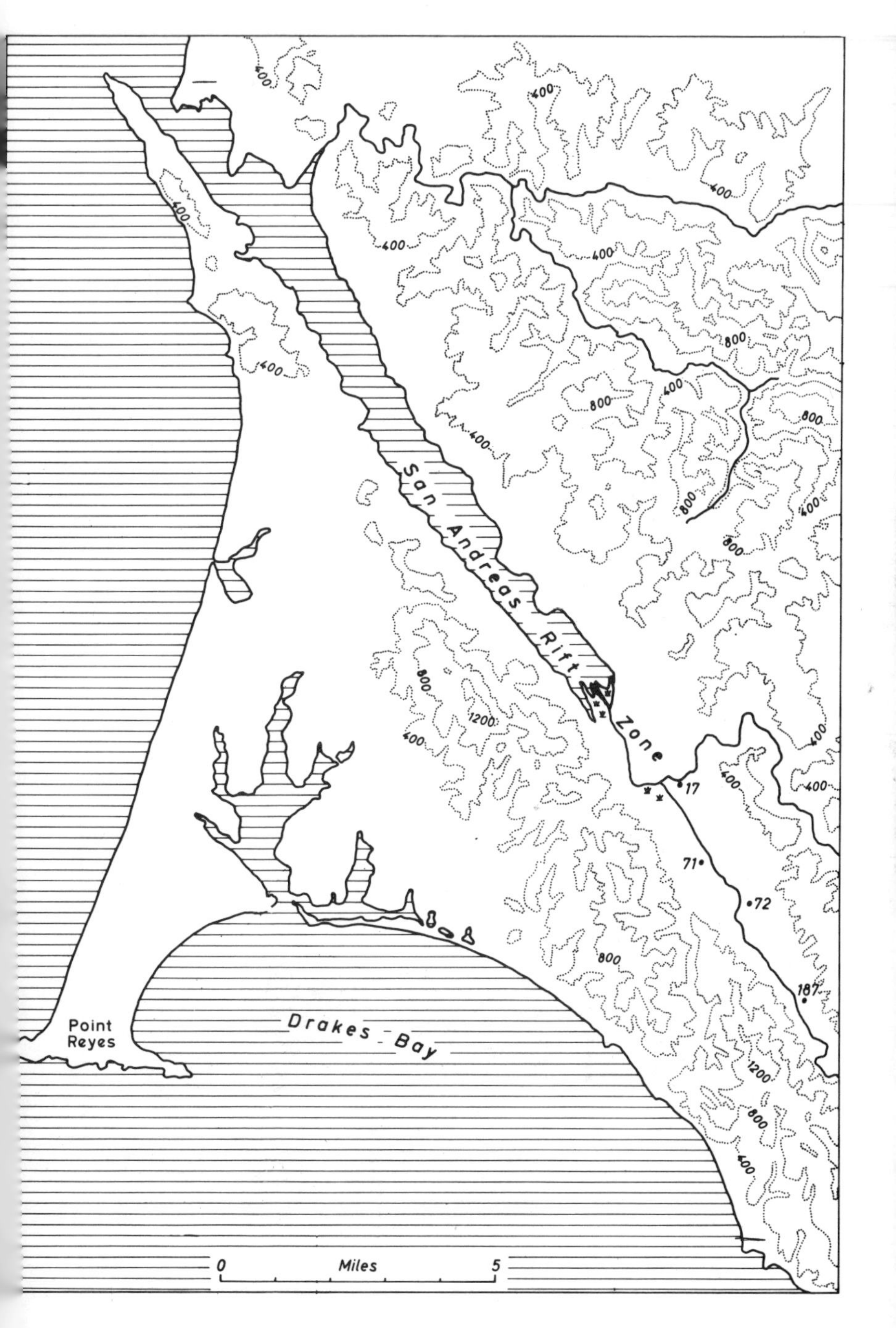
San Andreas Rift Zone
Drakes Bay
Point Reyes
17
71
72
187
400
800
1200
0
Miles
5

water reaches these streams from the west, for this is the drier, rain-shadow flank of the Coast Range; but a row of parallel streams descends from the Sierra Nevada, and their deposits have tended to push the main-stream towards the western side of the valley.

Unlike the Willamette valley, water-supply here tends to be deficient. Even in the north the annual precipitation reaches only 23 inches; and in the south it is as low as 6 inches. The more southerly 'tributaries' of the San Joaquin are intermittent in flow, and 'Lake' Tulare is usually dry.

Beyond the southern rim of the Great Valley, formed by the Tehachapi mountains, lies the Mojave desert, and its south-western boundary corresponds with a fault scarp. Farther south-east, the Pacific trough reappears in the shape of the deep valley that contains Salton Sea. This is bounded on each side by fault scarps, and is perhaps the clearest example in North America of a rift valley. Like the land bordering the Dead Sea in the Middle East, its surface lies well below sea-level – a condition that can continue only in an arid climate. Salton Sea was formed in 1900 by human intervention in the course of the Colorado river. The conversion of these former desert wastes into highly productive land is noticed below (p. 201).

The Coast Ranges. The Coast Ranges extend from Queen Charlotte and Vancouver islands in Canada, through the Pacific states, and on to form the peninsula of Lower California. They constitute the youngest element in the mountain systems of North America, and indeed movement still continues along the line of the San Andreas fault in the south: this was responsible for the disastrous San Francisco earthquake of 1906.

The ranges have resulted from the folding and faulting of marine sediments. North of Cape Blanco these are of Tertiary age; farther south they include Cretaceous, Jurassic, and Triassic material. The smooth coastline north of Cape Blanco contrasts strongly with the irregular shoreline to the south, with its many bays and headlands. In this southern section the ridges are fault-guided, and the line of the coast cuts the structure lines at a low angle, so that the seaward ends of the troughs have been drowned to form inlets, while the ridges form peninsulas. The San Andreas fault is only one of several fractures, but is particularly prominent, and has formed a remarkable mountain-girt valley and inlet in the neighbourhood of Point Reyes (Fig. 69). The troughs so formed are, with the aid of irrigation, of great agricultural value; and the bays that mark their seaward ends are sometimes useful in the development of harbours. The most striking example of the latter is the magnificent land-locked San Francisco bay.

A characteristic of the entire Pacific shore is its lack of any real coastal plain. There are small lowland embayments along the Columbia and Umpqua rivers and in the Los Angeles district; but apart from these, and the troughs described above, the mountains rise abruptly from the sea, and all the major agricultural areas are inland and rimmed by mountains.

CLIMATE AND VEGETATION

In mountainous country that stretches across seventeen degrees of latitude we shall expect to find a wide variety of climate and vegetation.

Confining ourselves first to the coastal districts, we notice an increase in temperatures but a decrease in total precipitation as we move southward. The rainfall is brought by eastward-moving depressions from the Pacific; but these are essentially winter phenomena, for during the summer the normal high pressure over the seas of middle latitudes restricts the depressions to more northerly paths. Everywhere, then, along the Pacific coasts there is a winter maximum of rainfall.

Very high totals are registered in north-west Washington, where Quinault, in the foothills to the south-west of Mt Olympus, receives 128·6 inches per annum, of which only 8 per cent. falls in the three summer months (June, July, and August). At Crescent City, on the coast in the far north of California, the mean annual rainfall amounts to 75·9 inches, of which about $3\frac{1}{2}$ per cent. occurs in the summer months. The transition to the Mediterranean type of climate is marked by increasing temperatures and decreasing totals of rainfall; and while it clearly is not possible to draw a precise boundary, we may place the limit in about latitude 40°, so that the whole of the Great Valley of California falls within the Mediterranean region (Fig. 70).

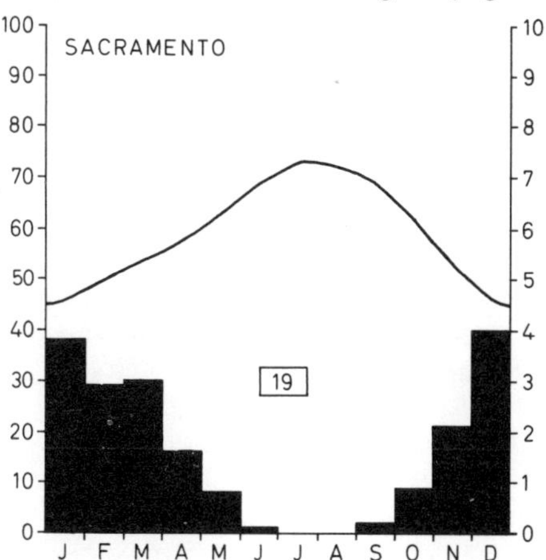

Fig. 70. SACRAMENTO: TEMPERATURE AND PRECIPITATION
For key see Fig. 46 (p. 117).

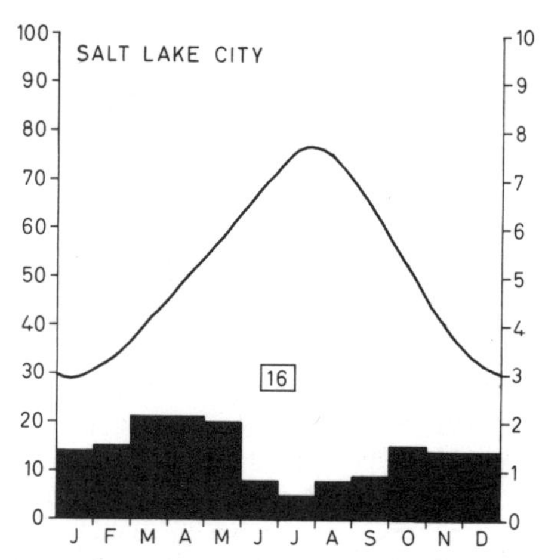

Fig. 71. SALT LAKE CITY: TEMPERATURE AND PRECIPITATION
For key see Fig. 46 (p. 117).

At San Francisco the annual total of rainfall has decreased to 20·2 inches, and at San Diego, in the far south, to only 10·1 inches. In both these places the summer proportion is only 1 per cent. of the total.

This simple pattern is profoundly modified inland, since the grain of the country runs at right angles to the direction of the main drift of the air. As one moves from west to east there are quite sudden changes in the total of precipitation. The exposed western slopes of the Coast Ranges in Washington and Oregon receive 100–150 inches of rain; yet the sheltered valley of the Willamette, a few miles to the east, has only 35–40 inches. On the windward side of the Cascades there are 75–100 inches, but in the rain shadow it drops to only 10 inches. By the time the air reaches the Rockies it has already lost most of its moisture, and their western slopes receive 30–35 inches.

In California large tracts of the Mojave desert experience as little as 4 inches (*cf.* Plate 5); and the computed average for Death valley is 2 inches, though in some years no rain has fallen at all. In Utah there are surprising differences over quite small areas – thus the eastern shore of the Great Salt Lake has 16 inches, while the western receives only 6 inches (Fig. 71).

Plate 5. AN ARID AREA NEAR BAKER, IN SOUTHERN CALIFORNIA
The photograph illustrates a portion of the eastern extremity of the Mojave desert, where the mean annual rainfall is between 5 and 6 inches. There are mountains at the top and dry water-courses and detrital plains at the bottom of the picture. There is not a single road, habitation, or tree in the entire area.

Photo by courtesy of the U.S. Forest Service

Vegetation

Plant associations are very sensitive to differences in the conditions of temperature and precipitation, and particularly to the seasonal incidence of the rainfall. But this relationship is not just the simple one of cause and effect, for similar climates in different parts of the world do not necessarily result in identical vegetations. California in particular has at least two characteristic forms of vegetation: these are the giant redwoods of the Coast Ranges and the ungainly Joshua tree of the Mojave desert. The latter, with its tufts of pointed leaves clustered at the ends of the branches, is among the tallest of the yuccas, and reaches a height of about 35 feet.

In the wet coastal strip of north-west Washington and Oregon are forests of Sitka spruce and western hemlock (Fig. 72). With a humid atmosphere, a heavy rainfall, and a growing season lasting eight months, their growth is rapid. But in most of the Coast Ranges and on the western slopes of the Cascades the typical forest tree is the Douglas fir: it occurs in both pure and mixed stands, grows tall and straight, and is of immense commercial value.

In California the forest belt narrows as one follows it southward; it becomes purely a coastal fringe, and terminates at San Francisco bay. Here the dominant and characteristic tree is the coast redwood. This is the world's tallest tree. The best specimens attain a base diameter of 25 feet and are over 300 feet high. The tallest known specimen, found in 1966, is in Humboldt State Park (near Cape Mendocino); it is 369 feet high. Redwood is valued both for furniture and constructional purposes, but the finest stands are preserved for the nation.

In California too is the only other species of redwood (Sequoia) to survive the Ice Age: this is the Big Tree, which grows in 71 scattered groves on the western slopes of the Sierra Nevada between 4000 and 8500 feet. It does not quite attain the height of the coast redwood, but exceeds it in girth. In the Sequoia National Park is the tree with the greatest-known bulk in the world. It has a diameter of 36·5 feet, is estimated to be 3500 years old, and its timber could build 40 houses of 5 rooms apiece.

In regions with smaller rainfalls and higher temperatures than those characteristic of Douglas fir the most important timber species is the ponderosa pine. For this, mean summer temperatures (June–September) of 59°–63°F. are typical, and a mean annual rainfall of 18–25 inches is sufficient. Ponderosa pine occurs above the Douglas fir of the Californian Coast Range, in the Sierra Nevada and Cascades, and in most of the Rocky Mountain forests except in the highest levels, where it is replaced by spruce and fir.

Thus Idaho, which comprises within its borders much of the northern

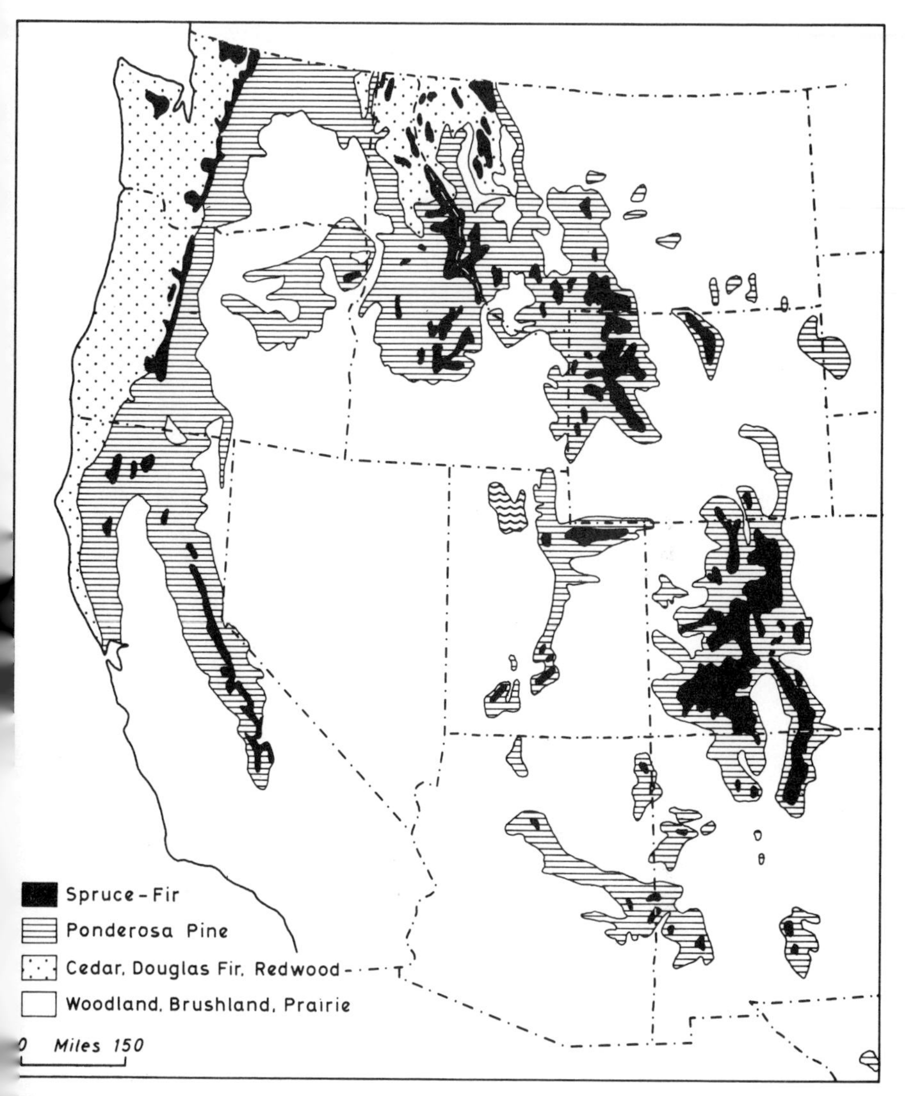

Fig. 72. THE WEST: DISTRIBUTION OF FORESTS

Rockies, is an important timber-producing state, and includes, in addition to its ponderosa forests, the finest stands in the continent of white pine. These occur farther north.

The vertical distribution of forest-land is very closely related to the westerly drift of the moisture-laden air. If we make a traverse at latitude 39° N. we encounter successively the Coast Range (rising to about

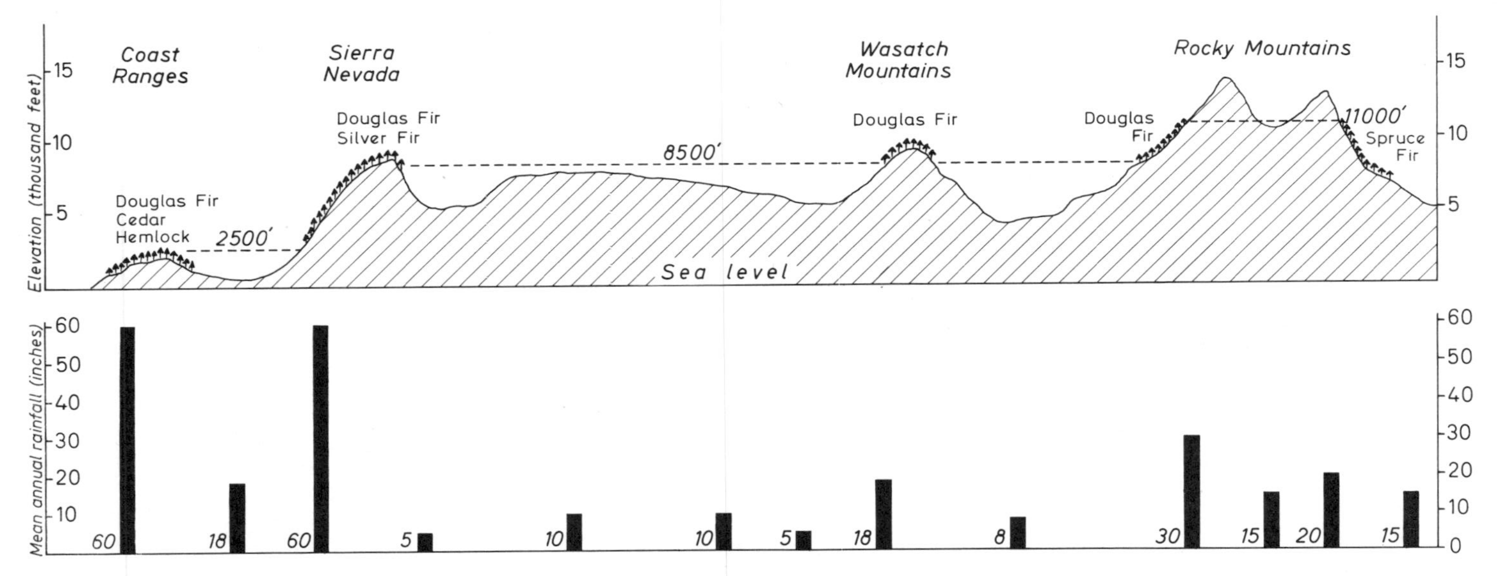

Fig. 73. THE RELATION BETWEEN RELIEF, RAINFALL, AND FOREST

This diagram represents a transect from the Pacific coast to the Rocky Mountains. Since the rain-bearing winds are predominantly westerly, each group of mountains casts a rain shadow to the east of it, so that its summit determines the lower limit of forests to its east. The forests on the eastern slopes of the Rockies are nourished by easterly winds from the Gulf of Mexico. *Modified from the 'U.S. Year Book of Agriculture', 1941.*

2500 feet), the Sierra Nevada (8500 feet), and the Rockies (13,000 feet) (Fig. 73).

The Coast Range is forested to its summits; but when the air descends on the far side it is warmed, and releases insufficient moisture to sustain forest. Here the natural vegetation consists therefore of grass or sagebrush; and this extends also up the western side of the Sierra Nevada. Beyond 2500 feet, however, the cooling is greater than that experienced by the air during its passage of the Coast Range: it releases more moisture, and above this limit the Cascades too are clothed in forest. Once again the intermontane areas are without trees, except for isolated ridges, such as the Wasatch, that exceed 8500 feet. Finally, the air rising up the slopes of the Rockies releases yet more moisture, and sustains forest above 8500 feet. There is an upper limit at about 11,000 feet, for beyond this the temperatures are too low or the exposure to wind is too great for the growth of trees. The eastern flanks of the Rockies receive little or no precipitation from the Pacific air streams, and the scanty growth here is nourished by moisture which may reach it from the Gulf of Mexico.

Within the non-forested areas are various types of shrubs and grasses, of which the most characteristic are bunch grass, sagebrush, and salt-desert shrubs. The bunch-grass type includes various grasses and flowering plants that grow in distinct tufts: it is developed most extensively in the Columbia Plateau, and offers useful grazing for both sheep and cattle. Sagebrush is a shrubby plant which together with other species forms an association typical of dry and cool regions with a seasonal rainfall. It too occurs in the Columbia Plateau, but extends over a much wider area, including most of the Great Basin. Sagebrush itself is of little grazing value, but the herbs and grasses that accompany it are useful as supplementary feeding for stock. The salt-desert shrub is a low, drought-resistant vegetation that occurs on saline soils in the drier parts of the Great Basin, and of southern California and Arizona. It is of little grazing value.

THE ADVANCE OF SETTLEMENT

For the purpose of historical geography it is convenient to subdivide the west into three zones: these comprise California, the Pacific Northwest, and the Rocky Mountains, together with the intermontane lands to the west.

California

The approach to California from the east across the mountains formed the last of a long series of attempts to explore and colonize the region. In the sixteenth century, when the story of white activity begins, the bases for exploration lay in Spanish Central America and the distant lands of eastern Russia, and the approach was made by sea.

But the coastal ranges run parallel to the shore and present an almost unbroken front. As we have seen, lowlands are restricted to a few embayments and valleys, and many of the latter have 'dead ends'. The mountain slopes are densely forested, so that suitable landing-places are often hidden. The site of San Francisco in particular is subject to fog, and for long its significance was overlooked in favour of Monterey. California thus provided a challenge to the explorer, and still in a sense does so.

Spanish penetration from the south was hindered by the southward-flowing California Current and the generally adverse trade winds: it was in fact easier for the 'Manila Galleons' to reach out to the Philippines and return to Central America using the Trades and the Westerlies than to attempt an inshore passage to California. Russian fishermen seeking the fur seal found a circumnavigatory voyage from the Aleutians much easier, but this involved them in immensely long journeys that took them thousands of miles from home.

An alternative route for the Spaniards was by land from the south. But between the established settlements of Central America and California proper there were formidable physical barriers. If he survived the deserts of Lower California the pioneer was still confronted by the mountains and basins of the coastlands.

Penetration along this hazardous land route began in the eighteenth century. Settlement took the form of missions and was confined to favourable coastal and valley sites. San Diego mission, founded in 1769, on the north bank of the San Diego river and about ten miles from its mouth, was the first of 21 Franciscan missions to be established in California. Sometimes a town grew later round the mission settlement: examples are San Rafael and Santa Clara, respectively north and south-east of San Francisco; often the mission remained an isolated centre. The last and most northerly of the chain of missions was established in 1823 at Sonoma, about 35 miles north of San Francisco: its secular object was to check the southward advance of the Russians.

The Spanish mission was based on agriculture and ranching, and it played an important part in assessing the possibilities of the land. Many, like that at San Gabriel, nine miles east of Los Angeles (and now surrounded by suburban buildings), had by the 1830's established gardens and vineyards, and reared cattle, sheep, and horses. This mission produced olives, oranges, and grapes for wine, and employed or supported up to 3000 Indians in addition to the Spanish settlers themselves. Elsewhere civil posts ('pueblos') were set up, without the panoply of mission agriculture; and such was the origin of Los Angeles (p. 211).

When in 1821 Mexico became independent of Spain white settlement in California reached beyond San Francisco. Mexican rule heralded a new era of ranching on an extensive scale, using the black cattle imported from the south. The only possible export consisted of hides, and this formed the basis of the famous trade around Cape Horn, between San Francisco and Boston. It has been well described in Henry Dana's classic, *Two Years before the Mast.*

In February 1848, at the close of the Mexican War, California was ceded to the United States. Hitherto the territory had been rather unpopular with migrants from the east, most of whom took the Oregon Trail to find a 'promised land' in the Willamette valley. But in January 1848, at Sutter's Mill, just south-west of Sacramento, gold was discovered. Immediately, and in their thousands, people flocked to the district. Some took the overland trail through Reno and the Donner Pass; others braved the ocean passage around Cape Horn. Between 1847 and 1857 over 350,000 came by sea to San Francisco, whose resident population grew from about 1000 in 1848 to 35,000 in 1852.

There was a fever of activity. During only seven and a half months of 1850 no fewer than 697 vessels anchored in the Golden Gate; and by the end of the year for lack of a return crew 500 remained abandoned there. The gold-rush had its effect on eastern industry, and the Atlantic shipyards during the years 1850–54 hastily launched 160 clippers to transport goods and men to San Francisco.

Until 1860 most of the prospectors were working the gravels of the Sacramento river and its tributaries, and they found plenty to occupy them, since in places the alluvium is 300 feet thick. After 1860 hydraulic methods came into use, and there was in addition some mining in the actual quartz lodes. Output of gold reached its maximum in 1853, and was valued at about 65 million dollars; but against this must be set the relatively high mining cost. The disturbance of the alluvia by hydraulic mining eventually led to the silting of the rivers, and in 1884 this method ceased. Since that date the gold-mining industry has never reached such proportions.

The influx of population provided an important stimulus to agriculture. Yet the farmers had their own problems. In the Sacramento valley there was still only a local demand for meat, and the cattle industry begun by the Mexicans grew slowly. Wheat-farmers found the summer drought an unusual experience, but extended their cultivation in spite of it. In the coastal valleys the settlers followed the Spanish lead in the cultivation of grapes and other fruits; in the San Joaquin valley agriculture was hampered not only by the low rainfall and the seasonal rhythm, but also by adverse reports and vague laws regarding the use of water. Modern irrigation appears to have originated in the Fresno district, when the local farmers, having failed to cultivate wheat, turned to the production of raisin grapes with the aid of river water. The salt and fresh-water marshes of the San Francisco delta lands were avoided until about 1870, when Japanese immigrants demonstrated that rice could be grown there successfully.

In the end a surprising range of crops was produced in California. The list includes wheat, vines, fruits, rice, olives, hops, and sugar-beet. The precise significance of the Spanish missions in guiding the development is difficult to assess; but it is clear that in the coastal districts, in the San Joaquin valley, and in the Los Angeles and San Diego lowlands at least, their influence was decisive.

The Pacific North-west

In the north of California Spanish place-names are rare, and beyond the Klamath ranges they are absent. This is a reminder of the effective barrier presented by these mountains to the settlers from the south. In the North-west we are concerned with the Russians, the English, and the Americans.

The Russians were active in the coastal waters in the eighteenth century, and though they were never dominant, they acted as a spur to English and American settlers. It is of interest that 70 miles north of San Francisco the Russians established a fortified post at Fort Ross: this is now preserved as a museum. About 30 miles to the south-east of this is a settlement with the suggestive name of Sebastopol.

In 1787 two Boston vessels under Gray and Hendrick reached the mouth of the Columbia river; and on a second voyage in 1792 Captain Robert George Gray entered the harbour that now bears his name, and christened the great river farther south after his ship, the *Columbia*.

The English too claimed a place in the North-west. The navigator George Vancouver insisted that his lieutenant Broughton had sailed up the Columbia river, while Gray (so he claimed) had only entered its mouth. This was the beginning of a long rivalry which had its counterpart on the land.

Representatives of the two English trading companies – the Hudson's Bay and North-west Companies – were probing westward in search of the 'gold of the north' – the fur-bearing animal. Mackenzie in 1793 and Thompson in 1811, together with Fraser, had traversed the Canadian cordillera and followed the Fraser and Columbia rivers to their mouths, incidentally perpetuating their names in rivers, settlements, and mountain ranges. During the same period American expeditions were in progress, such as that of Lewis and Clark in 1804. Both the English fur-traders and the American Pacific Fur Company set up rival posts on the Columbia river, and their respective Governments each laid claim to the sovereignty of the Columbia and Oregon country.

The 1830's saw the beginning of the trek by American settlers to the Willamette by way of the Oregon Trail. Most of them were farmers who sought the inviting valley of the Willamette or the smaller Yakima river. Until 1846 some uncertainty was caused by the lack of a settled boundary with Canada; but in that year the two countries agreed on the 49th parallel (which had already been adopted farther east). The California gold discovery of 1848 proved a counter-attraction; but the balance was partially restored when gold was found in the North-west itself, in eastern Oregon and in the intermontane area of Idaho.

Mining, whether in California or in Idaho, created a demand for farm produce, and the Willamette farmers responded by producing wheat and other grains, and fruit, and by rearing livestock. The Cascades and the Coast Ranges were rich in timber: this was cut both for local use and for 'export' to California. Exploitation, however, was restricted to the most accessible areas, particularly those that were within the reach of water transport. As a result only a small proportion of the timbered land passed into private ownership.

The resources of the sea and rivers were also tapped. The Columbia is one of the great salmon rivers of the world, and the settlers were quick to follow the example of the Indians in utilizing the salmon and trout runs. Markets were local at first, except for a limited export of dried fish. As with timber, the fisheries could be exploited fully only when communications were improved and markets widened.

Development until about 1880 was focused mainly on the Willamette valley, and helps to explain the political events. Oregon progressed from a 'territory' to a state in less than ten years; but, owing to the slower economic growth north of the Columbia, the state of Washington required more than a generation to emerge. From the area of the original Oregon Territory, Oregon state was established in 1859, and Washington in 1889. With the arrival of the railway in 1883 we may date the beginning of the 'modern' period.

The Rockies and the Great Basin

During the first half of the nineteenth century the Rocky Mountains, in common with the Great Plains to the east, were essentially zones of passage.

The most famous of the early expeditions was that of Meriwether Lewis and William Clark, which extended from May 1804 until September 1806. From St Louis they travelled up the Missouri as far as Fort Benton, in the heart of what is now Montana. They entered the Rockies north of Helena and emerged near the Palouse country at Walla Walla; they then followed the Columbia river to reach the Pacific Ocean.

It was a splendid achievement; but this northern route was not easy to follow, and in the early 1840's it was overshadowed by a trail through the Wyoming Basin. Trekkers across the Great Plains followed the

North Platte river as far as Fort Laramie, and traversed the South Pass, which became the gateway to the west. At Soda Springs (now in south-eastern Idaho) the trail divided. The Oregon Trail led the pioneers north-westward to the Willamette valley, and was the favoured route until 1848. After the discovery of gold in California, as we have seen, the southerly branch – the California Trail – came into its own (Fig. 74).

There was in addition a route across the mountains farther south: this was the Santa Fé trail. It led from Kansas City to the Cimarron crossing of the Arkansas river, and thence through the Rockies to Santa Fé, in what is now north-western New Mexico.

At first the mountain ranges and interior basins were regarded as barriers to be traversed quickly, and of no intrinsic value. Then, ten years after the California strike, gold was found at Cherry Creek, near the site of Denver, and there followed further discoveries along the mountain front in Colorado, at Clear Creek and Pike's Peak. In the 1860's the mountain and plateau lands farther north came into prominence, with discoveries at Alder Gulch, in Montana, and Boise and Silver City, in Idaho. Some of the recently arrived settlers in the Willamette valley began to turn back into the mountains and plateaux through which they had just hurried.

The most active mining district lay in Nevada near Carson Sink, where the Comstock Lode, high up on a mountain ledge, had been noticed in 1859. By 1865 about 50 mills were busy here crushing the gold quartz, and the Gould and Curry workings were reputedly recovering gold to the value of 2 million dollars a year. But by 1868 the boom was nearly over, and the principal centre, Virginia City, which had boasted 15,000 people in 1863, had declined to about 9000. There was a revival in 1873, when the Big Bonanza mine came into production, but after five years of profitable working this too began to fail; and by 1900 Virginia City had become a ghost town. The story is typical of many other mineral centres that in their day were the talk of the nation.

Mining was the chief, but not the only, activity in the region, for it contained many districts of potentially good farm-land. Many of these produced meat and grain for the mining camps and prospered or declined with the fortunes of the mines. Others, near major routeways or with particular physical advantages, became permanent: they usually depended on valley irrigation and on summer grazing on the hillsides.

Fig. 74. THE WAY TO THE WEST

The map illustrates the main staging points and mining centres together with the trails which led the pioneers to the West. The Oregon Trail led from Omaha via Fort Laramie and Soda Springs to Portland, Oregon. The California Trail led south-westward from Soda Springs to Sacramento. Farther south the Santa Fé Trail led through Dodge City and Santa Fé to Los Angeles.

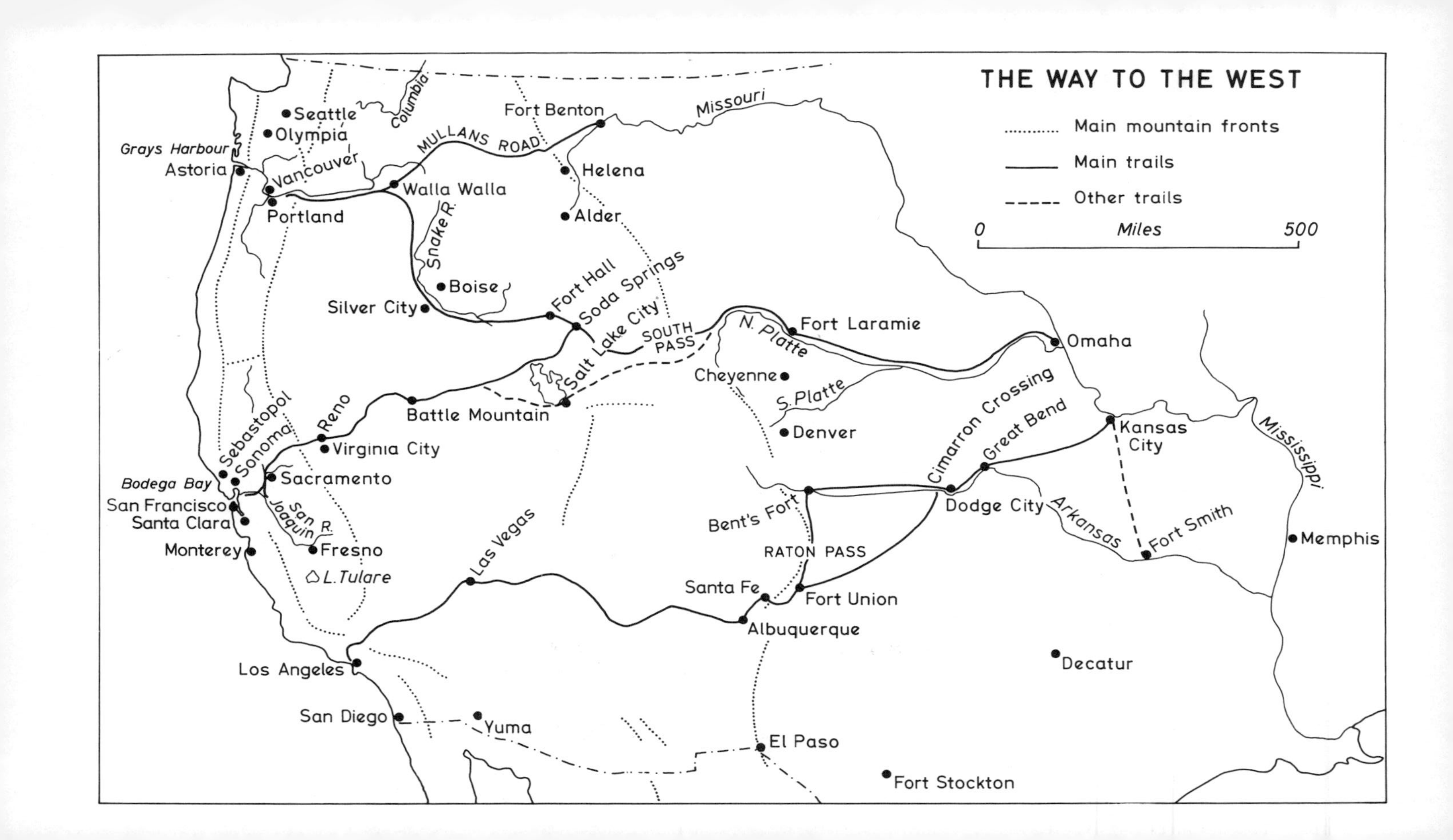
THE WAY TO THE WEST
Main mountain fronts
Main trails
Other trails
0
Miles
500
Seattle
Olympia
Columbia
Fort Benton
Missouri
Grays Harbour
Astoria
Vancouver
MULLANS ROAD
Helena
Walla Walla
Portland
Alder
Snake R.
Boise
Silver City
Fort Hall
Soda Springs
Salt Lake City
SOUTH PASS
Fort Laramie
N. Platte
Omaha
Cheyenne
S. Platte
Denver
Battle Mountain
Sebastopol
Sonoma
Reno
Virginia City
Sacramento
Bodega Bay
San Francisco
Santa Clara
Monterey
San Joaquin R.
Fresno
L. Tulare
Las Vegas
Cimarron Crossing
Great Bend
Kansas City
Mississippi
Bent's Fort
Dodge City
Arkansas
Fort Smith
Memphis
RATON PASS
Santa Fe
Fort Union
Albuquerque
Los Angeles
Decatur
San Diego
Yuma
El Paso
Fort Stockton

The most successful of these settlements was in Utah, in the valley of the Jordan river between Great Salt Lake and the fresh-water Lake Utah. The Mormons arrived here in 1847. They were seeking a settlement where they could practise their faith and manage their own affairs in peace, and the district seemed eminently suitable. To the east of the lake floor lay the massive mountain wall of the Wasatch. The main valley was watered by streams from the mountains, fed by snow and sufficient in volume for agriculture. It was an isolated area, and they were not to know that the discovery of gold in California would bring hordes of fortune-seekers along the trail that passed north of the lake at Soda Springs.

By 1860 the strip of country at the foot of the Wasatch was settled, with an economy based on irrigated crops and supported by the dry farming of wheat and the grazing of animals (Plate 6). Its capital was Salt Lake City, magnificently planned and spacious even in the 1850's. On a commanding site south-east of the lake, it dominated the settlement. Its streets, '8 rods wide', and its $1\frac{1}{4}$-acre residential plots gave it an almost unique character among early Western cities.

The settlement has continued to prosper, and has provided an example for others. Its long history of irrigation has also revealed the inherent dangers of farming in the West. Silted channels, the risk of backflow from higher to lower fields, of soil erosion and the undermining of buildings – all have been manifest, and have been attacked with characteristic vigour.

ECONOMIC DEVELOPMENT IN THE WEST

Among many modern activities in the West are two outstanding projects: these are the harnessing of the two great rivers of the region – the Columbia in the north and the Colorado in the south.

The Columbia River Project

The Columbia river basin covers almost 260,000 square miles, of which 40,000 are in Canada and 220,000 in the United States. In volume the Columbia ranks fourth in North America, after the Mississippi, the Mackenzie, and the St Lawrence. Its ample flow stems mainly from its

---

Plate 6. AN IRRIGATED AREA IN THE JORDAN VALLEY, UTAH

This view illustrates the extreme south of Salt Lake valley. Immediately behind the lorries is the shallow valley of the Jordan, whose water, derived from mountain streams and distributed by canals, allows cultivation in this semi-arid district. In the background are the Wasatch mountains, whose abrupt western face is formed by a fault scarp. The terraces at their foot represent the beaches of former Lake Bonneville (p. 169). The latest equipment is in use for the digging, topping, and loading of sugar-beet; behind the lorries sheep are feeding on the beet-tops.

Photo by courtesy of the Utah–Idaho Sugar Company

important northern tributaries, which descend from the rainy mountains and plateaux of British Columbia. The course of the river is complex. It rises in the small Lake Columbia on the western side of the Canadian Rockies, and flows first northward and then southward to round the Selkirk Range. Passing through the two Arrow lakes, it receives the Kootenay (which has rounded the southern end of the Selkirks), and enters the United States. It immediately receives also the Clarke Fork, which drains almost the whole of the Rockies of Montana. The main-stream then turns south and west, and incorporates the Okanagan from the north. Again it turns south, and cuts its great canyon into the lava sheets of the Columbia Plateau. In the south of Washington state it receives its chief American affluent, the Snake, which has drained virtually the whole of Idaho. The combined rivers then cut a great trench westward through the Cascades and the Coast Ranges to reach the Pacific in a broad estuary (Fig. 75).

In its natural state the river was interrupted at many points by falls and rapids, though the last 160 miles were free from obstructions. The Columbia has now been harnessed in accordance with a comprehensive scheme for the development of power and navigation, comparable with that of the Tennessee (p. 99), and, in addition, its water is being used for irrigation. Nine main-stream dams have been completed, and are equipped with power-plants, navigation locks, and fish passes, and four others are authorized for the Snake river. Limited navigation even now is possible as far up-stream as Lewiston, just inside Idaho, and the scale of this traffic will be increased when the project is complete.

Power-development is on a large scale. Four of the dams are generating more than a million kW of energy each, and the largest – at the Grand Coulee – nearly 2 million. The potential power available on the Columbia system, amounting to 30 million kW, is greater than in any other river system in North America. Of this immense total, over 8 million kW are already developed, and it is planned to raise this to nearly 13 millions. The Grand Coulee project has far-reaching implications and needs to be examined more closely.

The Grand Coulee was a temporary course of the Columbia river occasioned by the glacial damming of its valley. The northern portion of this trough has been sealed off by a dam at each end, and is utilized as a great equalizing reservoir; it is also sufficiently high to provide an effective head of water for the irrigation system.

Fig. 75. THE PACIFIC NORTH-WEST

The map illustrates the Columbia river system, and names the places mentioned in the text. T main dams are numbered as follows: 1: Bonneville; 2: The Dalles; 3: John Day; 4: McNar 5: Ice Harbour; 6: Priest Rapids; 7: Rock Island; 8: Rocky Reach; 9: Chief Joseph; 10: Gra Coulee.

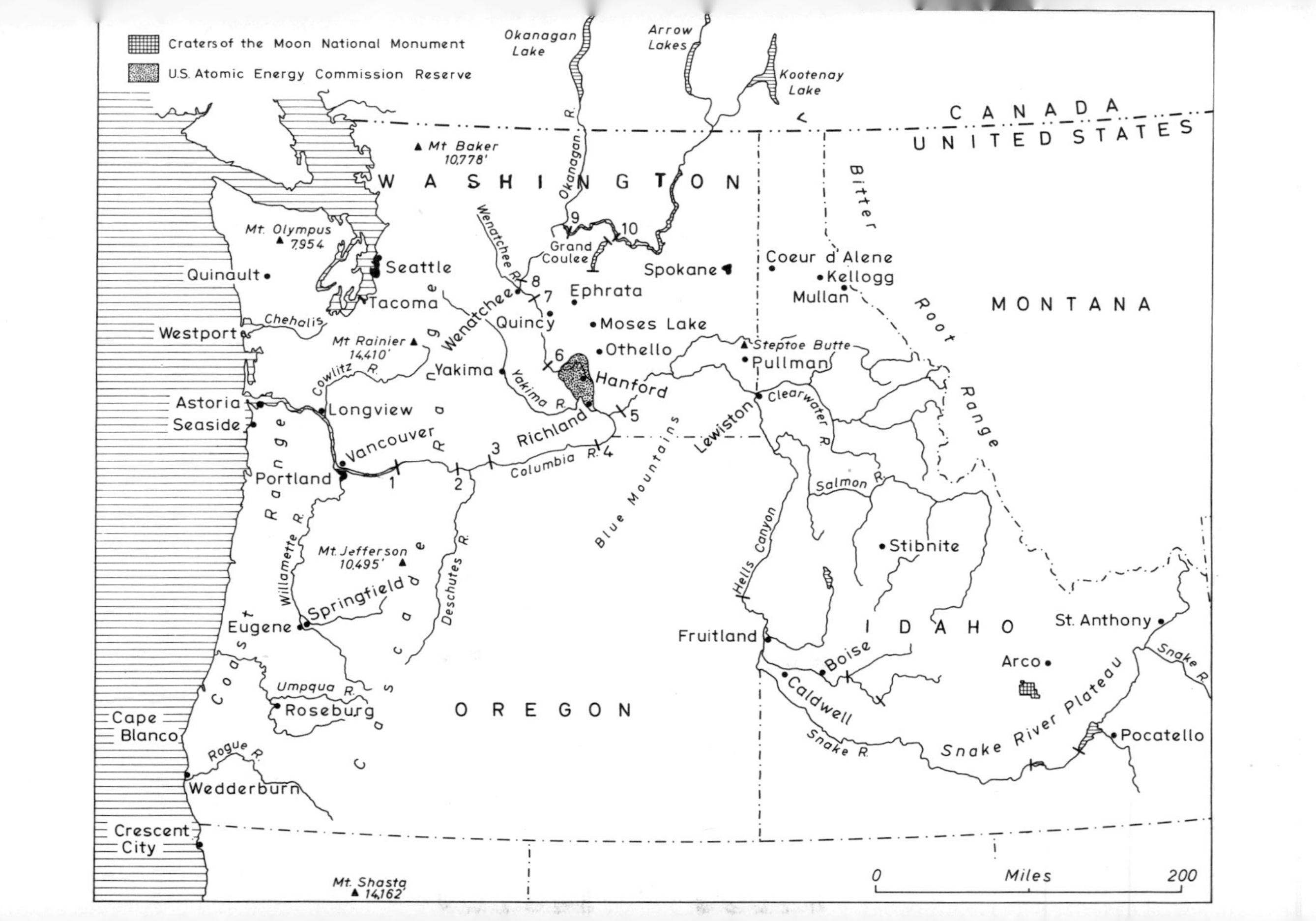
Craters of the Moon National Monument
U.S. Atomic Energy Commission Reserve
Okanagan Lake
Arrow Lakes
Kootenay Lake
CANADA
UNITED STATES
Mt Baker 10,778'
WASHINGTON
Okanagan R.
Bitter Root Range
MONTANA
Mt. Olympus 7,954
Seattle
Tacoma
Quinault
Westport
Chehalis
Wenatchee R.
Wenatchee
Grand Coulee
Spokane
Coeur d'Alene
Kellogg
Mullan
Ephrata
Quincy
Moses Lake
Othello
Mt Rainier 14,410'
Cascade Range
Yakima
Yakima R.
Hanford
Steptoe Butte
Pullman
Cowlitz R.
Astoria
Seaside
Longview
Vancouver
Portland
Richland
Columbia R.
Lewiston
Clearwater R.
Blue Mountains
Salmon R.
Coast Range
Willamette R.
Mt. Jefferson 10,495'
Deschutes R.
Springfield
Eugene
Hells Canyon
Stibnite
IDAHO
St. Anthony
Fruitland
Boise
Arco
Caldwell
Snake River Plateau
Snake R.
Pocatello
Umpqua R.
Roseburg
OREGON
Cape Blanco
Rogue R.
Wedderburn
Crescent City
Mt. Shasta 14,162'
0 Miles 200
1
2
3
4
5
6
7
8
9
10

The main dam, at a lower level on the Columbia river, is a tremendous structure, and in 1940, when it was completed, it was the largest in the world. It contains 10·2 million cubic yards of concrete, is 550 feet high and 4173 feet long, and weighs about 22 million tons. It has impounded a reservoir, Roosevelt Lake, that stretches 151 miles up-stream as far as the Canadian border. In terms of the United Kingdom this compares with the distance between Brighton and Nottingham, or between Nottingham and Newcastle upon Tyne.

The power-plant at the dam generates 1944 MW, and a small proportion of this is used to raise some of the water 360 feet into the equalizing reservoir. This is accomplished by six huge pumps, any one of which would be sufficient to supply the whole of Chicago with its water requirements.

An important element in the Grand Coulee scheme is the supply of irrigation water to potentially fertile farm-land. The scheme comprises 500 miles of main canals, 28 miles of siphons, and 7 miles of tunnels. In 1952 Grand Coulee water first began to reach the farms; and 480 holdings, each of 80 acres, were irrigated. Additions are being made at the rate of about 60,000 acres annually, and the total irrigated area is planned to amount to 1,029,000 acres. The farmers are growing wheat, maize, sugar-beet, beans, and potatoes, and the hitherto small established centres are growing into what are virtually new towns as the area expands: they include Ephrata, Quincy, Moses Lake, and Othello.

Farther east, in the Palouse country, wheat has long been grown on the rich soils of the lava plateau. It is a soft, autumn-sown wheat, suitable particularly for cakes and pastries, and the yields, at 35 bushels per acre, are the highest in the nation. Pullman, in the south of the area and close to the Idaho border, is the seat of the state university, and has a particular interest in the breeding of wheat varieties.

Farther west are the valleys of the Yakima and Wenatchee, two right-bank tributaries of the Columbia that drain the eastern slopes of the Cascades. The Wenatchee specializes in apples, and the orchards spread into the neighbouring areas of the Columbia. The annual rainfall amounts to only eight inches, and must be supplemented by irrigation from wells and canals.

The Wenatchee industry utilizes modern aids: helicopters spread insecticides over the orchards, and when frost threatens the air is stirred by tall fans. In Wenatchee town the state university maintains a tree-fruit research station. In a good year the harvest forms 20,000 lorry-loads, and is valued at 50,000,000 dollars. Wenatchee, with its annual blossom festival, is dubbed 'apple capital of the world': its population is 13,000.

There are extensive apple-orchard lands also in the American portion of the Okanagan valley (p. 304), in the Yakima valley, and in the lower

Deschutes valley, and to a smaller extent in the Willamette valley. With over $3\frac{1}{2}$ million trees, Washington state in fact produces a quarter of the entire nation's apples, and, in spite of high freight charges, competes successfully in eastern markets.

The Yakima valley is more diversified in its agriculture. In addition to important apple crops, it grows plums, peaches, apricots, sugar-beet, potatoes and other vegetables; and in the production of cherries, pears, and hops Yakima county leads the nation. In this remote area much of the fruit must be preserved, and there are 17 canning or freezing plants in the district.

The commercial centre for the Columbia Plateau is Spokane (190,000), the second city of Washington. It is the regional capital for the 'Inland Empire' – an extensive tract of land that includes the wheatlands of the Palouse country, the fruit areas and new irrigated districts, the mineral centres of the northern Rockies, and even the fruit valleys of Canada. Spokane is the only large city between Denver and the coast.

The hydro-electric power developed in the Columbia system amounts to over a quarter of the national total. Even this huge output is insufficient to meet all the demands of the region, especially in winter, when the rivers east of the Cascades are at their minimum flow. Accordingly, thermo-generators are pressed into service, and there are more than two dozen of these along the Pacific shore and around Puget Sound, and a further score or so in the Willamette valley and lower Columbia district. How is all this power used?

The largest single consumer is the Hanford atomic plant, which operates within an extensive area on both sides of the Columbia river above the junction of the Yakima: it employs about 8000 skilled people in the production of plutonium from uranium. Most of the power is used in pumping cooling water through the plant, and in this process Hanford uses as much electricity as the entire city of Washington, D.C. Its supply base and 'headquarters town' is Richland, which has grown from a village of 250 people into a flourishing centre of 28,000. Richland has one of the youngest populations in the United States, for the average age of its citizens is below 27 years.

The second consumer of power in the region is the aluminium industry. This dates only from the Second World War, when there was a greatly increased demand for aluminium in the manufacture of aircraft. The industry was established in the North-west chiefly because there were large supplies of cheap electricity: this is an essential requirement in the smelting process.

There are now six reduction plants in the region. These are at Troutdale, Vancouver (Washington state), and Longview, all on the lower Columbia river; at Tacoma, on Puget Sound; at Wenatchee (linked with Rock Island Dam); and at Spokane. By 1950 half of the aluminium capacity of the United States was concentrated in these plants; but the region has not since retained this exceptional share of the industry, since it has proved difficult to harness further sources of water-power. By 1956 the proportion had declined to 37 per cent., and it is expected to become stable at about 30 per cent.

The raw material for these works consists of alumina, which has been processed from the natural bauxite in mills in the South; and it has a long haul by rail. Plants at Vancouver and Spokane produce aluminium sheets, plates, tubes, rods, and transmission wires, and several hundred smaller firms manufacture consumer goods; but the industry serves the nation rather than the region, and most of the metal is shipped for manufacture to California and the eastern states. The largest single consumer within the region is the Boeing aircraft factory at Seattle, which covers nearly 3000 acres. With a labour force of 60,000 people, this is the largest employer in the state.

Farming and Forestry

Nearer the Pacific, the chief farming district is the Willamette valley, which, as we have seen, was the goal of the pioneers following the Oregon Trail. It has a growing season of more than 200 days, and its relatively high rainfall (30–50 inches per annum) and nearness to urban populations have established the pattern of its farming.

Oats are more characteristic than wheat, and poultry more typical than sheep or cattle. All branches of the poultry industry are represented, from commercial egg-farming to chick hatcheries and the rearing of table birds. Turkeys form an interesting specialization, and are even supplied to eastern markets. The mild and damp atmosphere encourages the growth of green vegetables such as peas and beans, but perhaps the most valuable single crop is seed grass, cultivated for a nation-wide market. Other characteristic products comprise nuts and small fruits. In this quite small area there are nearly 2 million nut-trees, which yield up to 12,000 tons of filberts and the same quantity of walnuts annually. Strawberries and raspberries are grown in larger quantities than are needed locally, and most of these are frozen or canned. Here too are about 19,000 acres of trellised hops, and one of the most important concentrations of cherry-trees in the United States. Farming in the

---

Plate 7. AN AREA WITHIN THE FORESTED COAST RANGE, WASHINGTON STATE
The white patches represent the clearings that have resulted from logging operations the strips of forest between them have been preserved to assist in natural regeneration of the cleared areas. The region experiences annual rainfall totals that are exceeded in the United States only in Alaska: the 90-inch isohyet hugs the coast; a few miles inland 120 inches are experienced. There is a small settlement at the mouth of the gravel-strewn river, but the timber is being moved out by road across the river.

Photo by courtesy of the U.S. Geological Survey

Willamette valley is thus highly specialized; it is a district where human skill applied to a relatively small area wrings a surprising variety and quantity of products from the soil.

The Columbia Basin and its adjoining areas form the nation's leading producer of timber. They supply over one-third of the total output, and nearly half of the softwoods. Within the region forest industries employ half of all those engaged in manufacture, and they supply half of all the freight traffic on the railways.

In spite of the long distances involved, 80 per cent. of all this timber is transported to other parts of the United States, especially to the North-east and the mid-West; and most of this travels by road or rail. Fifteen per cent. is used locally, and only 5 per cent. is exported.

The most extensive and commercially the most valuable species is the Douglas fir, which extends, often in pure stands, from the eastern limit of the coastal fogs as far as the summit of the Cascades: this is an almost continuous belt, interrupted only by the farm-lands of the Willamette valley. Douglas fir supplies two-thirds of all the timber cut in the region (Plate 7).

Much of the original virgin forest has now been cut; the total milling capacity is greater than the sources of supply, and some mills have been forced to close. Nevertheless, the industry as a whole is expanding, and the new mills are linked with programmes for continuous cutting and the use of second growth. The North-west produces only a small proportion of the total output of paper and pulp; but in the manufacture of plywood from softwoods it is dominant. Oregon, with 40 plants, is the leading producing state, and the region as a whole manufactures over 80 per cent. of the national total.

Timber is also cut in the northern Rockies, in western Montana and northern Idaho, particularly in the neighbourhoods of Coeur d'Alène and Lewiston: these are districts of ponderosa pine, which is second only to Douglas fir as a commercial timber. But it is the Pacific areas that dominate the timber industries. Two counties (Lane and Douglas), towards the south-west of Oregon, are in the lead, each producing over 750 million board feet a year. Important centres here are Eugene and Springfield, on the upper Willamette, and Roseburg, on the South Umpqua. At Springfield are pulp and paper mills, together with plants for the production of resin glues, formaldehyde, ethyl alcohol, and other wood derivatives. Roseburg was the source of the 130-foot-long piles that were used to salvage the vessels sunk at Pearl Harbor during the Second World War.

The whole Pacific zone has its logging camps, and its paper and pulp mills (Fig. 76). Fourteen sites have access to tidewater, and another seven are in the Willamette valley. An interesting site is that of the planned town of Longview, which was built in 1923–24 on former

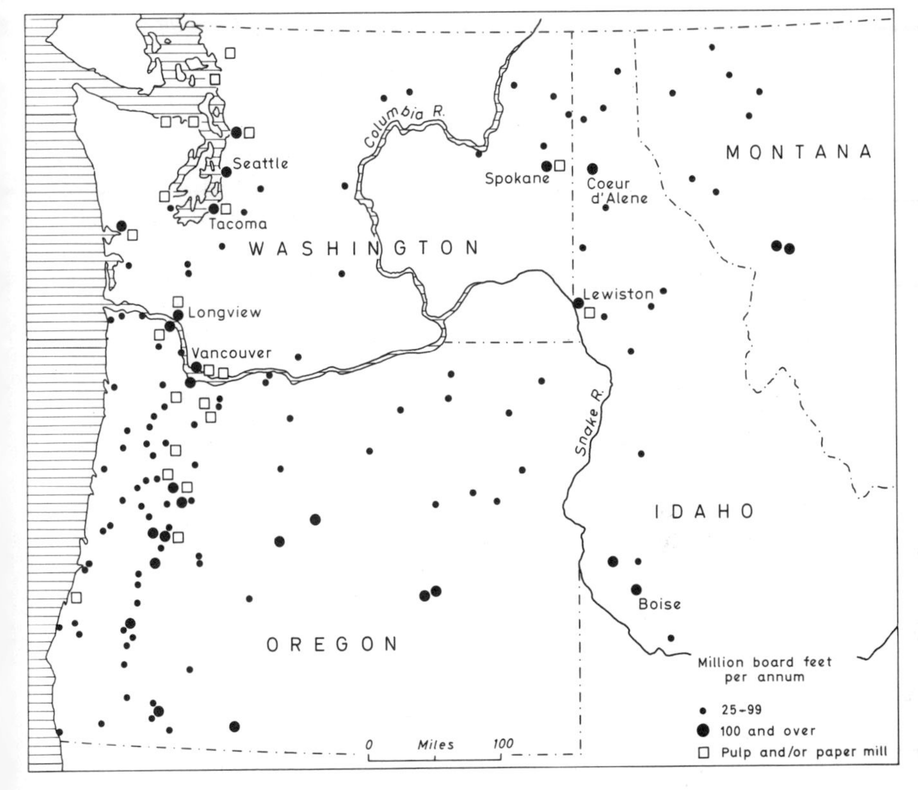

Fig. 76. LUMBERING IN THE PACIFIC NORTH-WEST
After the 'Atlas of the Pacific North-West', 1957.

swamp-land about 50 miles up-stream on the Columbia river. Its population of over 20,000 is almost completely dependent on forest products, and finds employment mainly in two concerns: one produces lumber, poles and piling, hardboard and furniture; the other, the firm of Weyerhaeuser, ranks as the largest integrated forest-products plant in the world. It includes a power plant, three sawmills, two pulp and paper mills, a plywood plant, and factories that process bark and reclaim sawdust. Longview is a town of wide avenues, handsome buildings, and pleasant parks, and is a thriving port.

Fisheries

We examine the salmon fisheries of British Columbia and Alaska on pp. 310 and 348. On the Washington and Oregon coasts also the salmon fisheries are of great economic importance, and yield a total value of about 65 million dollars each year. This is three times as great as their nearest competing species, and approximates to half the value of all the United States fisheries combined.

The size of some of these salmon is truly startling. An average Chinook (King) salmon weighs 24 lb; but exceptional individuals have been known to weigh as much as 75 lb. The state and Federal authorities maintain fish bypasses at the dams, guard against pollution, and operate hatcheries.

Convincing evidence of the life-cycle of the Pacific salmon was obtained when workers in the University of Seattle reared young silver salmon in their tanks. Eighteen months later the young salmon, marked and released, made their escape down a fish ladder, through the Lake Washington Ship Canal and Lake Union, past the locks, and into the Pacific. In 1951, three years after hatching, 75 mature salmon, recognizably marked, returned to the same pond in the fishery building where they had been hatched.

Seattle is not only interested in the local fishing industry, but is also the headquarters for the Alaska fleet. Much of the Alaskan catch is landed, canned, and marketed in Seattle. Westport too, at the base of the Olympic peninsula and at the mouth of the Chehalis river, is the centre of a flourishing salmon fishery; here in a good year 135,000 are caught. The Columbia is probably the greatest of the salmon rivers, and Astoria, on the left bank at its mouth, is the 'fishing capital of the north-west'. In the harnessing of the river, particular attention has been paid to the preservation of the salmon runs. In the far south of Oregon, the Rogue river too is rich in salmon: its centre is Wedderburn.

Seattle and Portland

Seattle was founded little more than a century ago, when in 1851 24 pioneers landed from a schooner. They found themselves in a deep-water harbour, amid timbered country where the waters teemed with salmon. The weather was pleasantly mild, and close by there was promising farm-land. The California gold-rush was in its early days, and the townsfolk were soon able to supply some of the construction timber that was in great demand in the rapidly growing settlements farther south.

For about 50 years Seattle remained a small lumbering and saw-milling centre; but in 1897 the steamer *Portland* arrived in the port, carrying 'a ton of gold' from the newly discovered Yukon goldfield. Seattle now became the base for prospectors bound for Alaska (p. 344); and, as we have seen, it retains some of its connections with the north.

Seattle is the nearest American port to the Far East. This advantage was first utilized in 1896, when regular shipping services began with Japan. Until the 1920's a staple item in the trade of the port was the shipment of raw silk from Japan: this was forwarded by fast train right across the continent for manufacture in New York. There are still firm links with the Far East, though since the 1940's the traffic has consisted largely of military supplies.

We have already mentioned the aluminium and aircraft industries of the city. It has also shipyards and steel-mills; the latter are based almost entirely on the use of scrap. With its fruitful hinterland, Seattle possesses 17 freezing works or canneries for fruit and vegetables, and is the largest food-processing centre of the North-west. It is the cultural and commercial centre for a very wide region, and has a cathedral and two universities. The city alone contains about 600,000 people, and within the metropolitan area there are 1·1 million (1960 census: 1,107,213): there is no larger city within 600 miles!

Portland, the largest city of Oregon, is situated on the south side of the Columbia river, at the junction with the Willamette. It is an outlet for the Columbia Basin, and the commercial and manufacturing centre for the Willamette valley. In addition it is one of the five major seaports of the Pacific coast (in order of tonnage handled these are: Los Angeles and San Francisco, about 27 million metric tons annually each; Vancouver, B.C., 18 million; Portland, 12–13 million; Seattle, 10 million).

The Willamette valley was the first district of the American West to be settled, by those valiant pioneers of the 1840's who followed the Oregon Trail. The 'official' terminus of the Trail is commemorated in a monument at Seaside, on the coast a few miles south of the mouth of the Columbia. Portland was founded in 1845 by two sons of New England, and named after Portland, Maine. Like Seattle, it was able to supply some of the needs of the California gold-seekers, so that its early growth was rapid.

With easy road and rail communication with the Willamette valley, Portland has developed fruit and vegetable canneries, flour-milling and wood-working industries; and on the southern outskirts of the town a large paper-mill derives its power from the Willamette. The lower Columbia has been dredged to provide a 35-foot shipping channel as far as the city, and port installations have been constructed, mainly at the Willamette junction. Up-stream, as we have seen, navigation on the Columbia extends as far as Idaho, and this traffic is growing.

During the Second World War Portland quickly emerged as a shipbuilding centre. Six main yards were established here: they constructed over a thousand vessels, and at their peak employed 125,000 people. Most of the yards have now been cleared to make room for factories and warehouses, but shipbuilding survives, though on a greatly reduced scale. The port ships timber, grain, canned salmon, and fruit and vegetables. In common with Seattle its chief single import consists of petroleum products. The population of the metropolitan area in 1964 was 821,897.

The Colorado River System

The Colorado is little more than half the length of the combined Mississippi–Missouri; yet it is 2000 miles long, and ranks as one of the major rivers of North America. It drains the whole of Arizona and about half of Utah, together with smaller portions of Wyoming, Colorado, New Mexico, Nevada, and California.

The river rises about 35 miles west of Denver, Colorado, in the southern Rockies, and its head streams drain the western slopes of the Front Range. Its chief right-bank tributary, the Green, plays a part in the draining of the southern Rockies, as well as of the Wyoming Basin; and its first important left-bank affluent, the San Juan, descends from the San Juan mountains of the south-west Rockies. All this Rocky Mountain catchment area enjoys 20–30 inches of precipitation, so that the main-stream has an assured flow. Tributaries lower down, however – the Little Colorado, Virgin, and Gila rivers – are of more doubtful strength. Before the Virgin is reached the rainfall has shrunk to less than 10 inches; and beyond it only 5 inches is experienced. Like the Nile, the Colorado flows into a desert region, and in a similar way its water has been harnessed for both power and irrigation.

We have already mentioned the tremendously deep canyons that the river has cut in traversing the plateau. Below the Grand Canyon the river enters a region where deep gorges cut in tough material alternate with wide basins floored with weaker sediments. In its natural state the river was exceedingly erratic in flow, so before it could be harnessed a very large storage reservoir was needed. This has been accomplished by blocking one of the gorges and flooding the basin up-stream of it.

So was built Boulder Dam (Hoover Dam), which has impounded above it Lake Mead, a vast reservoir which stores two years' normal flow of the river. Above it the dam – one of the highest in the world – rises 726 feet; and the reservoir covers 227 square miles. It was completed in 1936, and immediately the generation of electricity was begun. Boulder Dam now supplies about half the power needs of Los Angeles and a quarter of those of southern California. It has fostered a rapid growth of manufacturing in San Francisco and San Diego, and has brought cheap power to the farmer. Californian farms use more than seven times the national average of electric power, and 96 per cent. of them are electrified.

In 1939 the now regularized flow of the river was utilized to supply water to Los Angeles, by way of an immensely long aqueduct that leaves the river at Parker Dam (Fig. 77). This has since been extended to San Diego, and ranks as the largest and longest aqueduct in the United States. It is 621 miles long, of which 104 miles are in tunnels. Five

Fig. 77. SOUTHERN CALIFORNIA

The Colorado river is utilized for power, water-supply, and irrigation in southern California; and virtually the whole of its water is used, so that soon after entering Mexico it ceases to flow. The map also indicates the Friant–Kern Canal, together with places mentioned in the text.

pumping stations urge the water on its way to serve the needs of $6\frac{1}{2}$ million people.

Plans for irrigation took a little longer to bear fruit, but in 1942 Colorado water began to flow to the thirsty land of the Imperial valley. The main irrigation channel is the All-American Canal: this is a great artificial river, 20 feet deep and with a maximum width of 232 feet. In 1946 a new branch was constructed to water the Coachella valley, and the project was complete.

Today these former deserts are fruitful farm-lands. In the Imperial valley, south of Salton Sea, 800,000 acres of reclaimed land support 60,000 people, and form the largest irrigation district in North America. Here you might see 2000 migrant workers in a single field picking carrots, on a farm which during the harvest season sends out 42 railway truck-loads each day. The farmers in the Imperial valley grow cotton, sugar-beet, alfalfa, and vegetables, and they rear cattle and calves. Among the vegetables they pay special attention to lettuces: these are grown as a winter crop, and are highly valued in the eastern states, which have no other source of supply at this time of year. Lettuces alone from the Imperial valley bring a return of about 16 million dollars a year.

The Coachella valley, north of Salton Sea, is smaller, but nevertheless covers 80,000 acres. In addition to vegetables there are vineyards and groves of grapefruits; but the characteristic crop is the date. Here, especially centred on Indio, about 4500 acres of palms produce virtually the entire American crop of dates.

The Great Valley of California

The Great Valley deserves its name: 500 miles long and an average of 40 miles wide, it includes some of the richest land in the world. Yet it is not without problems, and the chief of these is an unfortunate distribution of water-supply.

The total quantity of water appears to be ample, but it occurs in the wrong places and at the wrong time of year. As we have seen (p. 175), most of the rainfall takes place in the winter, whereas the greatest need for water is in the summer. Moreover, nearly three-quarters of it falls in the sparsely peopled north, leaving only one-quarter for the needs of the densely populated south. In the northern tip of the Great Valley, the bordering mountains receive as much as 110 inches annually in places, though the valley itself receives only 23 inches. In the far south the mean annual rainfall amounts to less than 10 inches, and much of this is lost by evaporation.

The problem, then, is to redistribute the available water; its solution lies in the storage of water from the winter to the summer months, and in the construction of long canals to lead it southward to places with greater needs. Actual examples illustrate these two principles.

Shasta Dam in the north is one of the largest storage works: it has impounded a reservoir on the upper Sacramento extending for about 20 miles along the main-stream and three of its tributaries: in this way the flow of the major river of the northern half of the Great Valley has been regularized. The tributaries that descend from the Sierra Nevada have also been impounded by a whole row of dams, so that the valley below receives regular supplies of water: one of the largest of these is the Folsom Dam and reservoir on American river (Fig. 78).

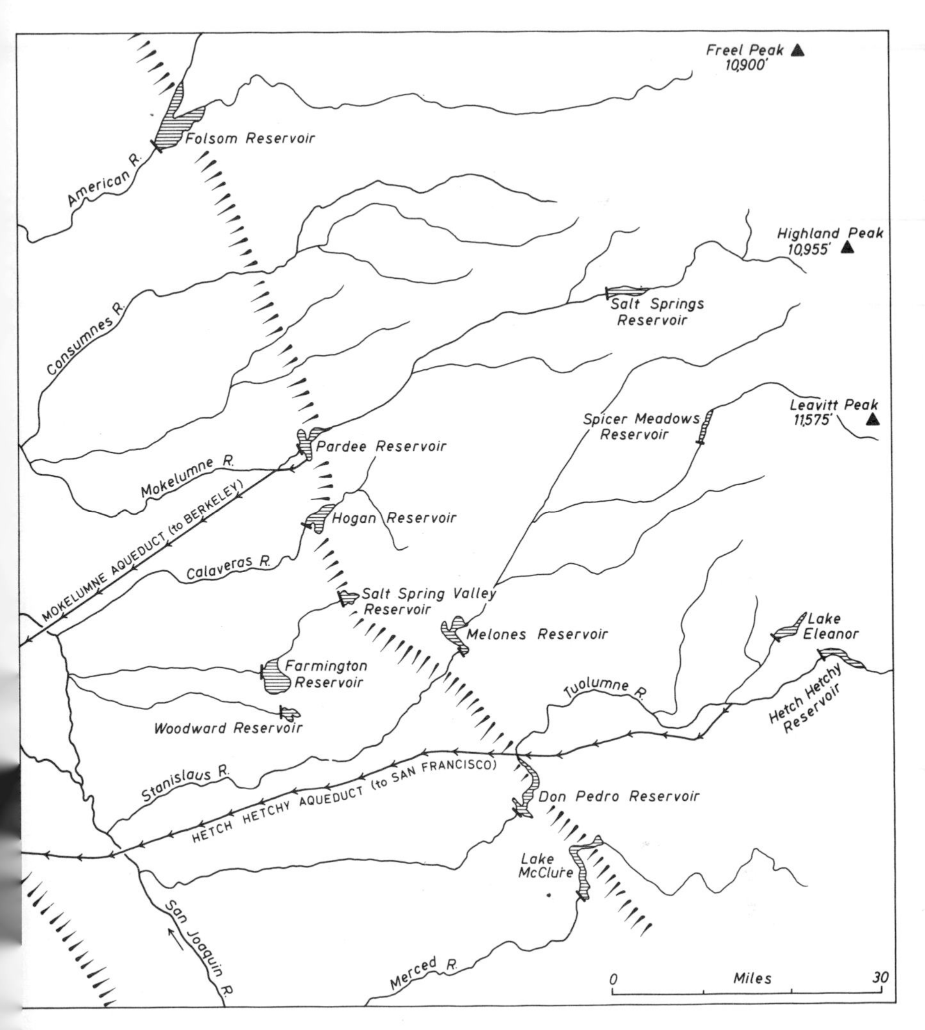

Fig. 78. WATER CONSERVATION IN THE GREAT VALLEY

The area lies in the Great Valley to the east of San Francisco. A row of reservoirs store water from the streams descending from the Sierra Nevada, and Berkeley and San Francisco are served by two long aqueducts. The hachures indicate the approximate limits of the Great Valley, which is here about 50 miles wide.

Farther south the upper San Joaquin has been dammed at Friant, and two long canals lead its water away for irrigation. The Madera Canal supplies the Chowchilla district, 36 miles to the north, and the Friant–Kern Canal, 160 miles long, conducts the water south as far as the Bakersfield district. Here the rich valley land in Kern county is the nation's greatest producer of cotton. With an average yield of 770 lb to

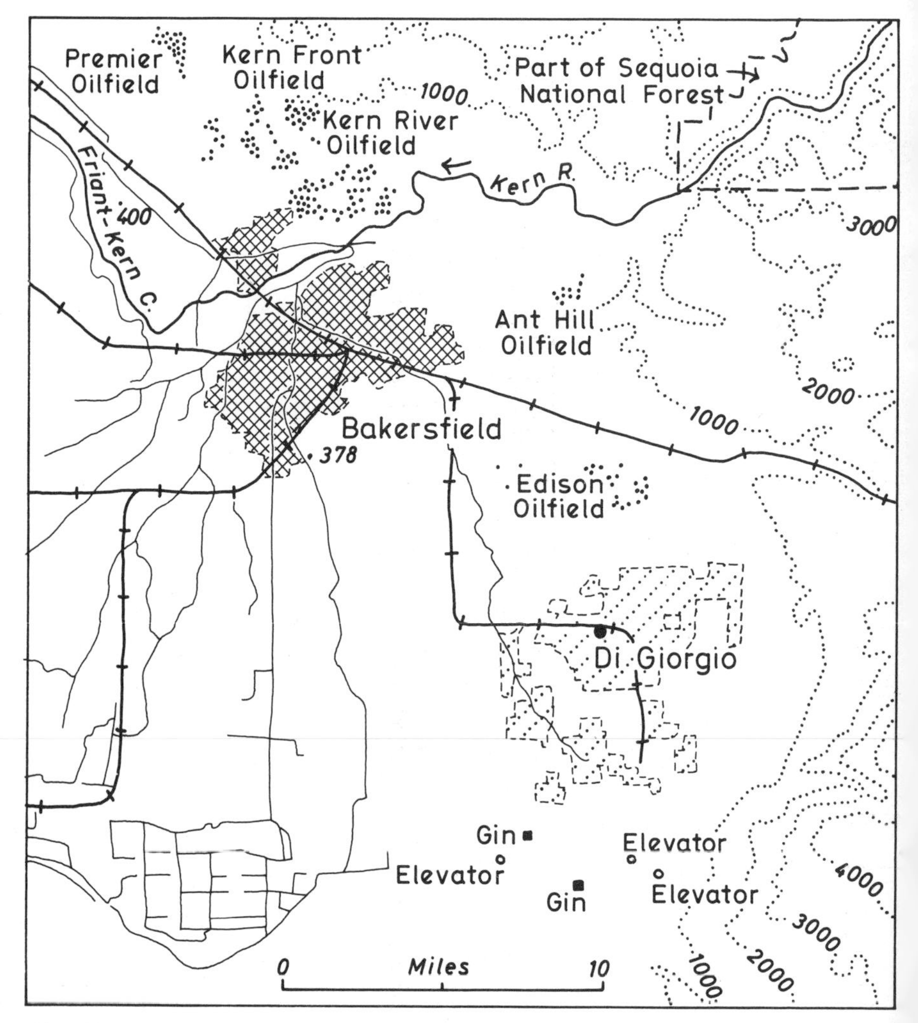

Fig. 79. IRRIGATION IN THE GREAT VALLEY

The map illustrates part of Kern county in the south of the Great Valley of California. To the east are the foothills of the Sierra Nevada, while south and south-west of Bakersfield the land is below 400 feet. The dotted lines represent contours, at 1000-foot intervals; the continuous lines are irrigation canals. Notice the oilfields (some of which have been omitted), the Di Giorgio orchards, and the two cotton gins. A small part of the Sequoia National Forest is also shown. *Based on the official 1 : 250,000 map.*

the acre, this single county produces more cotton than the entire state of Oklahoma (Fig. 79).

Thirteen miles south-east of Bakersfield are the headquarters of one of the world's largest orchard and vineyard concerns, the Di Giorgio

Fruit Corporation. Stretching over 15,000 acres, the estate employs 1800 people, and includes 6200 acres of vineyards, 1200 acres of plums and peaches, and 1100 acres of potatoes. The Friant–Kern Canal also waters important stretches of olive groves farther north at Lindsay, east of 'Lake' Tulare. Yet in a state of nature all this land was desert.

The Central Valley Project is even more daring. Water stored behind Shasta Dam is carried down almost the entire length of the Sacramento river; near Stockton this water is raised 200 feet into the Delta–Mendota Canal, and this conducts it a further 150 miles or so southward, parallel with the course of the San Joaquin, but flowing, of course, in the opposite direction. At Mendota the water is fed into the San Joaquin, after having travelled about 440 miles away from its source in Shasta lake. One of its functions is to nourish the important raisin grape industry which centres on Fresno (about 35 miles east of Mendota); this is the home of Sun Maid raisins (Plate 8).

The most obvious district of intensive cultivation in the region is the southern portion of the Great Valley; but the neighbouring smaller valleys too are highly productive. One of these is the Salinas valley, a fault-guided trough whose river reaches the Pacific in Monterey bay. It forms a vegetable garden famous for its lettuces and carrots; and to preserve its produce the town of Salinas manufactures 4200 tons of ice a day. Farther north, Stockton is a noted canning centre for tomatoes, while the San Francisco suburb of Oakland packs the well-known Del Monte peaches.

In the far south of California some of the valleys and plains beyond the Great Valley have also been turned into 'fruitful' land. Near Ontario, about 30 miles east of Los Angeles, is one of the world's largest vineyards; and farther east, San Bernardino is a centre of orange-cultivation, and has its National Orange Show each March.

It is not surprising that California is the nation's leading state in respect of the value of its farm produce. California grows more than half the national output of lettuces and the entire crop of figs, olives, and lemons. The fig crop amounts to over half a million tons a year, and the lemons fill 15 million boxes. California leads in the production of sugar-beet, with an output of about 5 million tons a year; it grows practically all the nation's grapes, and in the production of cotton it is second only to Texas.

Oil

The commercial production of oil in California dates from 1875, so that the industry is an old-established one. California still ranks high among the oil-producing states of the U.S.A., being third in importance, after Texas and Louisiana. The annual output is at the rate of about 45 million tons – that is, rather more than the total production of Canada.

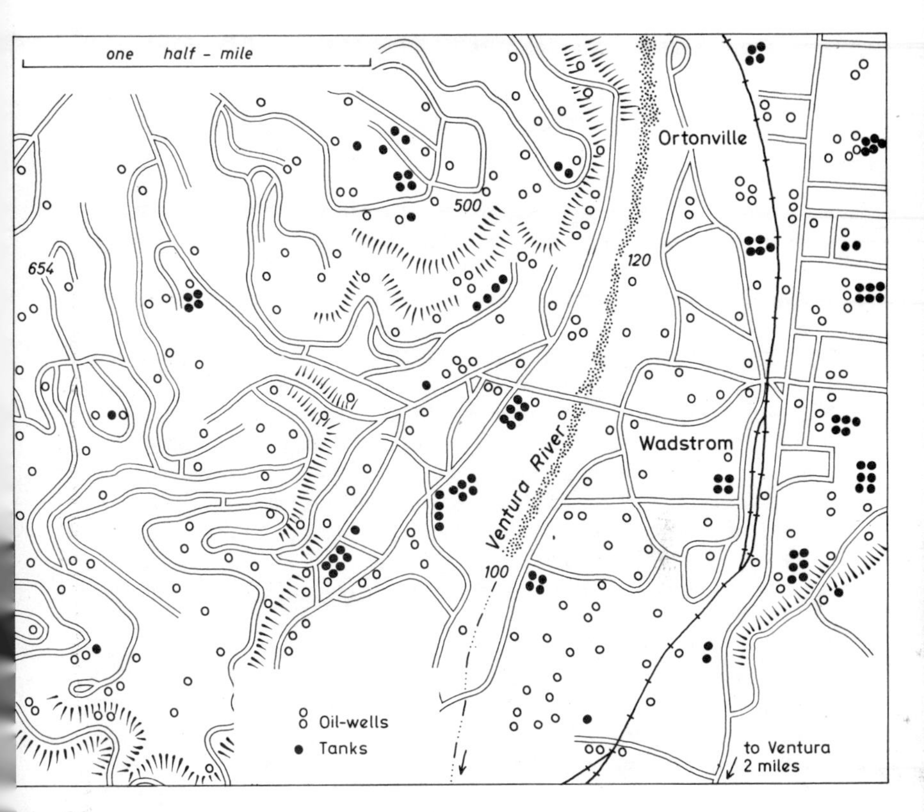

Fig. 80. PART OF THE VENTURA OILFIELD

This area lies about 60 miles west-north-west of Los Angeles. A broad valley, now occupied only by the intermittent Ventura river, has been cut into the plateaux of the Coast Range, whose summits are 500–600 feet above sea-level. The oil wells are very close together, and have been drilled successfully both in the valley and in the hills. To service them a complicated system of access roads is needed whose sinuous curves are necessary to preserve acceptable gradients. The only major road is that which runs north and south to the east of the railway. *Based on the official 1 : 24,000 map, 1951.*

The oilfields occur in the south of the state, both within and to the south of the Great Valley: they are therefore conveniently close to the large concentrations of population in Los Angeles and San Diego; and, with eight refineries, Los Angeles is one of the major oil-refining centres

---

Plate 8. AN IRRIGATED DISTRICT NEAR FRESNO IN CENTRAL CALIFORNIA

Fresno, whose suburbs appear in the bottom of the photograph, is one of the major commercial centres of the Great Valley of California. The district has a mean annual rainfall of only $9\frac{1}{2}$ inches, so that cultivation is possible only with the aid of irrigation. This district, one of the earliest to be irrigated in California, now benefits from the Central Valley Project, and some of its water has travelled 440 miles from the north of the state. In the photograph the irrigation ditches can be discerned as pale parallel lines among the citrus orchards and vineyards. The Fresno area is the home of Sun Maid raisins.

Photo by courtesy of the U.S. Forest Service

of the United States. Some of the crude oil is carried northward by pipeline to San Francisco, where there is a further group of four refineries.

In all there are over 26,000 oil-wells in the state, together with nearly 300 gas wells. Nevertheless, in neither is California self-sufficient. The local gas supplies are supplemented from Texas and New Mexico; and about one-third of the oil requirements of the state must be imported.

Fig. 80 illustrates the conditions in the Ventura oilfield, about 65 miles north-west of Los Angeles. Here an elongated oil pool underlies part of the Santa Ynez mountains, which rise to about a thousand feet. In a narrow zone about ten miles long and a mile wide there are about 500 wells. The surface topography bears little relation to the underground structure, and wells have been drilled both on the hilltops and down on the alluvial plain of the intermittent Ventura river. The wells are serviced by a maze of roads that twist like serpents in their search for acceptable gradients. At intervals are groups of tanks to store the crude oil. The railway and the main road lead to Ventura; but the pipeline system by which the oil is transported is not shown on the map.

San Francisco and Los Angeles

Of the two major cities of California, the site of San Francisco is the more arresting. It is centrally placed, where the Sacramento and San Joaquin rivers jointly reach the sea, so that their fruitful valleys combine to form its hinterland. The city looks both westward to the Pacific and eastward on to one of the finest harbours in the world. San Francisco Bay, about 50 miles long from north to south, and with an average width of about 10 miles, is clearly the result of the drowning of a system of ridges and valleys whose structural grain runs N.N.W. and S.S.E. (Fig. 81). The notorious San Andreas fault reaches the sea close to the south-west corner of the city boundary; nearby, in the floor of the rift, is San Andreas lake (Fig. 69, p. 173).

San Francisco occupies a north-pointing spur of the Santa Cruz mountains, converted by subsidence into a peninsula. Within the city limits three peaks rise to over 900 feet; and a hill only two miles south of the boundary reaches 1314 feet. At both the northern and southern ends of the bay silting has given rise to shallows and marshy flats; but the central portion of the bay remains very deep, and among the eight miles of quays and wharves of the port are berths sufficiently deep to receive the largest vessels afloat.

The entrance to the bay – the Golden Gate – is so well hidden from the sea that it was missed for two centuries, and was eventually discovered from the landward side, by Spanish soldiers on the march in 1769. Until 1848 the town remained small, and in that year contained only about 900 people. The discovery of gold drained the town of

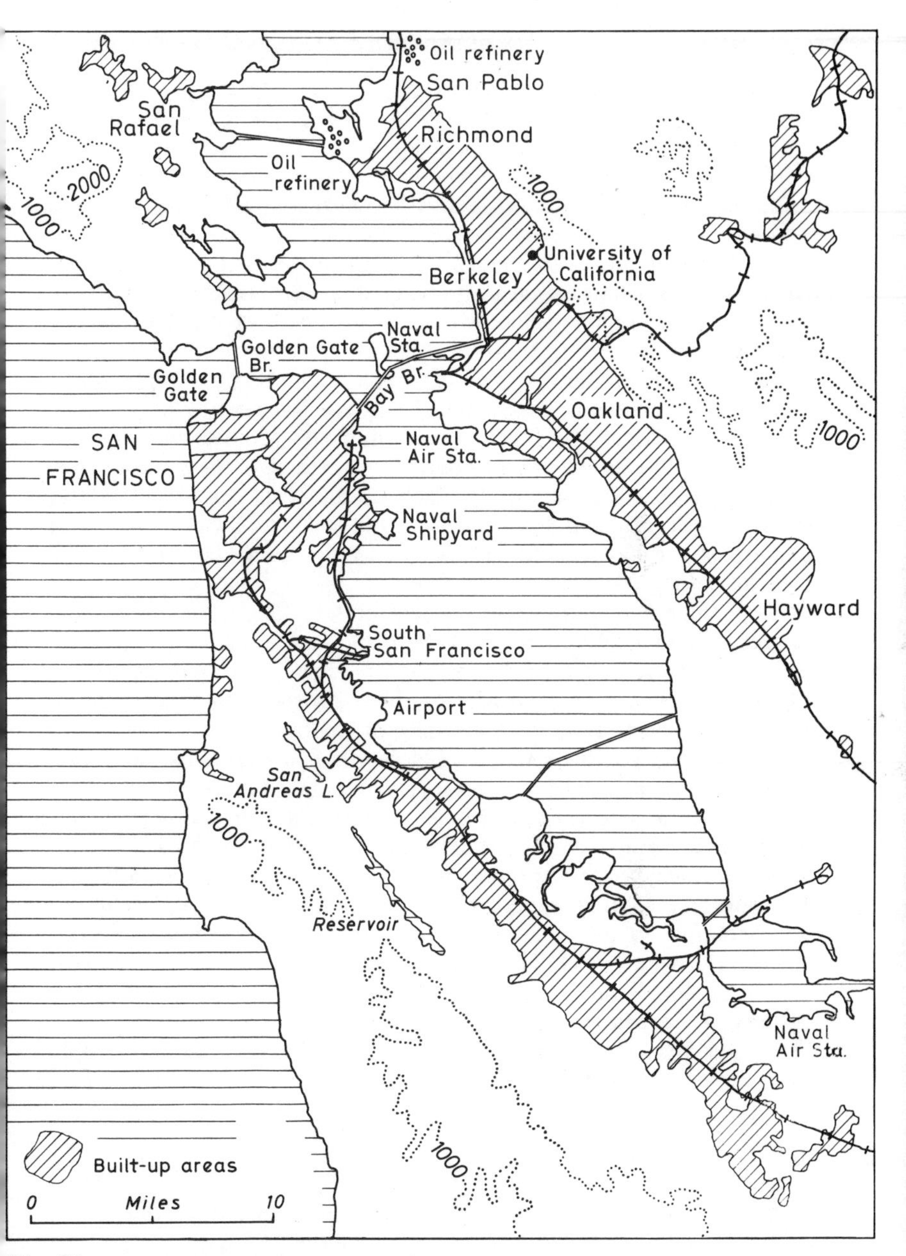

Fig. 81. THE SETTING OF SAN FRANCISCO

Built-up areas are lined obliquely. The seven-mile crossing near the south of San Francisco Bay consists mainly of causeway but incorporates a toll bridge. It connects the suburb of San Mateo on the west shore with Hayward on the east.

virtually all its inhabitants; but subsequently it grew rapidly, for it was now the gateway to the goldfields. In 1849 its population was about 2000; a year later it was about 22,000, and by 1852 nearly 35,000. The nearby river gravels were now becoming exhausted of their gold; but in 1859 the Comstock Lode of Nevada began to yield its treasure of gold and silver, and mining took on a new lease of life.

In 1860 San Francisco gained a through railway connection with the east, and its growth continued. Its population reached 150,000 in 1870, and on the eve of the disastrous earthquake of 1906 numbered about 350,000.

Modern San Francisco is the centre of a metropolitan region which has almost doubled its population during the last generation, and now numbers 3 million. The Bay poses an immense problem of transport, but it has been attacked with vigour. Here are three of the world's major bridges: the Golden Gate bridge includes a central span of 4200 feet; the Bay bridge, joining San Francisco with Oakland, is eight miles long; and Richmond has recently been joined to San Rafael by a new bridge four miles long.

San Francisco is the headquarters of the Bank of America – the largest private-enterprise bank in the world; and as a financial centre it is second only to New York. Higher education is represented by Stanford University, at Palo Alto on the south shore of the bay, and by the Berkeley campus of the University of California.

Immediately south of the city, in South San Francisco, are meat-packing plants and steel-works; beyond are light industries (especially electronics) interspersed with residential districts. The heavy industries are located mainly across the bay, in the Oakland area: this is continuously built up for 25 miles between San Pablo in the north and Hayward in the south. Here are four giant oil-refineries; and petroleum accounts for 60 per cent. of all the tonnage handled in the port. Associated with the oil-plants are petro-chemical works. Other typical industries include the processing of foodstuffs, particularly brewing and canning. Of great significance in the life of the city are the defence establishments: these include three air bases, two dockyards, a supply base, an arsenal, and a naval training centre.

Los Angeles

Los Angeles is the third city of the United States in respect of population. The following figures, which relate in each case to the population within the city limits, are from the 1960 census.

New York	7,781,984
Chicago	3,550,404
Los Angeles	2,479,015

The population within the Los Angeles metropolitan region, however, is far greater, and at 7 million this is the second largest metropolitan area in the United States. This immense population has accumulated in spite of serious physical difficulties. The Los Angeles river is tiny and unnavigable, and the port is quite artificial (Fig. 82). The city has virtually no hinterland, and its landward communications are restricted by mountains and deserts. Climatically the district is a semi-desert; local water resources could support only about half a million people, and the metropolitan area depends on distant sources, especially the Colorado river. Los Angeles, indeed, represents a triumph of man in an environment that, in some of its aspects, at least, was hostile.

How then is the emergence, survival, and prosperity of this city to be explained? The town was founded in 1781, when California was being governed from Spain, and was named El Pueblo de Nuestra Señora La Reina de Los Angeles de Porciuncula (The Town of Our Lady the Queen of the Angels of Porciuncula). Like San Francisco, it remained small until gold was discovered in the region. The strike of 1842, about 30 miles to the north-west, proved to be of little extent; but further discoveries in 1848 in the foothills of the Sierra Nevada led to an influx of diggers; the town supplied their needs, and prospered.

By the 1880's it had gained railway links with the east, and in 1892 oil was struck within the city boundary. This soon developed into a major industry. Today, with seven large refineries and several smaller ones, Los Angeles vies with Philadelphia as the leading refining centre of the United States. Half the overseas tonnage of imports consists of crude oil, and about 20 per cent. of its overseas shipments consists of refined products.

Two other important interests of the city are related to its sunny climate: these are the film and aircraft industries, and in each of them Los Angeles is the chief centre of the United States.

The motion-picture industry originated in 1907, and was established in Hollywood in 1913. Bright sunshine and the proximity of mountain and desert scenery were advantages, and there are now 800 firms in operation: they employ between 25,000 and 30,000 people. Television, far from acting as a competitor, provides a staple outlet for the main companies, which contract to occupy a regular number of hours each week.

In terms of employment, however, the film industry is far outstripped by the manufacture of aircraft and space equipment: this too finds the settled, dry, and sunny climate an advantage. Seven plants in Los Angeles and a further four in San Diego together employ over 200,000 people; San Diego, in fact, is almost completely dependent on the industry. The California Institute of Technology at Pasadena (on

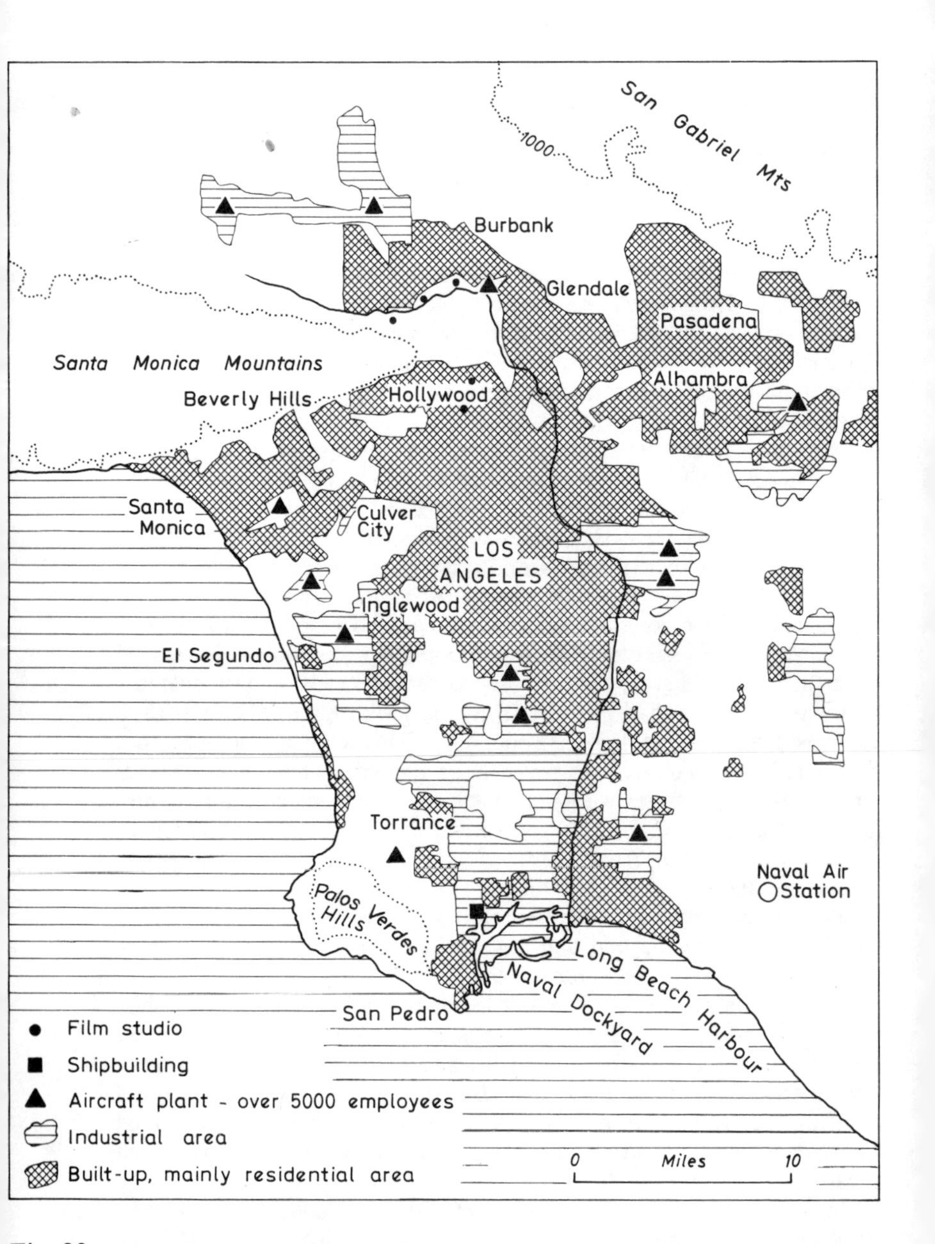

Fig. 82. THE SETTING OF LOS ANGELES

The nucleus of the town was on the banks of the Los Angeles river (which is indicated but not named); its harbour is quite artificial. Notice the film studios and the defence establishments. There are oil wells and tanks in the Torrance district and in many parts of the eastern outskirts.

the north-eastern outskirts of Los Angeles) specializes in space technology, and provides a valuable aid to the industry.

The clear atmosphere is of value in another department of science – namely, astronomy – and here are two of the world's major observatories. The Mount Wilson telescopes stand at an altitude of 5700 feet close to Pasadena; the Mount Palomar observatory is about 100 miles to the south-east, nearer San Diego.

One other manufacture calls for comment: this is the steel industry at Fontana, about 50 miles east of Los Angeles. It is the only integrated steel-plant in the West, and the only advantage it possesses is the presence of a metropolitan market. Its ore is brought 160 miles from Eagle Mountain, in the desert beyond Salton Sea; and most of its coal travels even farther, from mines in central Utah, 800 miles distant. With such expensive raw materials there is an incentive to make the most of the available supplies of scrap. This is a large plant: with four blast-furnaces and nine open-hearth steel furnaces, it has an output of about 2·6 million tons, and employs 11,000 people. It compares in size with the works at Hamilton, Ontario (p. 58).

Originally an inland centre, Los Angeles now reaches the coast. Its artificial harbour is the leading port of Pacific North America, and its coastal suburb of Long Beach is a major resort.

Other resorts have been built in the desert, and are linked to the city by modern highways. Palm Springs has grown from an Indian camp to a town of 13,000 people, with golf-courses, 300 hotels, and over a thousand private swimming-pools. Here, between their pictures, movie stars relax in 'gardens' of crushed and painted rocks, climbing roses, and transplanted Joshua trees. Its mean annual rainfall is 5·6 inches.

The Intermontane Area and its Economic Development

The intermontane area is a vast region: it includes the whole of Idaho, Nevada, Utah, and Arizona, and portions of their eastern neighbours. Its economic development is based on lumbering, ranching, irrigated crops, minerals, and, more recently, on tourism. We cannot examine the entire region in detail, but glance at some of its more important aspects and districts.

Idaho is essentially the basin of the Snake river; it possesses important timber resources, mining areas, and irrigated districts. In the centre and north of the state the Bitter Root mountains receive as much as 40 inches of precipitation annually, and here are some of the finest stands of white pine in the United States (Fig. 72). Farther south are yellow (ponderosa) pine, Douglas fir, and larch, together with other useful timbers. The Clearwater Basin is renowned for its white pine, and at its outlet Lewiston houses one of the largest sawmills in the nation. A net of fire-fighting stations is maintained in the timber areas, and a constant watch is kept against the danger of fire.

Idaho is also rich in minerals. In 1860 one Captain Pierce discovered gold at what is now Pierce City, in the 'panhandle' of the state; rushes began and many settlements were established in the district. Mining remains active in the Coeur d'Alène area, where a line of mineral centres stretches south-eastward as far as the Montana border. Kellog is the headquarters of the Bunker Hill and Sullivan Mining and Concentrating Company: it produces lead, zinc, antimony, and cadmium; Mullan has made a reputation in the output of zinc. Here too is the Sunshine mine, the largest producer of silver in the United States. Farther south, nearer the centre of the state, is Stibnite, close to the largest-known deposit of antimony in the nation.

Irrigation in Idaho is best developed in two districts: on the upper reaches of the Snake, in the east of the state, and on the Boise river, in the west. Some of the headstreams of the Snake are draining the northerly spurs of the Wasatch mountains, and receive an assured rainfall. The lava soils can be very productive, given sufficient water, and this has been drawn from the river at Idaho Falls and American Falls. At the latter point a Federal project has impounded a reservoir 26 miles long: it supplies many neighbouring farming districts, and conducts water even to Gooding, 100 miles distant. The farmers concentrate on the growing of seed vegetables, and have gained a national reputation for their products. St Anthony is a collecting centre for the local produce, especially for seed peas; at Pocatello are flour-mills, cheese-factories, railway workshops, an oil-refinery, and a branch of the University of Idaho.

The Boise river drains the southern slopes of the Sawtooth mountains, which rise to 10,000 or 11,000 feet. In the 1860's gold was discovered in the lower Boise valley, and was still being recovered in the 1940's at Placerville; but the cluster of towns in the valley is supported by irrigation water from the Arrow Rock and Anderson Ranch reservoirs. From them a great ditch carries 7 million tons of water a day into the Boise valley.

Caldwell is a centre of potato-production, and close by a large dehydration plant utilizes the smaller potatoes. Nampa is a dairying centre, but in response to the distance from the market the milk is condensed. Here too seed vegetables are raised, particularly seed corn. Farther north on the Payette river 22,000 acres have been irrigated, and here are famous orchards of apples, cherries, and peaches. The settlement of Fruitland is appropriately named. The commercial centre for the whole district is Boise, the state capital. Its name is a corruption of Les Bois, for the early settlers were struck by the wooded appearance of this area, hemmed in by mountains on one side and by desert on the other. Boise holds an annual agricultural fair and rodeo; and though its population is only 41,000, it is the centre for nearly a quarter of a million.

These two irrigated districts – the upper Snake and the Boise valley – between them grow nearly all the hybrid sweet-corn seeds of the nation, three-quarters of its turnip seeds, more than half its dwarf green seed beans, and half its seed onions.

Arizona

Other important irrigation and mining districts lie in Arizona, south-east of the Great Basin. The rainfall here is closely linked with altitude: at Yuma, in the far south-west (141 feet above sea-level), the mean annual rainfall is only 3·1 inches; at Globe (3525 feet) it is 16·7 inches, and at Flagstaff (6902 feet) it is 22·8 inches. The Salt, Gila, and Little Colorado rivers drain the state, but many of their 'affluents' are intermittent.

By 1930 seven dams had been constructed on the Gila and its tributaries, and the whole of its water is now used for irrigation: none is allowed to run to waste into the sea. Later extensions in irrigation were possible only through the use of underground sources; and more than half the irrigation water now in use is contributed by wells, which number more than 4500. Pumping, however, far exceeds the rate of recharge, and the water table is falling at an alarming rate – about five feet a year in the Salt river valley, and as much as eight feet annually in the lower Santa Cruz Basin. It is clear that if the economic development of Arizona is to continue additional supplies of water must be sought elsewhere. The Colorado river at once suggests itself, and an appraisal will be needed of the requirements of Arizona compared with those of California, which is at present the largest consumer of Colorado water.

Ranching and dairying have been overshadowed in Arizona by the production of cotton. This is a quite recent development: in 1945 Arizona ranked eleventh among the cotton-producing states; by 1950 she had risen to take the seventh place; and in 1964 she was sixth, after Texas, Mississippi, California, Arkansas, and Alabama. The whole of the crop is grown by irrigation, and the control of its water requirements has made possible an exceptionally high yield: in this Arizona leads all the states, with yields nearly three times as great as the national average.

Formerly the cotton was picked by Papago Indians, whose reservations are close to the chief cotton-lands; now the picking is largely mechanized. Usually several machines will be at work in the same field, and each replaces the labour of 110 men. The irrigated lands of Arizona total about 1½ million acres, and centre chiefly on Phoenix and Casa Grande.

The mineral deposits of Arizona lie in a zone of faulting and folding that extends from the centre of the state in the district of Jerome through Globe and Ray to the Bisbee district in the south-east. A little to the east of this line is Morenci. Lead, zinc, and silver are produced, but chief among the minerals is copper, which is recovered from half a dozen great open-cast workings, and Arizona is the leading copper-producing state in the United States. Jerome is now a ghost town, but Bisbee and Globe are still flourishing centres of production, and Bisbee itself is the commercial headquarters of the industry. At the vast open pit at Ray 23,000 tons of ore are mined daily by the power shovels. The pit at Morenci is larger still: it is fully a mile wide, and is worked in 23 enormous terraces.

Two other important copper-producing areas farther north must be mentioned: these are the Bingham district of Utah and the Butte area of western Montana. Bingham canyon is about 20 miles south of Great Salt Lake, and here a great open-cast pit covering 972 acres is claimed to be the largest copper quarry in the world. It is the most productive of all the copper pits, accounting alone for nearly 22 per cent. of the total U.S.A. output. Modern techniques make it economic to work unusually low-grade ores, and here the copper content is only 1 per cent., so that very large quantities must be extracted in proportion to the final product. The ore is concentrated at Magna, close to the lake, and smelted at nearby Garfield.

Butte lies amid the northern Rockies of western Montana, close to the divide between the Missouri and the Snake rivers. For over a century miners have been at work here, robbing the 'richest hill on earth'. Below the town there are now estimated to be 2700 miles of mine galleries. Lead, zinc, manganese, and silver have all been produced at Butte, but it is the copper deposits on which its reputation is based. Since 1955 large new operations have begun on a deposit of over 100 million tons of ore, whose copper content is as low as a half per cent. The ore is smelted at Anaconda, 25 miles to the north-west. With a population of 27,500 (estimate, 1962), Butte is the third largest city of Montana, and is the home of the state School of Mines.

No discussion of the economy of the West is complete without a reference to the tourist industry. It is difficult to assess the importance of tourism in quantitative terms, though in the early 1950's it was estimated that tourism in Arizona alone yielded a revenue of 175 million dollars a year. The large number of National Monuments and National Parks testifies to the significance of the industry: among the greatest attractions are Yellowstone Park, in the Rockies of north-west Wyoming, and the Grand canyon of the Colorado river; the latter attracts about a quarter of a million visitors annually.

Another sign of the tourist industry is the large number of Western towns which stage an annual rodeo. Thus at Tucson in southern

Arizona the rodeo, with its bands and processions of covered wagons, attracts between 5000 and 10,000 visitors. Finally, the growth of desert resorts and guest ranches should be mentioned. In south-east Arizona alone there are about 75 ranches, many of them operated by retired business-men, where the visitor can spend a week or fortnight sampling the life of the 'Wild West'.

CHAPTER EIGHT

ATLANTIC CANADA

The Atlantic Provinces consist of Nova Scotia, New Brunswick, and Prince Edward Island (commonly called the Maritime Provinces), together with Newfoundland; and to the Maritimes we may conveniently add that part of Quebec province which lies to the south-east of the St Lawrence river. These lands have a common outlook in that their life is permeated by the sea. They were the earliest parts of Canada to be settled. Far from the more closely settled parts of the Dominion, they have an air of detachment from the bustle of modern life, and their trading interests are overseas as much as Canadian.

NEWFOUNDLAND

Politically, physically, and culturally, Newfoundland has its own individuality, and may be examined first. The island was probably known to fishermen long before John Cabot made his voyage of 1497, but it was he who first advertised its rich fishing-grounds. Within a generation adventurers from Western Europe were fishing regularly off its coasts, and making temporary bases on the island. In 1583 Sir Humphrey Gilbert formally annexed Newfoundland for the British Crown, so that the island claims to have been the oldest British colony.

Nevertheless, a century later Newfoundland contained only 120 permanent residents, for the land was considered subsidiary to the fisheries. Settlement on a large scale, indeed, dates only from the nineteenth century, when immigrants arrived, particularly from Ireland: 11,000 Irish entered Newfoundland in 1814–15 alone.

The island was granted a bicameral legislature in 1832, and responsible government in 1855. During the Great Depression of the 1930's Newfoundland suffered severe financial hardship; the British Government assumed responsibility for her debts, and appointed a commission to govern the country. In 1948, when economic stability was restored, a referendum was held to determine the future status of Newfoundland. The population decisively rejected commission government, and, given the choice of independence or incorporation into Canada, by a quite small majority (78,823 votes compared with 71,334) chose the latter course. In March 1949 Newfoundland, together with its dependency of Labrador, became the tenth province of Canada.

Newfoundland is a little larger than Ireland and a little smaller than England; but its population, though growing quite quickly, is still only 493,000 (estimate, 1964) – that is, about the same as the city of Leeds, Yorkshire. There is only one large town – St John's – which has a population of 91,000; most of the remaining population is scattered in 1700 settlements along 6000 miles of coastline. The interior is virtually uninhabited.

Physical Basis

The general drift of air is eastward from continental North America, so that, in spite of its oceanic situation, Newfoundland experiences some of the characteristics of a continental climate. In particular, the island has a comparatively high range of temperature. Mean July temperatures at sea-level over most of the island are below 60°F., and mean January temperatures are below 20°F., so that the range is about 40 degrees. These are low temperatures for the latitude, for St John's is farther south than Paris! The rather cool summers and the intensely cold winters are largely due to the cold Labrador current, which brings Arctic water to the shores of Newfoundland.

Precipitation ranges from over 60 inches on the central south coast to below 30 inches along the west coast of the North peninsula, and much of it takes the form of snow. Climatically the most favoured districts lie in the south-west of the island, where there are July mean temperatures of over 61°F. and a relatively low rainfall (Fig. 83a and b). It is a fortunate coincidence that in this area are the most promising soils.

In detail the climate has much variety, for Newfoundland lies on the path of eastward-moving depressions, particularly in winter. Frequent changes in wind direction, and hence in rainfall, humidity, and temperature, are experienced. The most closely comparable climate would seem to be that of Hokkaido, the northernmost island of Japan.

Both in surface geology and in topography there is a distinct north-east and south-west grain in Newfoundland. This is the Caledonian trend. It is illustrated by the coasts of the North peninsula in the west, and of the Avalon peninsula in the east, and in the courses of almost all the rivers. It was established during the earth movements of Silurian and Devonian times, and corresponds with the similar trend in parts of Scotland, Northern Ireland, and North Wales. The rocks were subjected to renewed pressures during Carbo-Permian times, but these appear only to have reinforced the established alignment of the structure. Accordingly we now find in Newfoundland parallel belts of folded and faulted strata, which range in age from Pre-Cambrian to Carboniferous: no later rocks have been recognized apart from glacial drift and recent alluvium. Pre-Cambrian rocks form the main mass of the Long Range

55°
50°
55°
60°
60°
55°
0 Miles 100
Inches.
55 and over
50 to 55
45 to 50
40 to 45
35 to 40
35 and under
0 Miles 100

and are exposed over the whole of the eastern portion of the island, east of a line joining Bonavista and Fortune bays. The mass of Pre-Cambrian material forming the Long Range is bounded by two bold fault scarps, which explain the straight and parallel coasts of the North peninsula, and which appear in the Codroy valley (Fig. 86, p. 224) and elsewhere. Here, then, is a raised block – a horst – and one of the clearest examples of its kind in North America.

Ordovician sedimentary and volcanic material forms the basins of the Exploits and Gander rivers, and is found along the west coast. In limited areas south-west of the White bay and around St George's bay are sediments of Carboniferous age.

During the long period following the Caledonian earth storm the folded strata were peneplained and re-elevated more than once, and today level plateaux rather than towering peaks are characteristic of the interior of Newfoundland. At a relatively late stage the land was tilted down to the south-east (similar to Scandinavia and Scotland), so that the highest land is now in the west. As in the Canadian Shield and New England, the Pleistocene glaciers removed the loose material from the highlands, scoured the valleys, deposited drift in the lowlands, and left a chaotic drainage. The latest event has been a sinking of the land relative to the sea, resulting in a complex, indented coastline, fringed with islands and exhibiting many magnificent fiords.

The Long Range mountains rise to over 2000 feet, and their summits are above 2500 feet. They are crossed obliquely by a deep fault-guided trough, which extends from White bay to St George's bay, and contains Grand and Sandy lakes (Fig. 84). East of the Long Range is the High Plateau, whose general level is at about 1500 feet. The rivers wander aimlessly across its surface, and flow through innumerable lakes and bogs; in spite of the south-easterly tilt, the main-streams reflect the Caledonian trend, and the Exploits and Gander rivers flow north-eastward to empty into Notre Dame and Gander bays. Following the same alignment are the ridges rising 500 feet above the general plateau level and rejoicing in the name Annieopsquotch mountains.

Virtually all the land above 1000 feet is barren, with a tundra vegetation of lichens and reindeer moss; this includes a belt ranging from 50 to 75 miles wide running the length of the south coast, together with

---

Fig. 83a. NEWFOUNDLAND: JULY ISOTHERMS

The mean July sea-level isotherms are selected, since they are critical for farming. The accuracy of the map, however, is doubtful, for there are few records available inland.

Fig. 83b. NEWFOUNDLAND: MEAN ANNUAL PRECIPITATION

Again, the map is of doubtful accuracy.

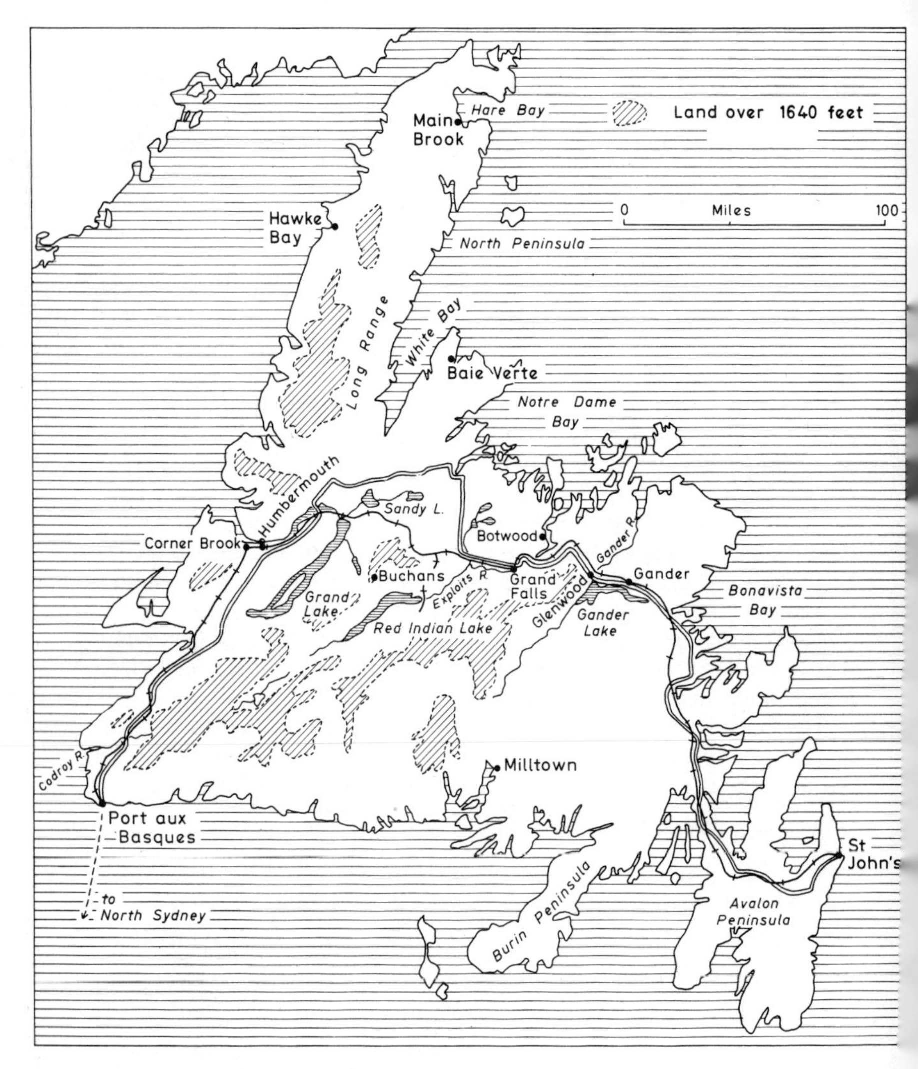

Fig. 84. NEWFOUNDLAND: LOCATION MAP

The map indicates the trans-peninsular railway and part of the Trans-Canada Highway, together with the places named in the text.

several smaller inland areas (Fig. 85). Most of the remainder of the plateau is under forest. The heavy and well-distributed rainfall favours tree-growth, which is as rapid as in eastern Canada, though the mature trees are not so tall. Conifers are dominant, and include black and white spruce, balsam fir, and white pine; but there are also hardwoods such as birch and maple. Black spruce is typical of the poorly drained areas.

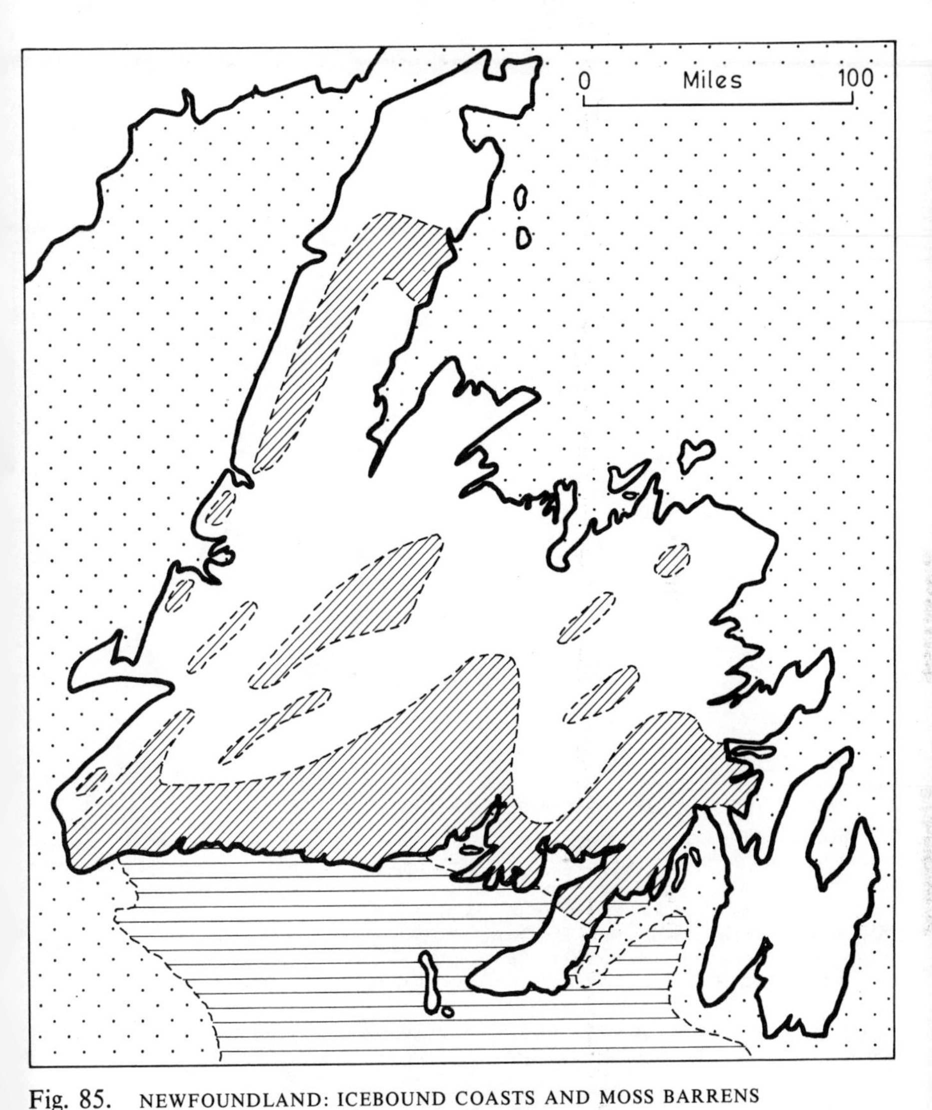

Fig. 85. NEWFOUNDLAND: ICEBOUND COASTS AND MOSS BARRENS

The areas ruled obliquely indicate the general distribution of moss barrens: much of this land is over 1000 feet high. The stippled areas represent seas that are closed by ice in March, when the ice is at its greatest extent. Fishing and shipping are therefore seasonal except along the south-west coast.

Human Response

It is estimated that only 157 square miles are devoted to agriculture in the whole of Newfoundland – representing less than half of 1 per cent. of the total area. The reasons for this are clear. Newfoundland is

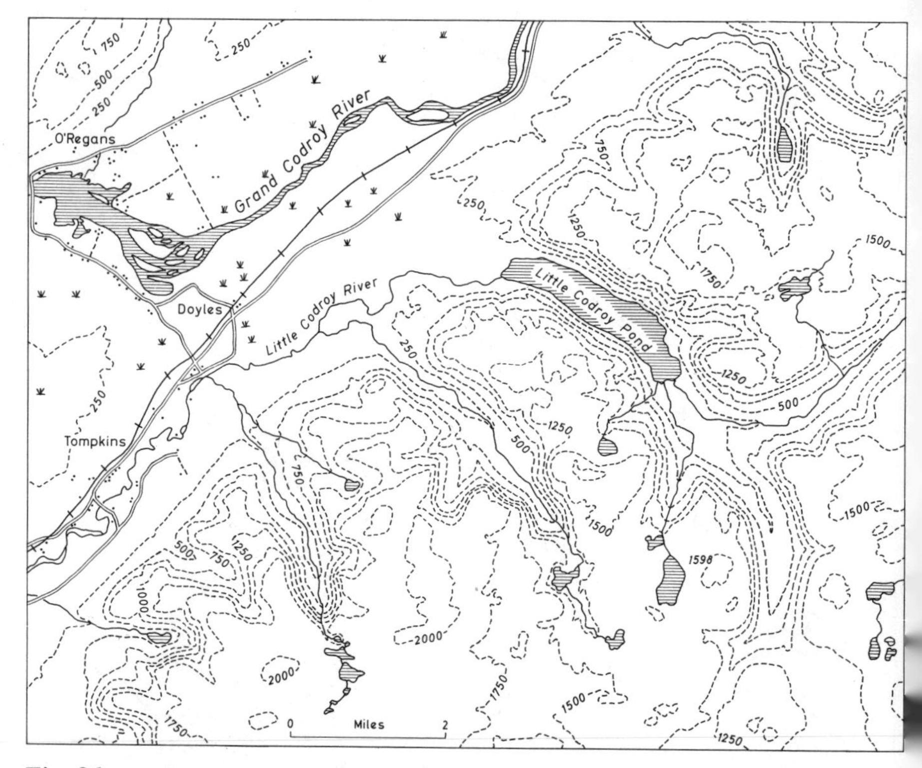

Fig. 86. A PORTION OF THE CODROY VALLEY

The area shown is in the south-west of the island. Running diagonally across it is the striking fault scarp that forms the north-western face of the Southern Long Range mountains: these are composed of ancient metamorphic rocks. The many lake-filled hollows (some of which have been omitted) are a sign of its intense glaciation. Part of the narrow-gauge trans-peninsular railway is shown; the main road is the Trans-Canada Highway. The Codroy valley has been excavated in Carboniferous sandstones, which form the youngest solid deposits in Newfoundland, and offer relatively productive soils to the farmer. The district also enjoys a relatively low rainfall and summer average temperatures of about 60°F. (see Figs. 83a and 83b). The farmhouses bordering the roads speak of a considerable rural population, which is rare in western Newfoundland (the black dots represent dwellings). *Based on the official 1 : 50,000 map, Codroy sheet.*

essentially a plateau of ancient metamorphic rocks, and there is little lowland suitable for farming. The rocks weather slowly, and the ice sheets have stripped off the loose soil-forming material, depositing in its place sterile coarse sands and gravels. Soils that have developed on this unpromising material are thin, stony, leached, and acid. Moreover, the province lies close to the climatic limits for agriculture. The mean July temperature of 57°F. appears to be critical, and there are few parts of the island which lie within this limit.

However, in the lower Humber valley and St George's bay districts there are mean July temperatures of over 61 °F., and here too the underlying rocks, of Carboniferous age, are more promising for agriculture. In the past this district has been considered too remote for farming; but settlement is extending, particularly in the neighbourhood of the railway and the Trans-Canada Highway (Fig. 86).

The Avalon peninsula in the east has not these advantages of climate and soil, but it has better communications, and the proximity of the capital as a market for farm produce. This is the traditional farming district of Newfoundland – such as it is. Newfoundland farms are small: few of them are larger than 50 acres; and hay and pasture account for more than half the area farmed. The climate is too cool for cereals except perhaps oats, and vegetables are the leading food crop, with an emphasis on potatoes. In some places raised terraces along the coast or at the heads of bays provide suitable sites for farms; but in many areas the fisherman finds it hard to discover a small plot to grow vegetables for his family. Soil fertility must be built up by means of compost, or by digging in large quantities of the tiny fish, caplin. Sometimes soil is moved bodily from an inaccessible site to one where it can be utilized. Inevitably the family diet lacks variety, and there is a real danger of deficiency diseases such as rickets.

Fishing

Cod, whether caught on the Grand Banks or inshore, is by far the chief catch of the Newfoundland fisheries. 'Cod is Newfoundland currency.' The inshore fishermen use small, streamlined, open rowing-boats, nowadays invariably fitted with engines. Two men and a boy form a usual crew. The boat puts to sea, and anchors in about 30 fathoms of water. The men bait their hooks with squid, and fish all day for cod, pausing only at noon for a meal of stewed fish, pork, potatoes, and onions, followed by hot tea. At dusk they return with the catch, which must then be cleaned, salted, and dried. The season is governed by the spawning time of the caplin, which is usually early in June, for it is these tiny fish that attract the cod inshore, providing food in plenty. The greatest catches are in June and July, but fishing continues till October.

A newer method of inshore fishing is by the use of the 'long liner': this is a larger boat, of about 40 tons, with a crew of six. A single line is used, with innumerable hooks on it, so that the fish are caught wholesale instead of singly. By this method a good day's catch could amount to ten tons.

The little fishing village is likely to be sited precariously on a rocky ledge overlooking the sea, with bare moorland behind. Along the harbour, perched on stilts above the water, are long rows of covered wooden sheds with wide entrances. Here the fish are unloaded and cleaned; then they are spread out on wide mattresses of interlaced spruce branches to dry in the sun. When it rains they must be gathered in quickly, for they represent almost the whole wealth of the village. The powerful smell of drying fish pervades the atmosphere. The family meal consists of fish, garden vegetables, home-baked bread, and wild blueberries.

Deep-sea fishing takes place in the Grand Banks – one of the most prolific fishing-grounds in the world. This consists of a portion of the continental shelf – a wide submarine undulating 'plateau' stretching for about 500 miles south-east of Newfoundland. Its average depth is in the region of 180 feet, though in places the sea is 600 feet deep. These depths are sufficiently shallow to allow sunlight to penetrate, and so encourage the generous growth of the minute marine 'vegetation', the phytoplankton. Squid, caplin, and herring feed on plant and animal plankton, and in their turn provide food for cod.

The traditional 'banker' was a wooden sailing schooner of up to 150 tons, with a complement of about two dozen men, and it would make three voyages a year to the Grand Banks, usually setting out from the south coast of the island. Each schooner carried seven to ten dories (small boats); and at the fishing-ground a pair of men would go off in each dory to fish with a long line, with perhaps a thousand baited hooks.

The schooners are fast dying out, and their place is being taken by trawlers. The trawler is more efficient: it is constructed of steel, and motor-driven. With a crew the same size as that of the schooner, it can catch more fish, and can make several journeys to the Banks in all weathers.

Mining

There are several known deposits of metallic ores, and coal-seams are known to occur in a downfold between Deer lake and White bay. At present, however, minerals are worked on a large scale only at Buchans, near the centre of the island, for the old-established iron-mines at Bell Island, off the north coast of the Avalon peninsula, were closed down in 1966.

The red hæmatite of Bell Island was considered one of the largest deposits in the world. Mining began in 1893, and gave rise to the town of Wabana, after which the district is usually named. The beds are contained in Ordovician rocks; they dip gently northward and continue below the floor of Conception bay. Shafts were sunk in the north-west of the island, and the galleries extended for a distance of about 2½ miles below the sea. Three ore beds were worked, and the output was at the rate of about 2 million tons per annum – representing an average of about one shipload a day. There is no local iron and steel industry: the ore was simply crushed into lumps of a size suited to the blast-furnace, and then shipped. Much of it was used in the blast-furnaces at Sydney, Nova Scotia, and the other traditional markets were the United Kingdom and Germany. These underground mines, however, were unable to compete with the modern open-cast workings of other iron districts; their closure has left a gap which the province cannot easily fill.

Buchans lies close to Red Indian lake at the end of a private spur of the railway, pointing southward towards the centre of the island. No road links it with civilization: all its material needs arrive by rail, and all its output departs in the same way. The ore yields $1\frac{1}{2}$ per cent. copper, $7\frac{1}{2}$ per cent. lead, and $15\frac{1}{2}$ per cent. zinc, and these materials are separated and concentrated at the mine. About 2100 people live in Buchans, and about one-third of them are employed by the mining company. Power for the mine and town is supplied from Bowater plant at Deer lake, which we notice below. The concentrates are shipped from the port of Botwood, situated at the mouth of the Exploits river, and on a north-pointing spur of the railway.

Other minerals are worked on a smaller scale: they include fluorspar from the St Lawrence district, at the southern end of the Burin peninsula, and limestone, at Aguathana, on the north side of St George's bay. Both are shipped for use in the steel industry of Sydney, Nova Scotia. Brick clays, gypsum, building stone, slate, and marble await development.

Forest Industries

Almost half the surface of Newfoundland is forested, and of this 83 per cent. is classed as exploitable. Nearly half the exploitable forest is at present untouched and self-regenerating. A small proportion of the timber is used locally for constructional purposes, and is prepared in about 900 sawmills scattered round the coasts, each employing three or four men. Furniture, barrels, and casks are manufactured to serve home needs, and the fishing-boats are locally built. Since coal is absent, timber is burnt for fuel, and for this purpose birch is used. But there are virtually no exports of lumber: mature trees are restricted in size as a result of the strong winds and low temperatures, and are inferior to the best timber of mainland Canada. However, logs of small diameter can be utilized in the pulp and paper industry, and two large companies between them control 80 per cent. of all the timber in Newfoundland. These are the Bowater Newfoundland Pulp and Paper Mills, Limited, with headquarters at Corner Brook, and the Anglo-Newfoundland Development Company, Limited, whose mills are at Grand Falls.

Fig. 87 indicates the location of the timber concessions of the two companies. The A.N.D. company owns timber in the North peninsula and in the land drained towards Bonavista bay, but its main concession lies in the basin of the Exploits river. Its mills at Grand Falls were established in 1909, and the site was well chosen. The Exploits river and its tributaries bring down the logs to the mill, and just here the water can be harnessed for hydro-electricity. From the first the mill was on the trans-insular railway (opened in 1896), and it is connected by way of a short private spur to the port of Botwood, about 25 miles distant, from which its products are shipped.

The Grand Falls mills have developed into one of the largest plants in the world, with an output of 900 tons of newsprint and 80 tons of woodpulp a day. Their hydro-electric plant has a capacity of 70,500 horse-power, and if necessary this could be doubled.

The logs are plucked from the river, debarked, chipped and ground or chemically 'digested', and mixed with water. The creamy 'soup', consisting of 99 per cent. water and 1 per cent. pulp, is poured on to an endless, moving wire screen at the wet end of the paper-making machine. It emerges in the form of great rolls of newsprint for the papers of New York, Washington, and Buenos Aires. Grand Falls is the fourth town of the province, and has a population of 6605: it is the largest inland centre of the island.

The Bowater timbers are widespread. Estimated at 20 million cords (a cord of timber contains 128 cubic feet), they total just over half the entire commercial timber of Newfoundland. The operations of this company have had a tremendous influence on the development of Newfoundland, and in many districts they offer a more attractive alternative to the dwindling fishing industry. The timber concessions are distributed in three main blocks; in the North Peninsula, the Hudson Basin and the Grand Lake district, and the Gander Basin (Fig. 87).

The North peninsula until recently was a wilderness of untouched forest, unmapped and unknown. Now 700 miles of road have been constructed there, and eight loading depots established, each the centre of a logging operation. Unfortunately, this is the part of Newfoundland most devastated by the hemlock looper. This is a tiny caterpillar that eats the needles of the balsam fir, and as a result a great stretch of forest 40 miles long lies dead, brown and grey, and there are other smaller areas of infestation. Dead wood rots after five years, and would then be useless for pulping: but within that period up to 90 per cent. of the timber can be salvaged, so that much of the effort is devoted to this end. Infested forest is not irretrievably ruined, for the looper attacks only mature trees, and after a generation or so the younger timber will be ready again for logging.

One of the loading centres is at Hawke Bay (Fig. 87), with a long loading pier and a village of 30 families and a two-room school. Other families live farther afield, and in all Hawke Bay depot occupies 300 men

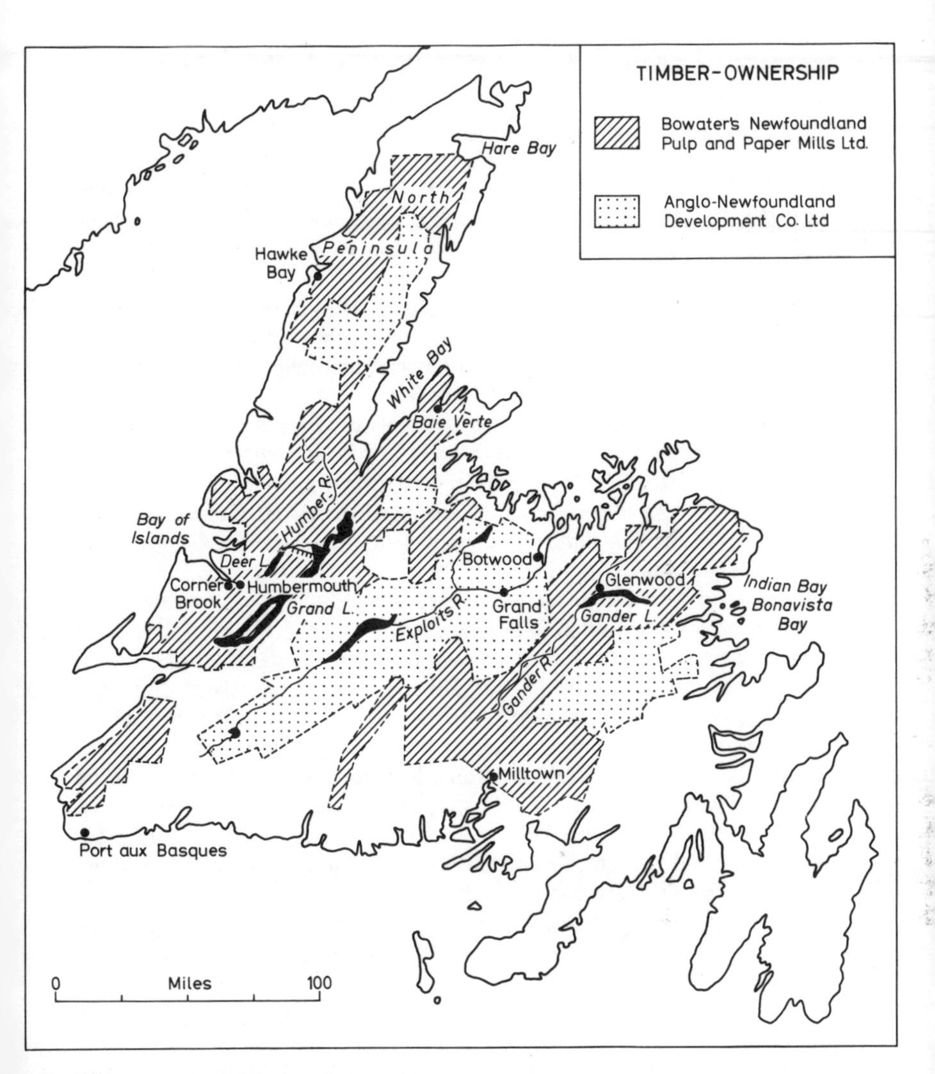

Fig. 87. NEWFOUNDLAND: TIMBER-OWNERSHIP

Broadly speaking, the Bowater Company controls the Humber and Gander basins, the Anglo-Newfoundland Development Company controls the Exploits basin, and the two companies share the North peninsula. Together they account for about 80 per cent. of the timber of the island. The larger areas of moss barren are avoided (see Fig. 85); even so, it is estimated that only about half of the concession areas contains commercially exploitable timber. The places named are linked with forest industry.

for most of the year and supervises a further 200 men 40 miles to the north. Close to the northern tip of the peninsula is Main Brook, a settlement of 650 people on Hare bay. It possesses all the services needed by a modern logging camp: machine shop, blacksmiths' and carpenters' shops, and retail and supply stores.

To the east of White bay is Baie Verte. Until 1937 this was a hamlet of only four families: it is now a thriving village of over 650 people, with three general stores, a restaurant, motor-repair shops, a hospital, and a loading pier, and it is linked by a new road to the Trans-Canada Highway near Sandy lake. Logs cut in the tributary districts are brought down to the bay, penned behind a boom, loaded on to self-propelled barges and shipped to Corner Brook – a journey of nearly 400 miles. Baie Verte ships 65,000 to 70,000 cords annually, Hawke Bay over 30,000, and Hare bay a further 30,000.

The Gander Basin district is a little east of the centre of Newfoundland. The timber concession area broadens considerably to the south, in the neighbourhood of the Gander headstreams, and reaches the coast at the head of the Bay d'Espoir. Loading is concentrated at two centres, Milltown, on the bay, and Glenwood, situated where the Gander river leaves Gander lake (Fig. 84).

Glenwood was established in the nineteenth century as a sawmilling centre, and its population has now grown to 700. It is the focus of 14 logging camps in the Gander country and it forwards about 76,000 cords annually to Corner Brook. The logs have a complicated journey to make. By horse, tractor, or lorry they are first hauled to the Gander headstreams and then floated down the rivers; they are towed across Gander lake in booms and so reach Glenwood. Here they are loaded on to flat railway trucks on the trans-insular railway, to form trains of 20 to 30 trucks. At Grand lake they are discharged, floated along the Humber Canal, which links it to Deer lake, and so down the Humber river. Finally, they are towed to the mill.

The long journey is necessary, for in order to conserve supplies the more distant timber must be used in addition to the nearby stands; moreover, the Gander timber includes a high proportion of spruce, which in paper-making needs to be mixed in definite proportions with the nearby fir.

Timber from the southern portion of this large concession is shipped from Milltown. Here is another full-scale depot, with offices, supply stores, sheds, and wharves. The village is in an attractive setting, and its few dozen substantial houses are well spaced along the road that skirts the bay, amid a fringe of meadow and gardens, and below the forest on which it depends for its existence.

From these and many other similar depots the pulpwood arrives at Corner Brook. Sixty per cent. of it arrives in great floating rafts hauled by a tug, either from Humbermouth or from neighbouring coastal depots. Another 30 per cent. consists of 'boatwood'; this, from Baie Verte, has a longer journey than timber to any other paper-mill in

Canada. Nine per cent. of the pulpwood arrives by rail, and only 1 per cent. by lorry.

The tidal location of the Corner Brook mill is an immense advantage, for during the ice-free period (here eight months) it can receive its timber and ship its products without the need for other transport. During the four months January to April, when the Bay of Islands is frozen, the products are forwarded by rail for shipment from Port aux Basques, the only important ice-free port of Newfoundland.

The mill is supplied by the company's own hydro-electric plant at Deer lake, 30 miles distant. With a capacity of 150,000 horse-power, this is the largest in Newfoundland, and though most of its power is required by the mill, there is a surplus available, which is used by other local industry and, as we have seen, by the mining company at Buchans.

The Corner Brook mill is the largest integrated paper-mill in the world. It consumes about half a million cords of timber a year (over a million tons) and it directly employs about 1750 people. The plant contains 10 great 'digesters' which cook chipped wood to make chemical pulp, and 41 grinders which reduce whole logs to pulp. The largest of the paper-making machines, No. 7, produces about 600 miles of newsprint 24 feet wide every day, while the whole mill manufactures 1000 tons of newsprint and 150 tons of sulphite pulp a day. These operations have a direct link with Great Britain, for pulp from Corner Brook supplies the English Bowater mills with some of their needs, while pulpwood is shipped from Indian bay, on the north shore of Newfoundland, to the Bowater mills at Sittingbourne, Kent.

The town of Corner Brook, with a population of 25,185, is the second city of Newfoundland. It began as a company town, and its prosperity still depends on the paper-mill; but it is developing a broader basis: recently established plants include representatives of the cement, gypsum, building, and lumber industries. Nevertheless, the great mills on the waterfront, with their wharves and jetty, their rail sidings and storage sheds, stockpiles of pulpwood and immense floating booms, will remain the economic heart of the town and, indeed, the source of much of the prosperity of Newfoundland.

Communications

We have referred at several points to the trans-insular railway. This looks rather like a toy: it is a narrow-gauge, single-track railway, with one train a day each way during the summer. It was built by a private company during 1881–96, and was taken over by the Government in 1923. Until quite recently it was a vital link in the economic life of the island, for there was then no through road. The railway begins at the capital, joins the heads of the bays of the north coast, crosses the Long Range mountains at a height of over 1500 feet, passes Deer lake and the Humber valley to reach Corner Brook, traverses the Codroy valley, and terminates at Port aux Basques. This trunk route is 547 miles long, and its several arms provide important links to inland and coastal settlements.

Road systems even today exist only in three districts of Newfoundland: these are in the St John's area, the Exploits district, and the Humber valley and St George's bay area. A few years ago these were isolated one from the other, but the construction of the easternmost section of the Trans-Canada Highway has joined them, and provided a much-needed road running parallel with the railway. There are still no roads in the centre of the island or along the south coast, but logging operations have already opened up much of the North peninsula, and will undoubtedly extend to other areas, at present inaccessible.

Many remote fishing-villages still rely for their contacts with civilization on the visits of the coastal vessels. Seven ships are constantly engaged on providing a regular service in summer; but this is interrupted by ice in winter. The detached Newfoundland section of the Trans-Canada Highway is linked daily to its mainland continuation by a 110-mile vehicular ferry passage between Port aux Basques and Sydney, Nova Scotia.

Newfoundland lies astride the great circle joining London and New York, so that an airport here is strategically placed to service trans-atlantic air-liners. For this purpose Gander was established between the wars, and has developed into one of the world's busiest airports. Few of the passengers who pass through it, however, see anything more of Newfoundland.

Distribution of Population

The interior of Newfoundland is virtually deserted, apart from a few small settlements along the railway, and centres of mining and forestry. It is estimated that 90 per cent. of the people live on or near the coast, and, more remarkably, that 45 per cent. live in the most easterly portion of the plateau, the Avalon peninsula. Even here the people cling mainly to the shores of the two inlets of the north coast – Conception and Trinity bays. In the former district are both the capital city and the former iron-mining district of Bell Island.

A scattered coastal and island population inhabits the north coast of the island, particularly round Bonavista and Notre Dame bays; but the North peninsula, apart from logging camps we have already noticed, is uninhabited, for it thrusts into a sea that is frozen in winter and infested with floating ice in summer. The south coast, in contrast, is open throughout the year, and affords sites for scores of small fishing-villages, many of them with fewer than 50 inhabitants. They are particularly numerous round Placentia and Fortune bays.

The west coast was settled rather late, in spite of its better climate and more fertile soils, for it is only in the present century that the French have relinquished their control of the local fisheries. Settlement clings mainly to three areas – the Bay of Islands, St George's bay, and Bonne bay. Here the pulp and paper industry and a growing farming community are added to the more traditional occupation of fishing, and result in an isolated corner of prosperity.

The only large town in Newfoundland is its capital, St John's. Its harbour consists of a drowned valley, protected from the ocean swell by a narrow entrance, only 200 yards across. Structurally this forms a breach in a steep ridge, rising to over 500 feet, which shelters the city from easterly gales.

During the eighteenth century the town was open to French attacks, and the harbour was guarded by an iron chain stretched between Pancake and Chain rocks. Within there were twin forts, and the road joining them was the earliest in the town. On the south-east side of the harbour the land rises steeply, so that the city is confined to the opposite shore.

Though the harbour has a depth of 90 feet, it is too small for large modern liners. Nevertheless, St John's is the chief general port for the whole of Newfoundland. Its exports include fish and paper, but these are greatly outweighed by the imports, which comprise provisions, tobacco, fuel, machinery, and clothing. The harbour is lined by commercial and industrial concerns. The city began as a fishing-settlement, and fishing remains an important interest. There are fish-processing plants, ship-yards, rope-works, and wood-working and clothing factories. At the southern end of the harbour are the dry dock, the naval dockyard, and the terminus of the Newfoundland railway. Unlike most American cities, St John's is not a planned chequerboard town, but its street pattern has evolved in accordance with its needs and in conformity with the physique of its site.

THE MARITIME PROVINCES

Today the three maritime provinces of Prince Edward Island, Nova Scotia, and New Brunswick appear something of an anachronism. Compared with the other provinces of Canada they are very small: even if we add all three together their area amounts to less than one-third that of Newfoundland (including Labrador), and less than a quarter that of the smallest other mainland province (Manitoba). Their populations, if totalled, are a little larger than that of British Columbia, but considerably less than one-third of those of either Quebec or Ontario.

These territories have had varied political status. New Brunswick formed part of Nova Scotia until 1784, when about 12,000 Empire

Loyalists, having settled north of the Bay of Fundy, petitioned for and were granted an independent administration. Prince Edward Island, when ceded to England by France in 1763, began as part of Nova Scotia; but six years later it was granted its own administration. Cape Breton Isle has had a chequered career: taken from France in 1758, it too was joined to Nova Scotia; but for the 36 years 1784–1820 it enjoyed a separate political life, only to rejoin Nova Scotia. There are thus many precedents for a future change of status, and in 1965 the Nova Scotia and New Brunswick parliaments authorized a study of the question of union. Should this be agreed, it is unlikely that Prince Edward Island would wish to stand aloof.

In material resources these are poor provinces. Incomes are low, and many of the most energetic inhabitants migrate to more prosperous regions in the west. They rely to a large extent on Federal aid, which takes two main forms: the placing of defence establishments in these provinces and the building of the Trans-Canada Highway.

We have mentioned the naval dockyard at St John's, Newfoundland. Halifax, Nova Scotia, is also a military and naval base. In southern New Brunswick an area 20 by 30 miles is destined to become the largest army training establishment in Canada: the village of Oromocto, on the lower St John river, is being expanded by the construction of 1400 new homes, and Camp Gagetown (as it is called) will entail an expenditure of 40 million dollars. Defence establishments in the Atlantic province are estimated to employ a total of 42,000 people.

All four provinces are deriving benefit from the project of the Trans-Canada Highway. This is to be a paved highway nearly 5000 miles long, with one terminal at Victoria, B.C., and the other at St John's, Newfoundland. New stretches of road are being built and existing roads improved. For the first time Newfoundland has a highway running the whole width of the island. In Nova Scotia a causeway across the Canso Strait now links Cape Breton Island to the mainland, and the former ferry across the Great Bras d'Or lake has been replaced by a causeway and bridge three-quarters of a mile long. Prince Edward Island is to be linked to the mainland by a nine-mile road and rail connection, part causeway, part bridge, and part tunnel. The proposal was announced by the Federal Government in 1965: it will take five years to build, will carry at least three times the amount of traffic using the ferry, and will cost 148 million dollars. These improved communications are very welcome: they reduce the costs of transport when complete, and while they are under construction they offer much-needed additional opportunities for employment to the local populations.

NOVA SCOTIA

Physical Basis

As in Newfoundland, the structure of Nova Scotia conforms with the Caledonian trend, and both geologically and topographically there is a north-east and south-west alignment, well seen in the parallel shores of the peninsula and the Bay of Fundy. The main peninsula is composed largely of Pre-Cambrian material, which has been intruded by masses of granite. In the south-west these two rocks extend across the whole width of the peninsula, excepting only the Annapolis valley, so that the prospects for farming are not very promising. Farther east they narrow, and terminate in the east-pointing Cape Canso. Beyond, to the north and north-west, is the rim of an extensive basin of Carboniferous rocks, which includes the eastern half of New Brunswick and the whole of Prince Edward Island. Cape Breton Island is complex in surface geology, but has extensive exposures of Carboniferous strata.

The striking longitudinal Annapolis valley has been carved from soft Triassic sandstones, and provides a structural link with New England and New Jersey. A great tilted sheet of lava, reminiscent of the Palisades of New York state (p. 22), extends for over 100 miles, separates the valley from the Bay of Fundy, and continues to form the rocky peninsula known as Digby Neck. The Trias is the youngest rock of the Maritimes, and its cover of glacial drift provides fertile soils, so that this is one of the most productive farming districts of eastern Canada.

Nova Scotia, though subject to the same general climatic influences as Newfoundland, is farther south, lower in elevation, farther from the Labrador current, and nearer to the Gulf Stream. Mean January temperatures are everywhere below freezing-point, but no part of Nova Scotia is as cold as the central plateau of Newfoundland, and its ports are open throughout the year. Summer in Nova Scotia is distinctly warmer than in Newfoundland: the whole province enjoys July means of over 60°F., while the north coast and upper reaches of the Bay of Fundy experience average July temperatures of over 65° (Fig. 88a). Even tobacco has been introduced successfully into the Annapolis valley.

Precipitation is rather high, but rarely excessive: it ranges from over 55 inches along the Atlantic coast to below 40 inches in the upper Bay of Fundy (Fig. 88b). Like Newfoundland, Nova Scotia lies in the path of depressions, and the occasional cyclone that strays from the normal path can cause great damage to the apple crop of the Annapolis valley.

These comparatively slight differences in temperature between Nova Scotia and Newfoundland are reflected in land use. There are virtually no moss barrens in Nova Scotia, and the northern coniferous forest of

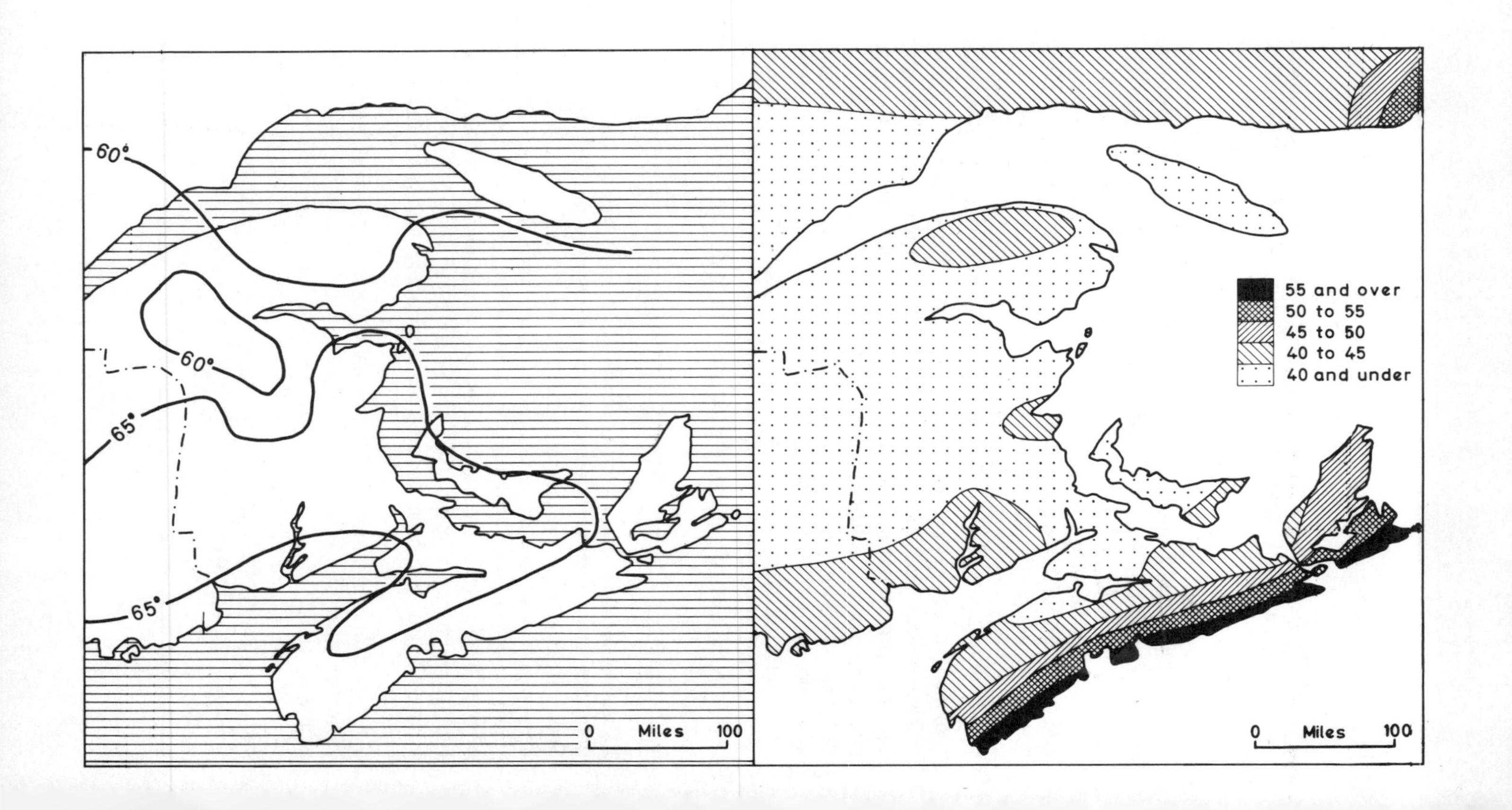
60°
60°
65°
65°
0 Miles 100
55 and over
50 to 55
45 to 50
40 to 45
40 and under
0 Miles 100

fir and spruce, typical of much of Newfoundland, is found only in the northern half of Nova Scotia. The natural vegetation of the south consists mainly of the so-called Acadian forest, containing many different species that include the sugar and red maples, black and white ash, yellow birch, white elm, beech, and red spruce. Along the Atlantic slopes, with their high rainfall and largely impermeable soils, there is much swampy land whose characteristic trees include black spruce, red maple, black ash, alder, and tamarack.

Settlement

In 1497 John and Sebastian Cabot sighted the northern tip of Nova Scotia, and claimed the territory for England. But it was the Frenchmen Samuel de Champlain and Sieur de Monts who first settled there, establishing Port Royal about 1594. This town, later renamed Annapolis, was one of the first permanent white settlements in the whole of North America. During the seventeenth century there was an extensive French occupation of the lowlands bordering the Bay of Fundy: the immigrants recognized the potential fertility of the wide areas of silt-covered tidal flats and set about reclaiming them by means of dykes, as they had done in Normandy and Brittany. Port Royal became the capital of the French province of Acadia, whose name was derived from a Micmac Indian word signifying 'abundance'.

Meanwhile in 1621 James I had granted these same lands, including all the territory as far north as the St Lawrence river, to the Scot Sir William Alexander. The name chosen for the new domain was Nova Scotia (New Scotland), after the King's native land.

The dispute between France and England was settled in 1713, and Acadia passed into British control. Port Royal was renamed Annapolis Royal in honour of Queen Anne. When the Hanoverian George II in due course acceded to the English throne he encouraged folk from his native Germany to settle in Nova Scotia. Some of them reached Mahone bay and founded the town of Lunenburg in 1753. It became an important centre for the building of schooners; it is still a significant fishing-port; and though the German speech and customs have now died out the German family names remain.

In 1755 the French were incited to revolt. Several hundred English

---

Fig. 88a. THE MARITIME PROVINCES: JULY TEMPERATURES

The map indicates the mean sea-level temperatures for July. A wide area enjoys summer temperatures of over 65°F. and hence is warm enough for crops to ripen.

Fig. 88b. THE MARITIME PROVINCES: MEAN ANNUAL PRECIPITATION

This map, when compared with the preceding one, shows that the land that is warmest in summer also enjoys a relatively low rainfall.

soldiers were massacred at Grand Pré, and as a reprisal the Acadians, numbering over 10,000, were expelled from their lands and homes and removed to scattered localities elsewhere along the eastern seaboard (they were allowed to return later, and many in fact did so). The vacant lands were occupied mainly by New Englanders, whose descendants still live in the Annapolis valley in farming-villages at the head of the Bay of Fundy, and in fishing-settlements along the south coast. Dating from this time are Yarmouth and Barrington in the west, Liverpool on the south coast, Windsor, Falmouth, and Truro in the Minas Basin, and many other settlements.

Scottish immigrants settled in 1772 at Pictou and other places along the north shore, and in Cape Breton Island: they were the forerunners of many others of their countrymen in the following century. At the close of the American War of Independence about 30,000 Loyalists moved into the region. Shelburne, in the south-west of the peninsula, was established by 470 families who set sail from New York to escape American domination. Dubbed 'true blues', they passed on their nicknames to Nova Scotians in general, who are still called 'bluenoses'. Most of the Loyalists, however, were allocated lands north of the Bay of Fundy; as we have seen, they petitioned for a separate political status, and the northern part of what was then a larger Nova Scotia was set apart as New Brunswick (1784), with a capital at Fredericton.

Human Geography

The Nova Scotia economy is more broadly based than that in Newfoundland. Forestry is important, but does not dominate; farming, coal-mining, and fishing each contribute approximately equally to the provincial income, and there are important steel-works at Sydney and other manufactures at Halifax.

The following descriptions of the Maritime Provinces are illustrated by the generalized land-use map, Fig. 89, and by Fig. 90. We begin with Cape Breton Island. For 36 years this was a separate province, and it retains a certain individuality of outlook. A bold plateau of Pre-Cambrian granite forms a bleak northern peninsula similar to that of Newfoundland, though on a far smaller scale. In the centre of the island some valleys following the Caledonian trend have been drowned to form the large marine lake, the Bras d'Or, now crossed by a causeway. In spite of its scenic grandeur, the interior of Cape Breton Island is almost deserted, and the population is coastal. There are many scattered fishing-villages whose inhabitants are part-time farmers. Most of these farmers are descended from Highland Scots: bagpipe and tartan are well in evidence, and it appears that Gaelic is better preserved here than in Scotland itself! St Ann's, about 25 miles west of Sydney, is a centre of Gaelic culture. French customs and language, on the other hand,

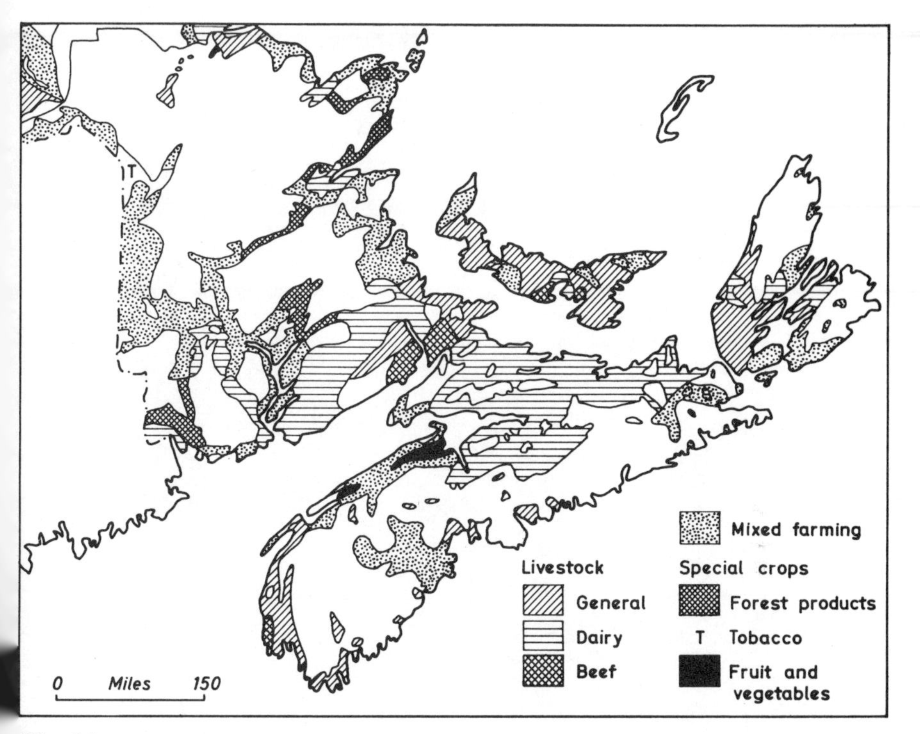

Fig. 89. THE MARITIME PROVINCES: GENERALIZED LAND USE

This map summarizes the farming types in the Maritime Provinces. It emphasizes the extremely high proportion of farm-land in Prince Edward Island, illustrates the dairy industry of northern Nova Scotia, the intensive cultures of the Annapolis valley, and the valley farming of New Brunswick. Areas left blank are largely forested.

survive in the Acadian settlements that focus on Arichat, on the Strait of Canso, and Cheticamp, in the north-west. A third racial group is the Irish, who have played a large part in establishing the coal-mining industry.

Nova Scotia produces about two-fifths of the entire Canadian output of coal, and most of this is derived from Cape Breton Island. The Coal Measures have been preserved in a series of furrows which now occupy the seaward ends of the peninsulas, and coal-seams outcrop for about 30 miles along the shore. The total thickness of workable coal reaches 47 feet, and this is of coking quality. The seams dip below the sea-bed, and are followed by galleries which extend up to $2\frac{1}{2}$ miles from the shore. Four coastal mining settlements in the Sydney district handle most of the coal: they are Glace Bay, New Waterford, North Sydney, and Sydney Mines.

The output from this field, together with the smaller coalfields of mainland Nova Scotia, amounts to about 6 million tons annually. It is

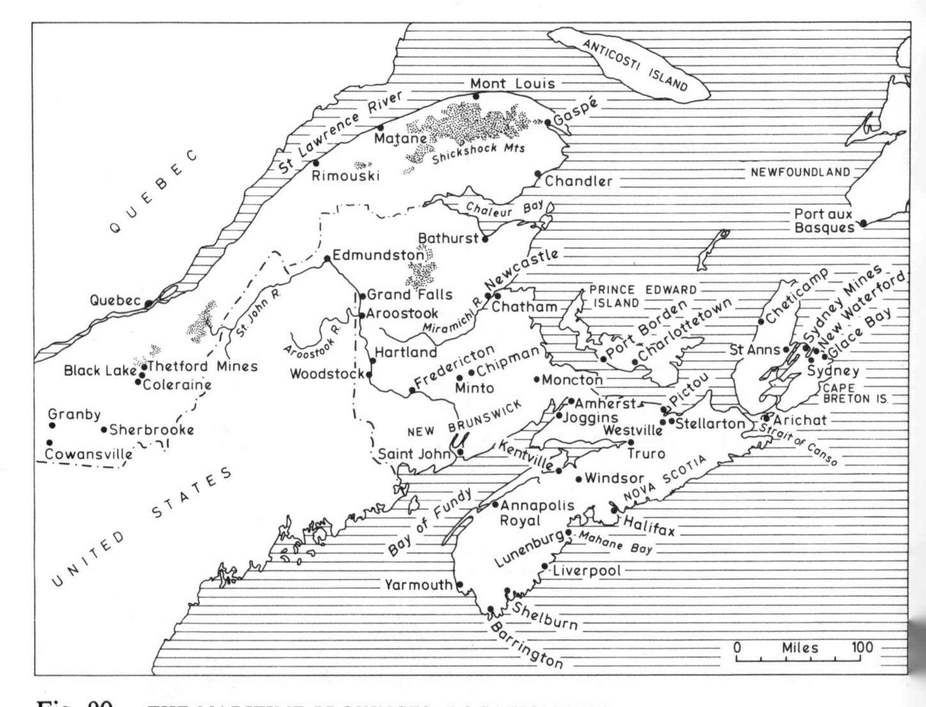

Fig. 90. THE MARITIME PROVINCES: LOCATION MAP

The map shows the position of towns and other features mentioned in the text.

used as fuel in Nova Scotia power-stations, and is shipped to some of the lower St Lawrence ports, but its major outlet is in the form of coke for the steel-works of Sydney.

The century-old Cape Breton Island coal industry, however, is beset by grave economic difficulties. For many years it has survived only with the aid of subsidies from the Federal Government: yet it forms the means of livelihood of 10,500 workers (over a quarter of the total male labour force of the island). The federal and provincial Governments are to assume responsibility for the coal and steel industries; the existing mines are to be 'rehabilitated' and improved. Yet closures, with all their attendant social problems, will be inevitable during the next 15 years. Efforts will be made to attract new industries to the area and to provide retraining schemes for the ex-miners.

Sydney was founded in 1784 by Empire Loyalists, and developed initially as a capital city for the short-lived province of Cape Breton Island. It enjoyed the advantage of a deep and sheltered harbour, and its stability was assured when it was chosen as the eastern terminus of the inter-colonial railway.

The local coal had been worked since the first half of the nineteenth century, but the industrial importance of Sydney dates from 1899, when a steel company was established, attracted by the possibility of combining the local coking coal with Bell Island ore. The company now controls most of the Newfoundland ore workings and many of the Nova Scotia mines; it imports its fluxing limestone from quarries at Aguathuna, on the west coast of Newfoundland. The steel-works have grown into one of the largest in Canada: they occupy a 460-acre site along the waterfront to the north of the city centre, and have an ingot capacity of about 1 million tons annually, and employ 6000 men. Sydney steel is rolled into rails, it supplies the engineering industries of Trenton, on the Pictou coalfield, together with the shipyards of Halifax, and it is shipped to manufacturing centres in Quebec and Ontario provinces, and overseas to Latin America.

We may divide mainland Nova Scotia into two regions: in the north are several isolated but populated mining and farming districts bordering the Minas Basin and the Northumberland Strait; in the south is a mountainous and largely deserted interior, with a row of coastal settlements, including Halifax, the capital.

Northern Nova Scotia

Several small and distinct agricultural lowlands flank the bays and straits of northern Nova Scotia. They are developed on relatively soft sandstones and limestones of Carboniferous and Triassic age, which are covered by glacial drift and (particularly around the Bay of Fundy) by marine silts. Climatically they are favoured by the large bodies of enclosed water, which reduce the risk of frost. July temperatures average about 65 °F., so that temperatures of sunny summer afternoons are well over 70°. Precipitation, at about 40 inches annually, is low compared with other parts of the Atlantic provinces.

These are districts of mixed farms, with an emphasis on dairying. Market centres include Amherst, on the New Brunswick border, Pictou, on the north coast, and Truro, at the head of the Minas Basin. Typical industries in these and similar centres include the processing of milk, woodworking, and the manufacture of textiles.

In addition there are two small coalfields – namely, the Cumberland and Pictou basins. Cumberland county adjoins New Brunswick, and stretches from the Minas Basin to Northumberland Strait (there is no town of that name). A series of disasters have resulted in the closure of the pits at Springhill, but mining continues at Joggins, on the shore of Chignecto bay. The Pictou coal-basin fronts the north coast, at the eastern entrance of Northumberland Strait, and here is a small but flourishing industrial district. Westville and Stellarton are mining-towns, Pictou is a port and shipbuilding centre, and Trenton has railway and automobile engineering works. The population of the district numbers nearly 25,000.

The most famous of the farming districts of northern Nova Scotia is the Annapolis valley, and this we may examine more closely. Its shape and situation are unusual, for, as we have seen (p. 235), it consists of a long and narrow lowland floored by Triassic material and sheltered by high ridges to the north-west and south-east. Coastal submergence has flooded the valley at each end to form the Minas Basin and St Mary's bay. In a state of nature wide areas were flooded by the phenomenally high tides of the Bay of Fundy, which at times approach 60 feet; now many farms in the valley (in common with others in the region) include stretches of rich pasture that were first reclaimed from the sea by the Acadian settlers.

The reputation of the Annapolis valley was made by its apple orchards, for which both climate and topography are favourable. Spring arrives late, for there are ice-floes on the surrounding seas: this delays the blossom until the danger of frost is past. Summer follows quickly; the sea becomes warm, and there is a long autumn, which lasts almost till November. This allows a long harvesting season without interruption by frost. As in Kent, the orchards are planted on sloping ground, which provides free drainage, both for ground-water and for cold air. The phenomenal tides of Fundy stir up the air four times a day, and this reduces the likelihood of frost.

During the Second World War the United Kingdom, for long the traditional outlet for Nova Scotia apples, was forced to reduce her imports, and this market has not fully been regained. Annapolis valley farmers have now reduced their orchard acreages, and are concentrating more on dairy and poultry farming. Poultry in particular has become a leading line: the district produces about 3 million table-birds a year, and has the greatest concentration of poultry in Canada.

The valley farmers have evolved an efficient marketing organization. Two railway lines serve the valley, and link with the export quays at Halifax. Refrigerated trucks and vessels ensure that the fruit will not suffer on their journey to Europe or the eastern United States. There are processing plants in the valley for converting the apples into sauce, essence, juice, or wine, or for canning them.

We illustrate from a farm near Kentville, in the eastern portion of the valley (Fig. 91). It covers 270 acres, and extends from the tidal

Fig. 91. A FARM IN THE ANNAPOLIS VALLEY

The phenomenal tides in the Bay of Fundy have enriched wide areas with marine silt. The early French (Acadian) settlers dyked much of this land to reclaim it, and the farm illustrated here includes 53 acres of dyked land. A generation ago the district depended on apples: these are still important but have now yielded first place to poultry. *The map incorporates information provided by courtesy of the Association of Agriculture.*

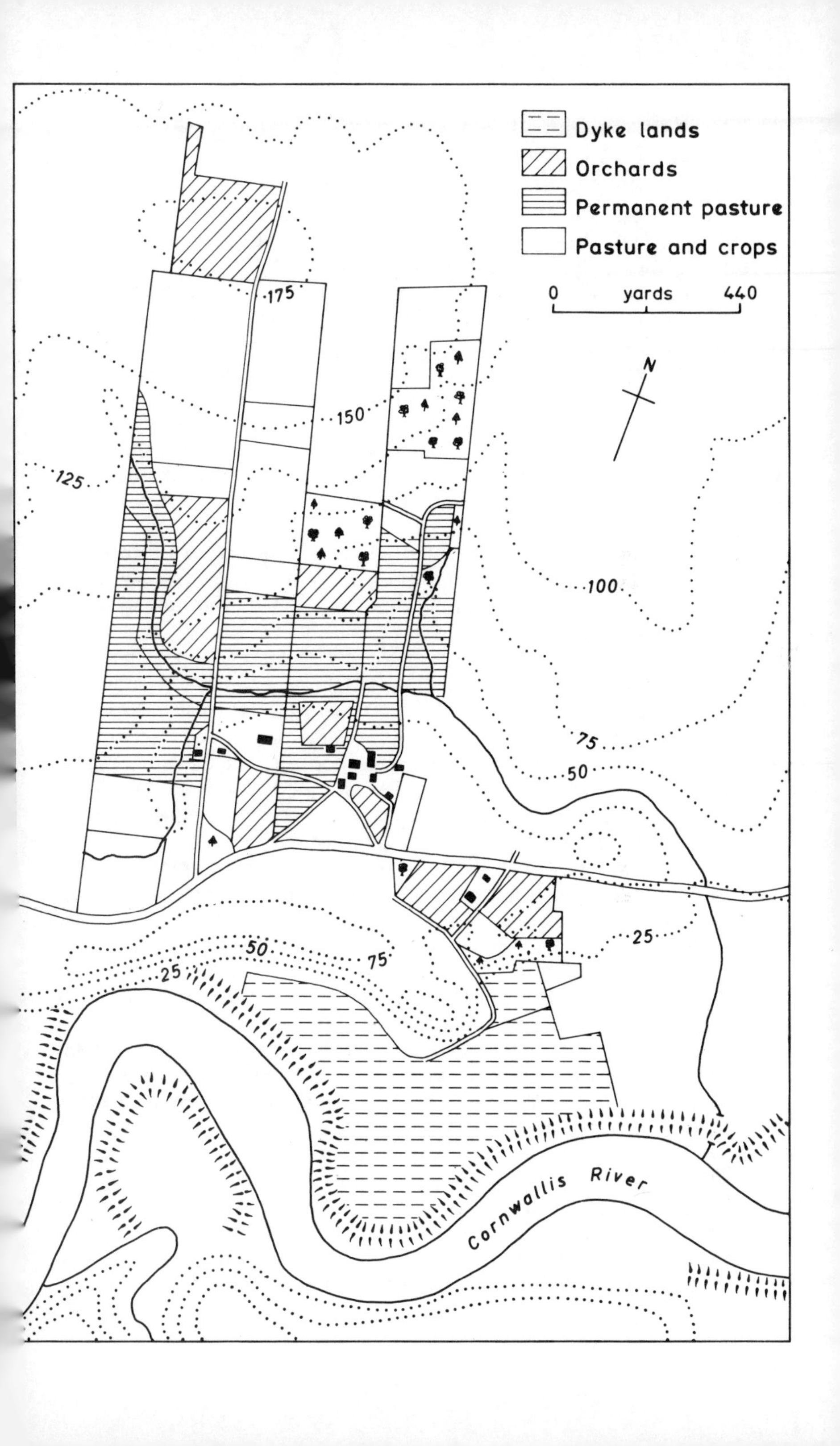

Dyke lands
Orchards
Permanent pasture
Pasture and crops
0 yards 440
N
175
150
125
100
75
50
25
50
75
25
Cornwallis River

estuary of the Cornwallis river to the crest of a ridge at over 175 feet above sea-level. A brook flows eastward through the middle of the farm and provides water for the dairy herd. The damper, heavier land in its valley is utilized as permanent pasture, and the cattle graze its 54 acres during June, July, and August.

Flanking the Cornwallis river are 53 acres of dyked land: this is managed on a four-year rotation, with a grass-clover ley for three years, followed by a crop of oats. The farmer first cuts this for silage and hay, then moves the cattle to graze it during September and October. On the remainder of the land there are reddish soils derived from glacial drift which itself rests on Triassic sandstones. This land is well drained and its soils are relatively light; consequently it is devoted to orchards (40 acres) and to cropping and pasture (68 acres). The latter, like the dyked land, yields hay, silage, and oats, and contributes to the winter feeding of the stock.

The dairy herd numbers 21 Holsteins (Friesians), with about 25 young cattle, and gives about 200 quarts of milk a day. About half of this is converted into cream, so that there is skimmed milk available for feeding the 25–30 young pigs.

The orchards, apart from four acres of pears and one of peaches, consist of several varieties of apples. During February, March, and early April the trees are pruned; from May to July they must be sprayed regularly against scab fungus, the codling moth, and other pests. September and October are the harvest months, but the work can be spread out, since the varieties ripen at different times; and all the labour can be concentrated on fruit-picking since by this time silage and hay-making and the oat harvest are finished.

Fruit-growing is not now the main source of this farmer's income, for since the War he has developed a major poultry interest. He rears and sells 7000 birds each year, and from the peak period of mid-August till the end of the year they are laying about 5000 eggs a day. The table birds are supplied mainly to Halifax and Sydney, but the eggs supply a wider region, which extends to Montreal, Newfoundland, and even Bermuda.

This is clearly a productive and efficient farm. Its output includes fruit, milk and cream, eggs, table birds, veal, and bacon, and all the varied activities are dovetailed neatly together. It is run by the farmer, his two sons, and only two other helpers.

The Interior and South Coast

The interior of Nova Scotia consists of rocky and forested country developed on ancient granites and metamorphic rocks; it receives a relatively heavy precipitation, 45 to 55 inches of 'rainfall', which includes about 75 inches of snow. There are considerable resources of timber, and several roads cross the peninsula, but there are few inhabitants. The only rail crossings link with Halifax.

Apart from the Halifax area, most of the people live in a row of small coastal settlements, and are fishermen and part-time farmers. Some of the villages have boatbuilding industries and sawmills, and there is a large paper-mill at Liverpool. The only large city is the capital, Halifax.

Halifax

Halifax was founded in 1749 as a military and naval base, on a rocky peninsula on the western side of a deep and sheltered drowned valley. There are still important naval dockyards and barracks in the city, and it was particularly active during both world wars. The outer harbour is exceptionally deep and wide, and will accommodate the world's largest vessels. The immediate surroundings of the port, however, are singularly unproductive (Fig. 92), and its importance springs from its wider hinterland.

Like St John's, Newfoundland, Halifax lies close to the arc of the great circle that joins the Rhine ports with New York, so that it is a convenient port of call for transatlantic liners. It is one of the few ice-free ports of eastern Canada, and its future was assured when it was chosen as the eastern terminal of the Canadian National Railway. During winter, when the St Lawrence is frozen, Halifax becomes the second busiest port in Canada (after Vancouver).

Halifax exports grain from the prairies, apples and other farm produce from the Annapolis valley, timber from southern Nova Scotia. It is an important fishing-port, and fish products figure largely in its exports. An important locally produced mineral is gypsum: it is quarried in the Windsor district to the north-west, and shipped at the rate of about a million tons annually, mainly to New York and neighbouring ports for the manufacture of plaster and plaster-board.

The industries of Halifax include oil-refining, shipbuilding, the manufacture of fertilizers, and the refining of sugar imported from the West Indies. In addition it is the centre of the provincial administration, and houses two cathedrals and Dalhousie University. The population of the city in 1961 was 92,511, and of the metropolitan area, 183,946.

PRINCE EDWARD ISLAND

Prince Edward Island is the smallest province in Canada: it accounts for less than 1 per cent. of its area and population. Yet of all the Atlantic provinces this is the most uniformly settled and the most completely agricultural, and it possesses the closest network of roads and railways.

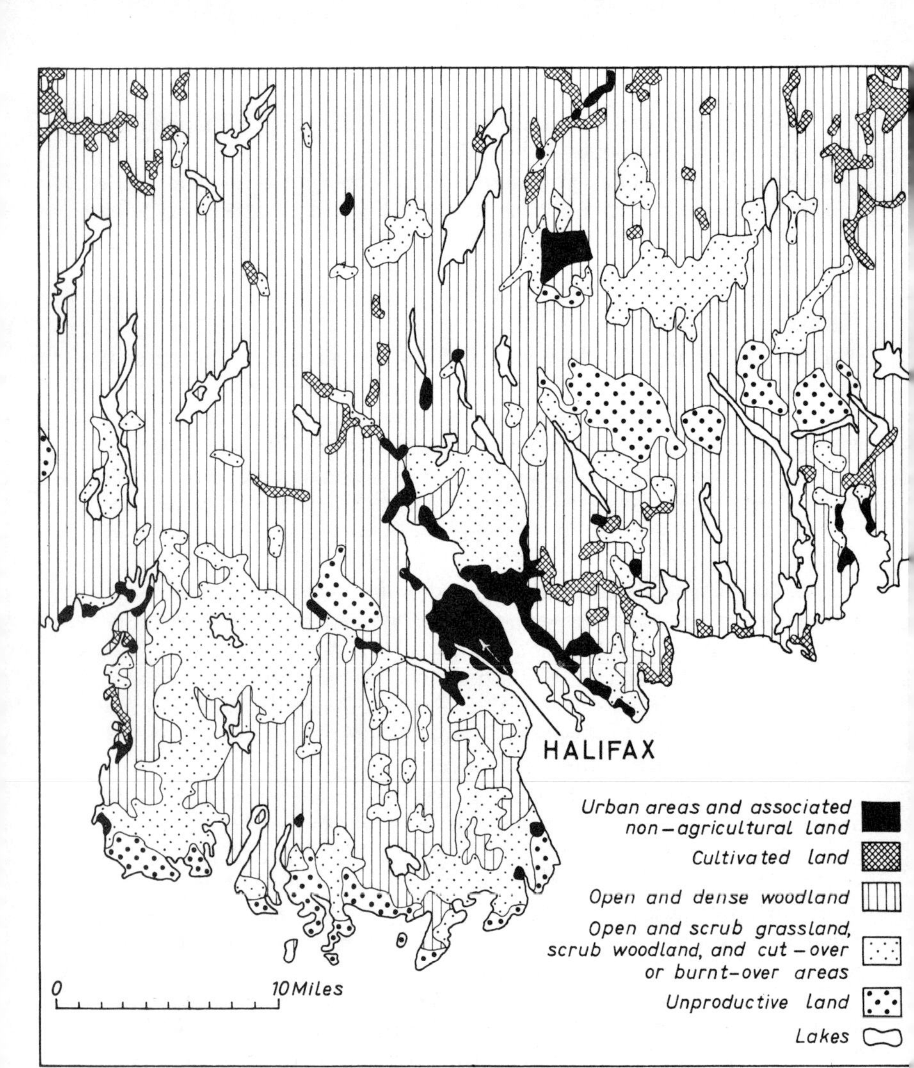

Fig. 92. THE HALIFAX DISTRICT: LAND USE

The immediate surroundings of this busy port do not offer much basis for trade. Most of the area is still under virgin forest, and cultivation is limited to a few favoured coastal lowland areas or sheltered valleys. Most of the nearby villages depend on fishing.

Structurally the island forms part of the floor of the Carboniferous basin whose rim appears in Nova Scotia and New Brunswick: its red sandstones, shales, and conglomerates dip gently north-eastward and are believed to be of Permian age. Almost everywhere, however, they are masked by thick deposits of glacial drift, which give rise to acid soils of little natural fertility. Nevertheless, the former cover of mixed forests has been largely cleared, and a quite prosperous farming system has been evolved, based largely on dairy cattle and seed potatoes. The warm, moist summers favour the growth of pasture, and potatoes flourish in these cloudy conditions and on the acid soils. There is consequently a remarkably high density of population, averaging over 47 per square mile. Few other rural districts of Canada can match this figure.

The population of 104,629 (in 1961) still reflects its origins: 30 per cent. are of Scottish ancestry and another 30 per cent. English, 20 per cent. are Irish, and almost all of the remainder Acadian. The capital, Charlottetown, possesses a fine harbour, 2 miles wide, 30 feet deep, and well protected from storms. It is mainly an administrative and trading centre, and its only important industry is the processing of foodstuffs.

A loop of the Trans-Canada Highway passes through the province for 75 miles, linking the mainland by ferries from Wood Islands and Port Borden. The latter, as we have seen, is to be replaced by a combination of bridge, causeway, and tunnel, and will greatly ease communications on this route.

NEW BRUNSWICK

The western half of New Brunswick represents a continuation of the Appalachian lands of the neighbouring state of Maine. Older Palæozoic rocks together with granitic intrusions give rise to plateau lands whose even summits rise to between 1500 and 2000 feet; these are deeply trenched by tributaries of the Saint John, Restigouche, and Miramichi rivers. An outlying portion of the plateau extends in the form of a highland belt close to and parallel with the north shore of the Bay of Fundy, and exposes Pre-Cambrian material to the east of Saint John.

The region suffers from a rather cold climate, is largely forested, sparsely peopled, and poorly provided with roads. Its wealth – present and potential – lies in its timber. The few towns have pulp and paper mills and are supply-centres for forest workers and sportsmen. They include Edmundston, a railway town on the Saint John river close to the United States frontier, Campbellton, at the head of navigation of the Restigouche river, and Dalhousie, a few miles farther east.

The eastern half of the province (east of a line joining Fredericton and Bathurst) forms the greater part of the Carboniferous basin that we have already met in Nova Scotia. Its rim is composed of limestones, which rise in rocky ridges to about 600 feet above sea-level; within this rim the surface is developed on the sterile sandstones of the Millstone Grit, though these are masked by glacial drift. The Quaternary ice sheets have disrupted the drainage, and there are many lakes and marshes. Coal is worked at Minto and Chipman, about 60 miles north of Saint John, and is known to outcrop along the shore of Chaleur bay.

The Carboniferous basin, with its lower altitude, enjoys warmer summers than the plateau to the west. Most of the land remains under forest, but there are small clearings where the forester or fisherman can engage in part-time farming. Bathurst, Chatham, and Newcastle, in the north of the basin, are lumber or pulp-mill centres; Moncton in the south is a commercial focus of roads and railways; and a dairy industry has been developed to supply the needs of these towns.

The valley of the Saint John river is more developed than other parts of New Brunswick, and may be considered a separate region. The river rises in Maine, and for 70–80 miles forms the frontier between that state and New Brunswick. Beyond the Grand Falls the river strays east of the meridian that forms the frontier; after passing Woodstock it turns almost due east to Fredericton, and reaches the Bay of Fundy at Saint John.

The upper portion of this valley, from about Hartland up-stream, shares in the important potato-growing industry which we have already noticed in Maine (p. 16). There are many storage sheds, and a starch factory at Hartland; while a hydro-electric plant at Grand Falls supplies power to the district.

Fredericton was settled by Loyalists in 1783, and in view of its central position was chosen as the capital for the new province. The town stands at the head of navigation of the Saint John river, is an administrative and commercial centre, and houses the University of New Brunswick. Its industries include woodworking and clothing, but are on a relatively small scale; its population amounts to only about 20,000.

Saint John, although not the capital, is by far the largest city in the province (population of metropolitan area, 1961, 95,563). In site and functions it is very similar to Halifax. Both are rail terminals (Saint John is the Canadian Pacific terminal); both are ice-free ports which enjoy a busy winter season; in both the harbours are formed by drowned valleys. In Saint John the harbour has three interlocking peninsulas, and its mouth is protected by two long breakwaters. In spite of a mean tidal range of 28 feet, the commerce is conducted at open piers. Repair facilities include one of the world's largest dry docks.

The strange reversing falls are at the head of the harbour, where it is constricted to 350 feet and is spanned by road and rail bridges. At low tide the river, penned between rocky cliffs, pours over a 15-foot ledge into the harbour below; but at high tide the sea water rises higher than the river, and the falls operate in reverse.

The industries of the port include pulp and paper manufacture, marine and locomotive engineering, sugar-refining and oil-refining.

New Brunswick depends largely on its forests: they cover 80 per cent. of its area, and their products are the chief source of its wealth and are valued at about 225 million dollars. Fishing occupies a much lower place in the economy: the catches consist mainly of lobsters from the coastal waters of the north-east and sardines from the Bay of Fundy. Farming is restricted to comparatively small, favoured districts. More than half the improved land is grazed or mown for hay, and dairying has developed round all the large towns. In the valley of the lower Saint John river there is a specialized fruit- and vegetable-growing area, but the leading single farm product by value is the potato crop of the upper valley: this provides fully one-third of the total farm income of about 55 million dollars.

Approximately of equal value to all the farm products is the total output of minerals in the province. Part of this is represented by coal, whose annual production is of the order of a million tons; but other minerals are known to be present in great variety. Those worked include granite, limestone, oil, and natural gas. The most significant venture is the exploitation of lead–zinc–copper deposits in the Bathurst–Newcastle district in the north-east of the province: two companies are in operation.

APPALACHIAN QUEBEC

We include Appalachian Quebec in this chapter since it has clear affinities with the Atlantic provinces. It comprises two main divisions: the Gaspé peninsula and the Eastern Townships, and these are joined by a narrow belt of rugged country, the Notre Dame mountains.

The whole region forms a continuation of the Appalachian zone of the United States, and exhibits the usual north-east and south-west trend, though the structural units are less well developed in Canada. The rocks are of early Palæozoic age, the most widespread being the Ordovician. A central belt of Cambrian material forms the core of the Eastern Townships: in the Gaspé peninsula Devonian and Silurian strata join with the Ordovician. Folded during Carbo-Permian times, the strata have been hardened into limestones, sandstones, shales, and conglomerates. Molten magma forced its way into the sedimentary rocks, and in these areas there are now valuable mineral deposits – the asbestos of the Thetford district and the copper–zinc of the eastern end of the Shickshock mountains.

The present landscape can be explained only in terms of its erosional history. As in North Wales, the surface has been peneplained and then re-elevated more than once, and newer platforms have been cut at the expense of older. Three erosion surfaces have been recognized. The highest, at over 3500 feet, is seen in the summits of the Shickshocks (Snowdon is about the same height); the middle platform, at over 1000 feet, is widely developed in the region; the lowest, below 300 feet, forms the coastal fringes and the St Lawrence Lowland.

As in the rest of the Atlantic provinces, the Quaternary ice sheets have left their marks in the form of smoothed and striated rock surfaces, U-shaped valleys, lake-filled rock basins, and disturbed river systems. The soils, especially in the uplands, are often stony, and there are many outcrops of bare rock. In the valleys and lowlands there are deposits of coarse sandy and gravelly outwash material whose soils tend to be leached and lacking in plant food. Only in restricted areas are there relatively fertile soils derived from loamy boulder clay, where farming is productive. Throughout the region forests occupy the greatest area, and usually form the chief source of income.

The Eastern Townships

The term 'Eastern Townships' is applied to the land bounded to the west by the St Lawrence Lowland and to the east by the international border. It signifies the land to the east of Montreal, which was surveyed when England assumed the administration of what had hitherto been French Canada. The early settlers included many Loyalists, but today almost everywhere French-Canadians are in the majority. It is a hilly land, but there are many lakes and potential water-power sites, and deep valleys where farming can be pursued.

As in Quebec province as a whole, the farmer concentrates mainly on his dairy herd. Most of the milk is condensed or converted into butter or cheese. There are scores of dairy plants throughout the region, and the Eastern Townships account for one-fifth of the provincial total of dairy produce. Specially favoured areas raise peas, beans, sweet corn, and tomatoes for canning, or grow apples, strawberries, and raspberries. Bordering Vermont, this is also the chief Canadian district for maple sugar. The average 'sugar orchard' contains between 500 and 3000 trees.

The landscape is very similar to that of the American region to the south, and the Eastern Townships have been named the 'New England of Canada'. Many towns engage in skilled industries, such as Granby (pop. 15,000), with its rubber and tobacco factories, and Cowansville (3600), with silk, footwear, and furniture industries. The largest commercial centre is Sherbrooke (1961 population: 66,554), an important road focus and at the junction of five railways. It draws hydro-electricity from the local 100-foot falls of the Magog river; its industries include hosiery, rayon, cotton and woollen textiles, the manufacture of mining machinery and locomotive parts, and the production of jewellery.

But, unlike New England, the Eastern Townships possess an important mineral district, where 60 per cent. of the free world's asbestos is mined. It occurs in veins of serpentine, and is worked in great open quarries which currently produce about a million tons annually. A row

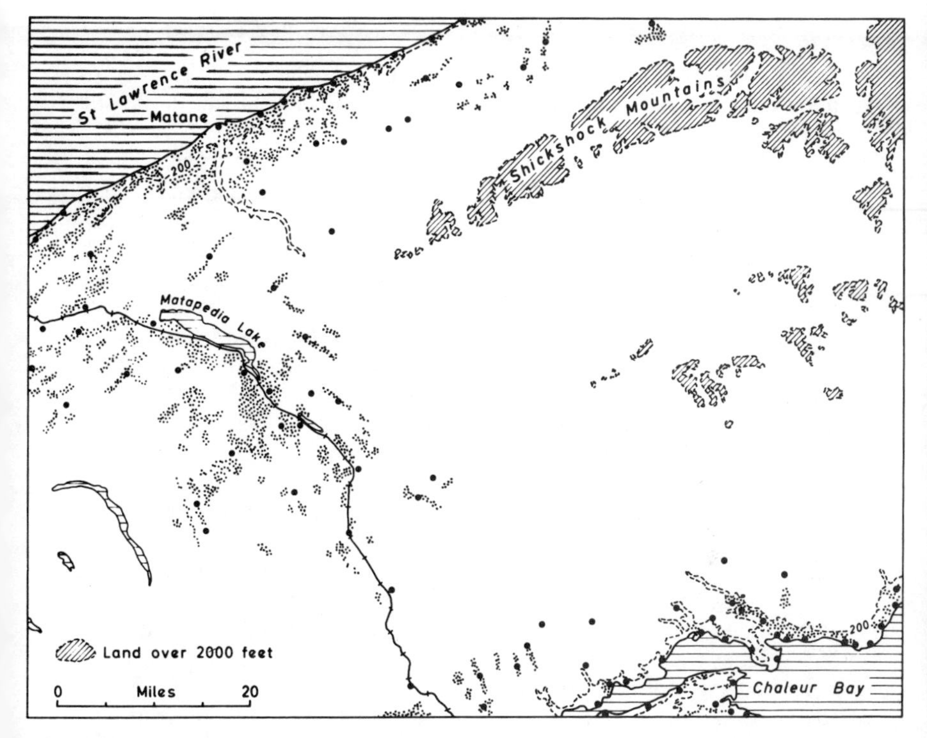

Fig. 93. PART OF THE GASPÉ PENINSULA

The map covers the western part of the peninsula. The black spots represent villages and hamlets, and the stippled areas cleared land. The rest is forest, and is uninhabited. Notice the contrast between the north and south coasts. The two contours are for 200 and 2000 feet. *Based on the official 1 : 250,000 map, Natane sheet.*

of settlements in the north-east of the region depends on the asbestos industry. It includes the appropriately named Asbestos, Black Lake, Coleraine, Robertsonville, Danville, and the largest of them, Thetford Mines (20,000). There are local manufactures of roofing, insulating, and fireproof materials, but the bulk of the material is exported in the raw state, mainly to the United States and the United Kingdom.

The Gaspé Peninsula

The Eastern Townships are joined to the Gaspé peninsula by a hilly, wooded district containing few inhabitants, and where communications are transverse rather than longitudinal. Thus the Trans-Canada Highway, following the Saint John river valley in New Brunswick, passes through Cabano with its giant paper-mill, then crosses the Notre Dame mountains to reach the St Lawrence at Rivière-du-Loup, and turns south to reach Quebec city. The narrow coastal plain is threaded by a single road, which links together sawmilling and woodworking towns and villages such as Montmagny (6500), Rimouski (15,000), and Matane (8000).

The Gaspé peninsula is composed of a mass of folded, peneplained, and raised older Palæozoic rocks. In their midst a long and narrow belt has been further raised, and is bounded by steep fault scarp edges: this forms the Shickshock mountains, which reach the highest elevations in eastern Canada (Mt Jacques Cartier, 4350). The northern shore of the peninsula is inhospitable, straight, bordered by cliffs, and is unsuitable for farming. The southern shore, however, is more indented, offers havens to fishing-vessels, and provides opportunities for small-scale agriculture. None of the settlements are large enough to be called towns: they are fishing-ports and sawmill centres. Where agriculture is possible – for example, in the Chandler district – the farmers grow potatoes and rear dairy cattle, sheep, and poultry.

Apart from coastal strips and land bordering the single transverse road, virtually the whole of the peninsula is under forest. There are more than 2000 square miles without a paved road, a hamlet, or school (Fig. 93). But since 1954 an important copper-mining venture has been inaugurated at the eastern end of the Shickshock mountains. There are 700 million tons of copper ore known to be present; a new town has been built at Murdochville, and new roads link the mine and town to the existing port of Mont Louis, on the north shore of the peninsula. The smelter is designed to produce 125 tons of metallic copper daily. The project appears to be prospering, and the company spent a further 12 million dollars during 1965–66.

CHAPTER NINE

THE PRAIRIES

Our title is deliberate: we discuss in this chapter not the prairie provinces but the prairies. Our purpose is to describe and explain the geographical regions of the United States and Canada, and these rarely correspond with political units. We are concerned here with a region in which a former cover of natural grassland has been transformed into one of the world's granaries – a region whose emblems are the elevator and the combine harvester. More than three-quarters of the provinces of Alberta, Saskatchewan, and Manitoba consist not of prairie but of the lake, swamp, and forest characteristic of the Laurentian Shield.

The extent of the region can be realized very readily from any map whose scale is sufficiently large to indicate the railway halts (Fig. 94), for to the prairie farm the railway is a lifeline. The north-eastern limit of the region is marked approximately by Winnipeg, and from here wheat-growing extends southward into North and South Dakota and the neighbouring strip of Minnesota. The American portion of the Wheat Belt, however, we consider with the Great Plains (Chapter Seven). In Saskatchewan the northern limit of the prairies is in the latitude of Prince Albert; in Alberta Edmonton marks their north-western corner, and the longitude of Calgary their western edge. They do not extend southward into Montana, where there is insufficient rainfall for grain cultivation.

Physical Conditions

Essentially the prairies form a level and relatively high plateau tilted slightly downward to the north and east. From about 1000 feet in the east the land rises to over 3000 feet in the west, where Calgary stands at 3450 feet above sea-level. Snowdon summit in Wales is only 100 feet higher.

Geologically the greater part of the prairies is developed on horizontally disposed strata of Cretaceous age; these rest with a major unconformity upon Devonian, Silurian, and Ordovician rocks, and it is these older strata which form the solid foundation of the Red River Basin to the north and south of Winnipeg. They strike N.N.W. and S.S.E. in three relatively narrow bands, each about 40 miles wide, and have influenced the surface topography: Lake Winnipeg lies in the Ordovician, Lakes Manitoba and Winnipegosis are in the Devonian, while the Silurian rocks form the slightly higher land between.

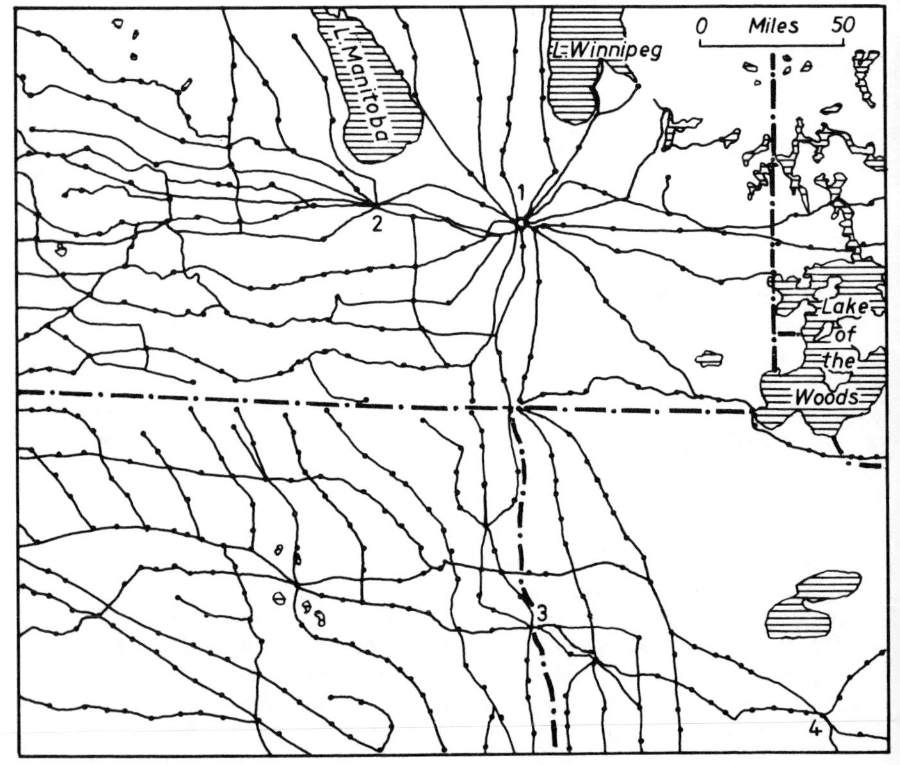

1 Winnipeg 2. Portage la Prairie 3 Grand Forks 4 Minneapolis — St.Paul

Fig. 94. RAILWAYS IN PART OF THE EASTERN PRAIRIES

Through the middle of this area runs the international boundary: to the north is Manitoba, and to the south are North Dakota and Minnesota. The boundary forms the conventional division between the prairies to the north and the Great Plains to the south. There is no sudden break in the physical conditions, but the map clearly shows an economic frontier along this line: few railways cross the border, and the Canadian and American systems are self-contained. The Canadian grain is channelled through Winnipeg, while much of the American grain passes through Minneapolis–St Paul. The black lines represent railways, and the spots stations. The railway net has a fairly clear eastern limit, which corresponds with the edge of the Laurentian Shield.

These lake plains may be regarded as the lowest of three prairie 'steps'. As we notice below, they formed part of the floor of glacial Lake Agassiz. Physiographically they are distinct from the main body of the prairies; but geographically they are a vital part of the region, and we have no hesitation in combining them with the prairies.

The lake plains are overlooked on the west by a broken scarp – the Manitoba escarpment – which represents the eastern edge of the Cretaceous beds: its highest parts are seen in the Porcupine, Duck,

Riding, and Pembina mountains, which rise to about 2000 feet above sea-level and break the monotony of the prairie landscape.

To the west extends the level, treeless, windy surface of the Cretaceous rocks, as far as the eye can see. This is the second prairie step. Its western limit is formed by the rising ground of a fairly gentle edge – sufficiently prominent, however, to be recognized and named by the early settlers. This, the Missouri Coteau, can be traced southward for many miles into the United States, where it runs east of and parallel to the Missouri river. The Missouri Coteau does not correspond to a geological outcrop, but appears to be the edge of an erosion surface.

West of the Coteau is the third prairie step – the highest and the widest of the three. There are, indeed, relics of an even higher surface in the form of remnants of Tertiary deposits, which account for the Cypress hills and Wood and Turtle mountains: these tracts of elevated and broken country interrupt the broad sweep of prairie farming.

The prairies were covered by the Quaternary ice sheets, so that the soils are derived from glacial drifts rather than from the underlying 'solid' deposits. Several advances and retreats took place, first, perhaps, from the north, later from the east. At one stage the Missouri Coteau formed a barrier to the ice advance; later its front rested along a line running to the north-west of Brandon, where there are prominent moraines.

When the ice had retreated to about latitude 55° N. a vast lake was impounded in front of it – 'Lake Agassiz' – whose remnants are now seen in Lakes Winnipeg, Manitoba, Winnipegosis, Rainy Lake, and the Lake of the Woods. At first Lake Agassiz drained southward, and only after a further retreat of the ice was the existing direction of drainage established – towards the Nelson river. In the bed of the lake, clays and silts accumulated to thicknesses of 10–50 feet, and although these overlap the edge of the Canadian Shield to the east, there is a fairly firm boundary to prairie farming in this direction, formed by the western edge of the Pre-Cambrian rocks (Fig. 95).

Mingling with the lake clays and silts are earlier glacial deposits: some of the smaller islands in Lake Winnipeg are considered to be drumlins, and the north–south alignment of the peninsulas thrusting into Lakes Manitoba and Winnipegosis are related to the existence of esker ridges.

The soils to the north and east of Winnipeg are thin and limy, but elsewhere in this lowest prairie step they are typically black soils: they are deep (1–2 feet deep), retentive of moisture, and rich in organic material. The black soils continue westward in the shape of a crescent, to form the outer zone of the prairies, passing through Brandon and Edmonton as far as Calgary. Grain yields are high, so that the farms are relatively small in area, averaging about 320 acres, and in this moister

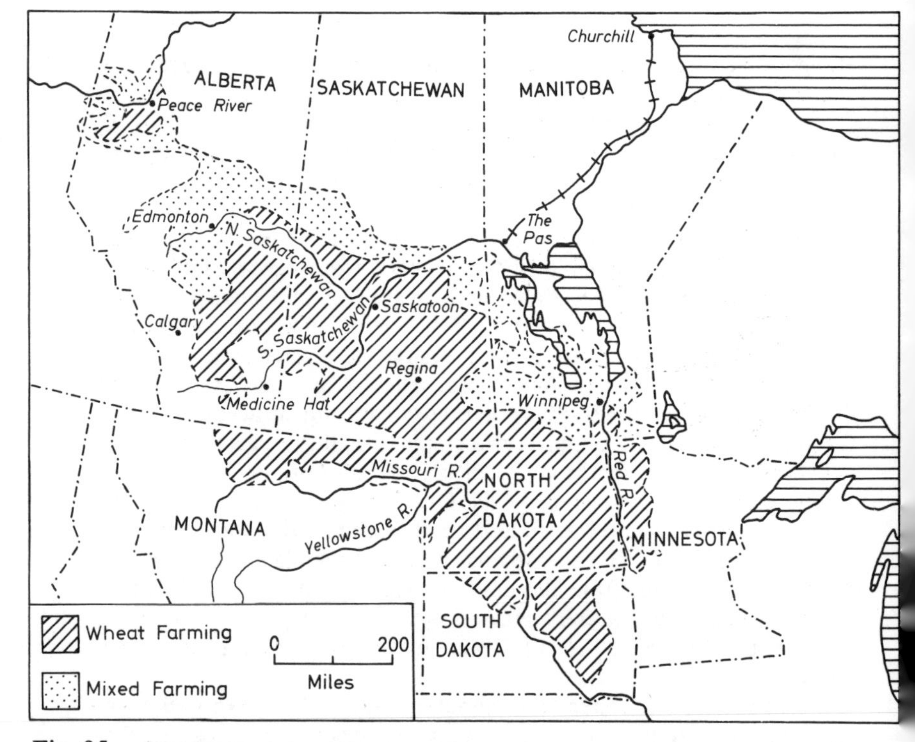

Fig. 95. THE EXTENT OF THE PRAIRIES ACCORDING TO OFFICIAL SOURCES
This map is compiled from Canadian and United States official maps relating to their respective territories. The Medicine Hat area of southern Alberta and Saskatchewan is too dry for extensive wheat cultivation, and these conditions continue south of the international border into Montana, so that the extension of the wheat-farming area here should be treated with some caution.

belt of the prairies mixed and livestock farms are more typical than purely arable farms.

As one moves south-westward the rainfall diminishes; the layer of deposited lime and other salts approaches nearer to the surface, the soil becomes shallower, and its colour changes through dark brown to brown. These soils contain a smaller proportion of organic matter, and in the driest areas are soon exhausted after repeated cultivation. Wind erosion can become a hazard, as it did in the 1930's: the prairies had their dustbowl similar to that of the American Great Plains; its centre was near Medicine Hat in Alberta (Fig. 96).

Climate

Far from oceanic influences, the prairies experience a continental climate. The summers can be exceedingly hot, with temperatures in the 90's; but the winters are bitterly cold. On the international border mid-winter average temperatures are about 5°F.; during the day the thermo-

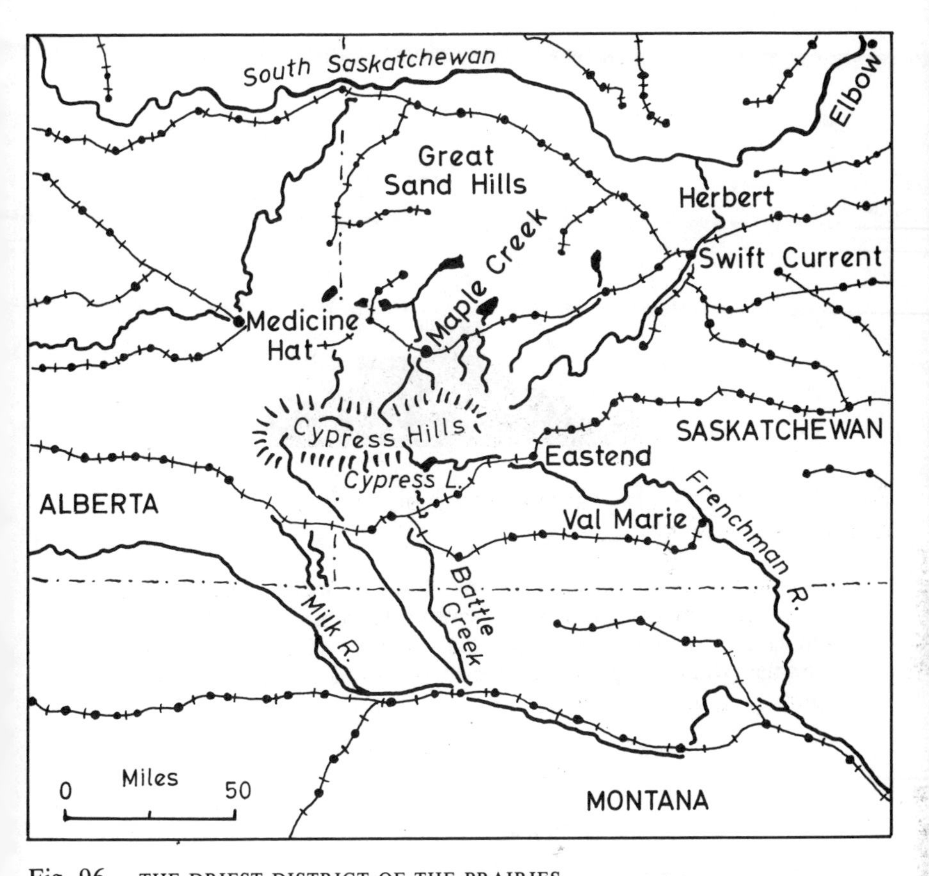

Fig. 96. THE DRIEST DISTRICT OF THE PRAIRIES

In the area illustrated, cultivation requires the aid of irrigation or dry-farming techniques. The places named are mentioned in the text.

meter rises to about 20° (still twelve degrees of frost!) and in the night it falls to −10°. At Winnipeg, where the north winds have blown over 400 miles of frozen lake, the average midwinter temperature is −4°F. (Fig. 97).

During the long, cold winter all outside farm work ceases. In May after the thaw the farmer with his hired help furiously operates the machinery for planting the seed. The grain grows for about twelve weeks; then there is another burst of activity, harvesting and transporting the grain to the local elevator. In many farms the work is finished in five months; and if he can afford it the farmer will take his family to Florida.

The average annual precipitation ranges from 20 inches at Winnipeg to less than 14 inches at Medicine Hat, but about half the area of the

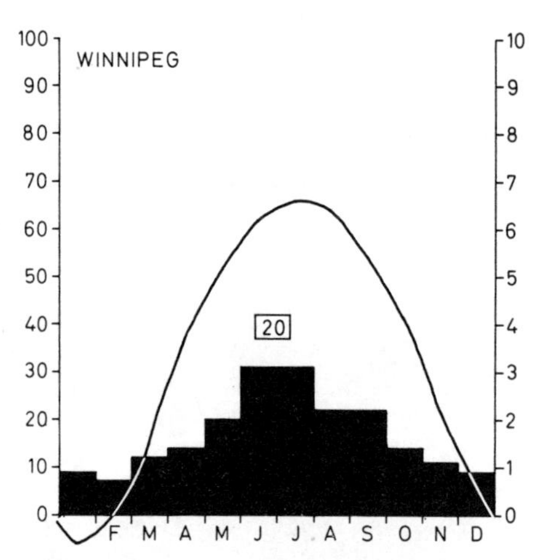

Fig. 97. WINNIPEG: TEMPERATURE AND PRECIPITATION
For key see Fig. 46 (p. 117).

Canadian prairies receives between 14 and 16 inches annually. In common with continental climates elsewhere, the prairies have the important advantage for grain-cultivation, that the bulk of the rainfall occurs in summer, when the plants have their greatest need for water. A typical rainfall regime is as follows:

Spring	4·4 inches
Summer	7·9
Autumn	3·1
Winter	1·5

If the climate were reliable many of the problems of the prairie farmer would be solved; but unfortunately there are wide variations from year to year, and within a run of years. North Dakota is sufficiently close to the Canadian prairies to be of interest: its average precipitation is computed at 16·9 inches per annum: in 1927, 21·5 inches occurred, but in 1936 only 8·8 inches. The climate of any particular season depends in fact upon the interaction of three variable elements: these are dry winds from the west; cold, dry air from the north; and warm, moist air from the south. The influence of the dry westerly winds is greatest in Alberta and least in Manitoba; that of the polar air is prominent in the northern limits of the prairies, where the growing season falls below 100 days; humid air is experienced in the southern border, where it brings its own problems.

An important sphere of Government activity has been the development of appropriate strains of wheat to suit these different climatic conditions of the prairie borders. Until 1910 the prairies were dominated by a single strain of wheat – Red Fife – named after an Ontario farmer,

David Fife, who in 1842 had the foresight to save a single plant which survived from a consignment from Danzig via Glasgow. Red Fife was crossed with a variety from India, and the resulting product was named Marquis. Marquis inherited the excellent milling and baking qualities of Red Fife, but it was more resistant to disease, and in addition it ripened a week earlier. By 1919 almost the whole of the prairie crop consisted of Marquis.

Marquis remained the dominant variety until about 1940, when it yielded in its turn to Thatcher, one of its offspring. The milling and baking qualities of Thatcher are superior to those of Marquis, and it is an even earlier wheat; and in 1961 Thatcher was sown in 52 per cent. of the prairie wheat area. Second in importance by area is Selkirk, which occupied 27·1 per cent. of the wheat-land: it has been developed to resist the fungus disease stem rust, which is liable to attack the grain in the warmer and damper parts of the prairies.

In the drier areas of southern Alberta and Saskatchewan the main pest is the sawfly: this lays its eggs in the stem; the grub travels down inside the stem, and at ground level chews it out in a ring, so that the wheat topples over. In 1946 Rescue was brought into general cultivation: this has a solid stem, and is thus resistant to sawfly. It was followed in 1952 by Chinook, which in addition is of higher quality, and has a greater resistance to drought. In 1961 these two varieties occupied 7·7 per cent. of the wheat area.

In the northern fringe, with its shorter growing season, quick-maturing varieties are available. Garnet is grown where frost is a real hazard, and since 1947 has been joined by Saunders. Together these two account for 4·9 per cent. of the wheat area.

The prairies have been divided into zones in which growth conditions are relatively uniform, and the agricultural service recommends varieties which are appropriate to each zone – not only for wheat, but also for oats, barley, and flax. These zones in Alberta are indicated in Fig. 98. Thatcher is recommended throughout; Chinook and Rescue in zone 1 and in most of 2; Selkirk in the north of zone 2 and in irrigated areas; and Saunders in zones 3 and 4.

The evolution and testing of new strains is a highly skilled procedure which requires the resources of Government organization. Only after exhaustive trials through eleven generations is a new variety released for general distribution.

The Course of Settlement

In its natural state the prairie consisted of a wide expanse of grassland. The individual grasses were from three to ten feet high, and were interspersed with a variety of flowering plants. Trees were to be seen only

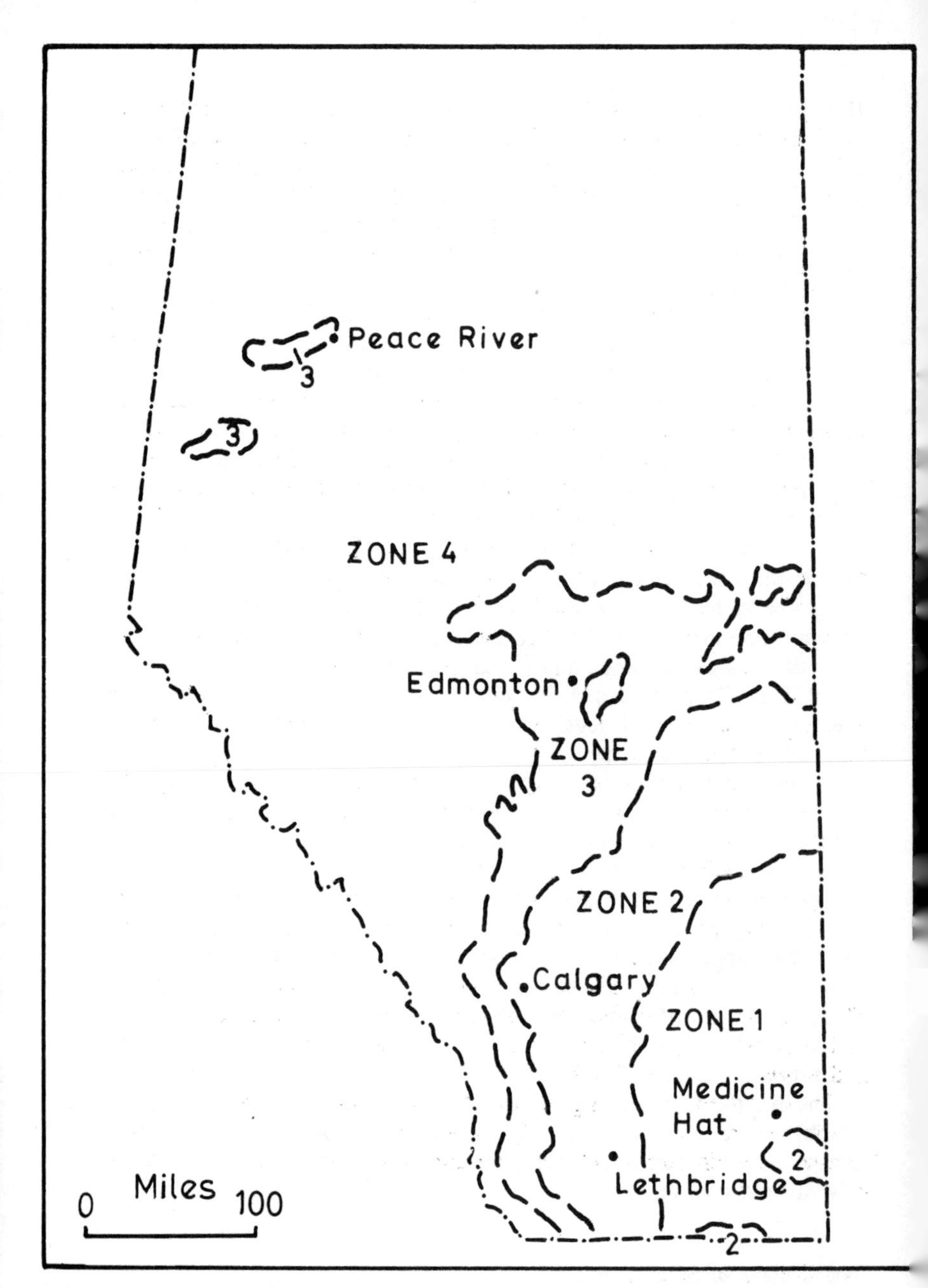

Fig. 98. VARIETAL ZONES OF ALBERTA

This map has been simplified from a pamphlet issued to farmers by the Alberta Department of Agriculture, and illustrates the results of research on climate and plant-breeding. In the original each zone is divided into sub-zones. The advice given relates to varieties of wheat, barley, oats, and flax appropriate to each sub-zone, and in addition the characteristics of each variety are listed.

along the watercourses. This was excellent grazing-land, both for the wild buffalo and for herds of cattle.

The westward-moving settlers reached the edge of this grassland about 1850. It was an unfamiliar landscape which met them; and there was a scarcity of water, timber, and road-building materials. The prairie sod was tougher than that farther east; but once its extraordinary fertility was demonstrated, the spread of cultivation was assured.

Effective occupation of the prairies, however, dates only from about 1870, and is thus less than a century old. By this time the settlement of the American Great Plains was already well advanced, and we need to inquire what it was that delayed the exploitation of the potentially fertile lands on the Canadian side of the border.

Their position in relation to neighbouring physiographic provinces provides the answer. Access to the region from the east was hindered by the Laurentian Shield, which pinches out the prairies against the international border, and presents a barrier of forest, lake, and swamp to would-be settlers. In contrast, the American Great Plains are bordered to the east by the fertile Central Lowlands with their long-grass pastures inviting penetration from this direction.

Until 1868, moreover, the prairies formed part of the vast domain of the Hudson's Bay Company – Rupert's Land – which had been granted to it for the purpose of the fur trade. The company established trading-posts such as the Selkirk settlement on the site of the later Winnipeg; but it did not encourage occupation; and at the last census of the company in 1856 their territory of about 2 million square miles had an estimated population of only 6600 'whites' and about 50,000 Indians.

In 1868, in accordance with the Rupert's Land Act, the Canadian Government was empowered to buy land from the Company, and for the first time effective settlement of the prairies became legally possible. An extensive survey of the region between Lake Superior and the Rockies had been carried out (1857–60) on behalf of the Government by Captain Palliser. Using the vegetation as his guide, he reported that the drier south-western 'triangle' was unsuited to close settlement, and that the most valuable land formed a crescent-shaped area to the north and east (the 'Park' Belt).

Palliser's survey strongly influenced the course of settlement, which was at first confined to the 'Park' Belt. Its occupation was hastened by the knowledge that the Americans were extending their railway net in the direction of the prairies. It is significant that the first railway into the prairies was American: it ran from St Paul to Winnipeg (1878). A considerable rise in the price of grain in 1867 provided an additional incentive to those who sought land in the prairies.

The early arrivals burnt grass as fuel, stored the rain-water in tanks, and dug wells 200 feet or more in depth, harnessing the wind to pump them. The problem of fencing was solved in the early 70's by the invention of barbed wire; reaping, threshing, and mowing machines were already in use, though they had to be drawn by oxen.

Close settlement, however, waited for the railways. With commendable speed, the Canadian Pacific Company surveyed and constructed an 'All Canadian' route across the Shield north of the lakes: it reached Winnipeg in 1883, and Vancouver only two years later. The second transcontinental reached the Pacific in 1896; and from these two trunk routes the prairie railway net evolved. With only horse-drawn carts to feed them, the railways were the only effective means of transport. The system was planned so that most farms were within five miles of a station, and about ten miles was adopted as the limit for a farmer's haul by cart.

First to be occupied were the fertile plains of the Red river: these were settled well before 1900, and their strip farms contrast strongly with the later rectangular layouts (Plate 9). From 1900 till 1909 the greatest advances were made in the 'Park' Belt of Saskatchewan and Alberta: they took the form of grants to settlers by the railway companies, which owned vast areas – thus the Canadian Pacific Railway had title to 25 million acres. In 1909 the prairies were thrown open to homesteaders, and lands were taken up to the south of the 'Park' Belt.

Settlement was based on a rectangular system which has impressed its pattern on the map and on the ground. Roads and boundaries were laid out parallel to the lines of latitude and longitude. A square of side six miles formed a 'township'; this contained 36 'sections', each of one square mile (or 640 acres). The usual grant to a settler consisted of a quarter-section, or 160 acres, though in later years these were often combined to form more economic units, as we see in the farm described later (p. 269).

The influx of settlers which began in the 1890's reached a peak about 1913. The farmer was offered free land, and the labourer profitable employment. The Canadian Government opened agencies on the continent of Europe, and the immigrants flocked in. Between 1901 and 1911 Alberta and Saskatchewan quadrupled their populations.

The fields were large, the growing season was short, and labour was scarce: all this favoured the extensive use of machinery. The busiest

---

Plate 9. PART OF THE RED RIVER VALLEY SOUTH OF WINNIPEG

The soils in this area are black, deep, and fertile loams and clays; they are derived from the silts of the former glacial Lake Agassiz. The winters are long and bitterly cold, but the summers are sunny and surprisingly warm. The growing season, of about 160 days, is sufficient for grain, sugar-beet, maize, sunflowers, and vegetables. Settlement in the district dates from about 1820: homesteads were built along the main road, and their lands ran back from it in long narrow strips. The layout is in striking contrast to the later rectilinear pattern of the surveys farther west.

Photo Royal Canadian Air Force.

times were the sowing season (April–May) and the harvest (August) – then the whole village would help in the fields – yet for the rest of the year there was little work to do. The father of one of the authors took up a teaching post near Winnipeg; but he left when he discovered that his contract included helping with the harvest!

The progress of settlement in Saskatchewan is revealing, for this province contains the core of the prairies. Between 1901 and 1906 its population almost trebled, and though later growth was never again so rapid, there was a 12 per cent. increase even during the years 1926–31. The early settlements were based on the trading-posts and the railways of the east, and by 1900 there was a triangle of close settlement with a base on the eastern boundary of the province and a spearhead at Regina. In the centre and west there was a rapid growth until about 1921, and many ventured into the drier south-west to practise dry-farming methods.[1]

While the largest single group of immigrants was of British origin, many were from the United States. In a single year (1913) 139,000 people crossed the border into Canada (though this may in part represent a redistribution of population within the prairies). Many came from the Continent, and the ethnic origins of the prairie farmers still reflect the period of early settlement. In the 1951 census returns the origins of the inhabitants of Saskatchewan were given as follows: British Isles, 42·3 per cent.; Germany, 16·3; Ukraine, 9·5; Scandinavia, 7·5; France, 6·2; Netherlands, 3·6; Poland, 3·1; Native Indian, 2·7; Russian, 2·3; Others, 6·5. Alberta shows very similar proportions.

During the five years between 1931 and 1936, however, the population of Saskatchewan was almost stationary: it increased by less than one per cent., and this is so far below the rate of natural increase that it implies that 50,000 to 60,000 people or more must have left the province. These bald figures describe in statistical terms the great human disaster of the 1930's. From 1929 onward for seven years there was drought. It was not confined to the prairies, for it spread south and west from the Kansas border as far as California, and everywhere it brought ruin to the farmer. The crops failed; the soil turned to dust; and the dust began to blow about. It clogged machinery and the wind-pumps; it piled against the fences and began to bury them; it irritated the throat and lungs; it blotted out the sun.

The drought years corresponded with a period of low farm prices – the Great Depression. The price of cattle was so low that it would not cover the cost of transport. Money was so scarce that the prairie farmer resorted to barter, and some began to speak of the establishment of a new independent state with an outlet at Churchill, on the new Hudson

[1] Stella W. Alty, 'The Influence of Climatic and Other Geographic Factors upon the Growth and Distribution of Population in Saskatchewan', *Geography*, XXIV (1939), pp. 10–23.

Bay railway. The shops and the schools closed, and 50,000 families abandoned their homes and left the western prairies.

The causes of the disaster were in part climatic and economic; but they were rooted also in bad farming. For a generation wheat had been grown almost continuously with little thought of restoring the fertility of the soil. It was invaded by weeds such as wild oats and wild mustard, and there were plagues of grasshoppers. Once the structure of the soil was damaged it was more likely to be blown by the wind. Often the farm was regarded not as a way of life but as a means to make money quickly – suitcase farming, as it has been described.

The bitter experience of the 1930's has brought about some permanent readjustments in prairie farming, particularly in the drier fringe. In addition to his grain, the farmer now rears cattle and poultry. He ploughs along instead of across the contours; he plants his land in alternate strips so that last year's stubble protects this year's corn from the wind; he leaves half his land fallow so that the crop can draw on the accumulated moisture of two years (Plate 10). The Government helps him to control weeds, to combat pests, and to conserve water.

In 1935 the Canadian Parliament passed the Prairie Farm Rehabilitation Act: this provided public money to restore parts of the prairies which had been damaged by drought and drifting soil, and authorized the resettlement of displaced farmers. In Saskatchewan about 200 irrigation projects have been inaugurated since the passing of the Act. We may illustrate from a small part of the far south-west of the province (Fig. 96, p. 257).

Here are the Cypress hills, which, with a summit at 4810, rise 1000–1500 feet above the surrounding country, and receive a precipitation of 21 inches, while the rest of the land is very dry. Formerly this water ran to waste with the spring snow-melt, so that in summer the creeks ran dry, or at best were mere trickles. Now the water is channelled into Cypress lake. From here it is released for irrigation purposes into Battle creek to the south, and into Frenchman river in the east. Frenchman river with its two reservoirs serves 9000 acres of irrigated land.

A farmer here in 1937 lost the whole of his crop and reduced his cattle herd to three animals. Now he cuts two hay crops a year from 90 acres of alfalfa and harvests 50 acres of oats. These crops feed his herd of 300 cattle in winter, and in summer they are allocated a proportion of the communal grazing land of the district. About 4000 cattle are grazing now where in 1937 only 150 had survived. Farther north there are similar schemes in operation. A dam at East End irrigates 4000 acres, and in an area of inland drainage north of the Cypress hills 2600 acres are irrigated at Maple creek. On Swift Current creek a dam supplies the town of Swift Current, and irrigates 30,000 acres of land between that town and Herbert.

None of these, however, is comparable in size to the great Gardiner Dam which was officially opened in 1967 about 60 miles south of Saskatoon. This is both an irrigation and a power project. The main dam is over three miles long, and rises 210 feet above the river-bed. When full the reservoir which it impounds will be 140 miles long, and its water, in addition to generating about 44,000 kW, will irrigate large areas between Elbow and Saskatoon.

Recent developments by the Prairie Farm Rehabilitation Administration should not imply that irrigation is a new feature in the prairies. For a generation or more irrigation has been practised in southern Alberta, particularly in the neighbourhood of Lethbridge (Plate 11). It is estimated that there are now almost a million acres of farm-land in the province where agriculture is independent of rainfall. Specialist crops of the dry areas of southern Alberta include oilseeds and sugar-beet, the output of the latter reaching about half a million tons annually. Eighty-five miles east of Lethbridge, in one of the driest parts of Alberta, is the small town of Taber: its prosperity is linked with its huge sugar factory, and it has also a potato-processing plant.

Prairie Farming

The prairies are not solely producers of grain: mixed farming is general in the northern and eastern fringes, where the climate is cooler and moister; and, as we have seen, in the drier parts too there has been a recent trend towards a more balanced system of farming (Fig. 99). In Manitoba nearly half and in Alberta about one-third of the farm income is provided by stock-rearing. Maize is also grown, in rotation, but it will not ripen satisfactorily and is used for silage.

Nevertheless, over large tracts of the prairies the characteristic enterprise is the specialist grain farm, without a single animal. Wheat is the chief grain, but it does not always dominate, except in the export trade. Oats come second, with barley third, and these two combined often exceed the acreage of wheat. Both are grown mainly for the feeding of livestock, and after the local needs of mixed farms have been met there is a considerable surplus available for the eastern provinces. Animals can digest barley more easily than oats, and it fattens cattle and pigs very well: since it has a short growing season, it is particularly valuable in the

---

Plate 10. A DRY-FARMING AREA IN SOUTH-WESTERN ALBERTA

At the top of the photograph (= west) is the small centre of Champion, about 40 miles N.N.W. of Lethbridge and about the same distance east of the foothills of the Rocky Mountains. In this relatively dry area (Lethbridge: m.a.r. 16 inches) it is necessary to conserve moisture, and this is achieved by alternating strips of sown crops with summer fallow – hence the striped appearance of the land. Eight of the wider strips comprise one square mile – a 'section' (see p. 262). The crop consists almost exclusively of wheat, but there are also small proportions of barley and oats. Notice the grain elevators along the railway at Champion.

Photo Royal Canadian Air Force. Crown copyright reserved

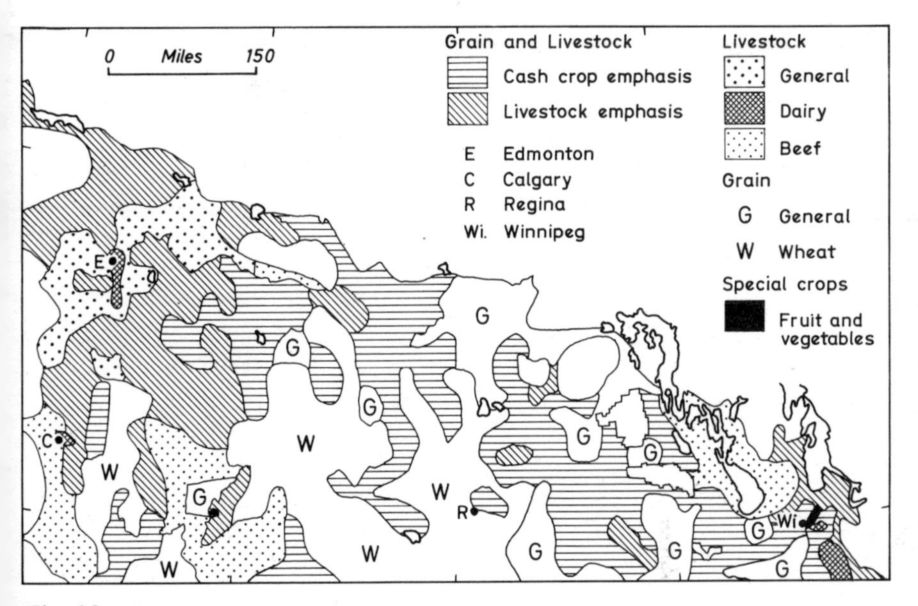

Fig. 99. THE PRAIRIES: GENERALIZED LAND USE

Specialized wheat farming is characteristic of the central prairies: for example, round Regina (where the land use is plotted on a larger scale in Fig. 106, p. 282). As one moves west livestock farming becomes more prominent, with an emphasis on beef cattle in the dry south-west. Dairy farming is restricted to the small districts in which the cities exert a demand for fresh milk.

cooler northern areas. As in the case of wheat, appropriate varieties of oats and barley have been evolved to suit the different climatic conditions of the prairie borders.

In addition to the grains, there are smaller acreages of specialist crops such as flax seed and sunflower (both grown for their oil), peas and beans, soya beans, and sugar-beet.

A Prairie Farm

We illustrate from a farm six miles west of Portage la Prairie and about 65 miles west of Winnipeg. It controls two outlying portions, but for the sake of simplicity we examine here only the Home Farm (Fig. 100). In the language of the surveyor, this comprises four quarter-sections, which

---

Plate 11. AN IRRIGATED DISTRICT IN SOUTHERN ALBERTA

The area shown lies about 50 miles west of Medicine Hat. The rainfall is not only low (annual average: 11–13 inches) but is also unreliable, and cultivation is possible only with the aid of irrigation. The growing season lasts about 180 days, and, given sufficient water, farming can be exceedingly productive. The crops include wheat, barley and oats, flax, sugar-beet, and alfalfa. Notice the sharp contrast between the irrigated area and the non-irrigated ranching land beyond the river.

Photo Royal Canadian Air Force. Crown copyright reserved.

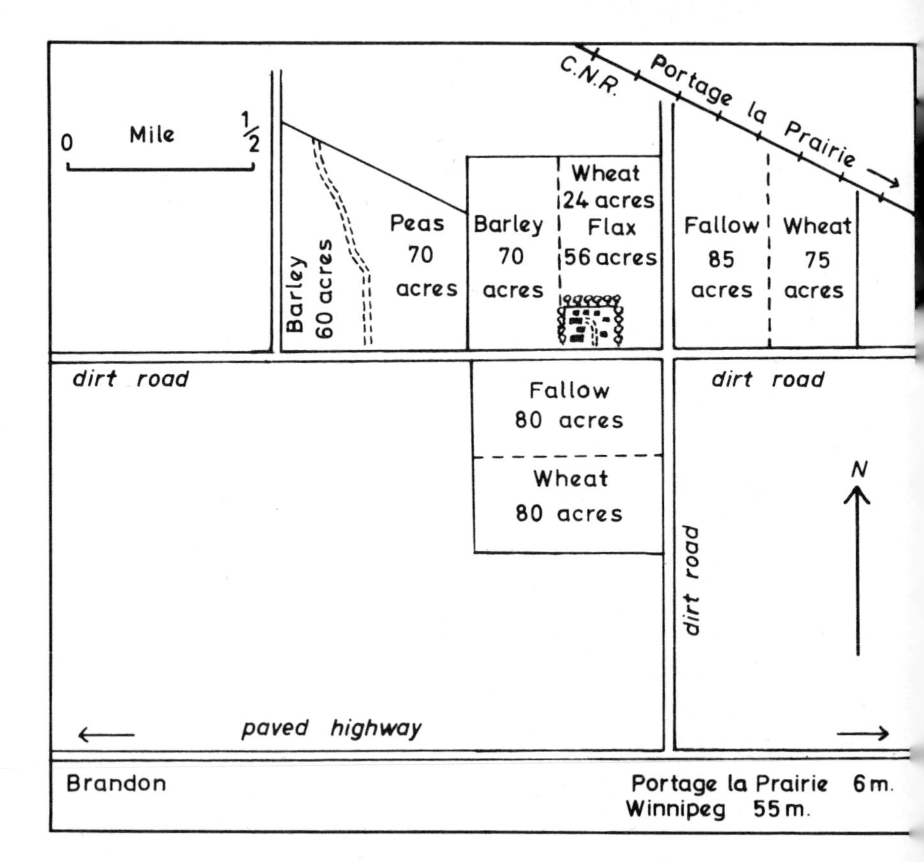

Fig. 100. A GRAIN FARM IN THE PORTAGE PLAINS

The farm lies in the Portage plains of Manitoba, about 65 miles west of Winnipeg. Its rectangular layout bears the mark of the land surveyor. The cropping indicated applies to 1962. Notice the windbreaks that shelter the homestead buildings. *By courtesy of the Association of Agriculture.*

are arranged in the form of a T. Apart from adjustments in the northern boundary, each quarter-section forms a square bounded by parallels and meridians and of side half a mile. For farming convenience each quarter-section is usually bisected, so that the Home Farm consists of eight fields, each of about 80 acres. This rectangular and regular farm layout contrasts strangely with the normal farm in the United Kingdom, and, as we have seen, reflects the work of the land surveyor. The Home Farm thus has a total area of 640 acres, or one square mile.

The cropping for a specimen year (1962) is shown in Fig. 100. About one-third of the land remains fallow: this is to conserve the moisture, and all the land is treated thus in rotation, once in three years. While it lies fallow, the soil is cultivated almost continuously – six or seven times during the summer–in order to check the growth of weeds. Farther west, where the rainfall is lower, the land will produce a grain crop only once in two years, so that half the land will lie fallow during the summer.

Wheat forms the chief crop, but this farm is exceptional in that the wheat is grown not for direct human consumption but for seed, which will later be sold to other prairie farmers. The thaw takes place in April, and the seed is sown in May, together with a nitro-phosphate fertilizer. It grows rapidly, and after three weeks is in leaf; the farmer now sprays the land with a chemical weed-killer. He hopes to harvest the crop in August; but rain may delay the harvest until October.

The grain is cut by a swather, and left in rows to dry for three or more days; then the combine harvester picks up the crop, threshes it, deposits the straw on the field, and delivers the grain into a lorry. On a hot summer day, with temperatures perhaps in the 80's, the farmer will harvest half an 80-acre field, using his tractor headlights to work far into the night.

The second crop is barley. The best quality is for malting or for seed, and any of lower grade is sold for animal feed. Barley has the advantage that it is not attacked by rust, and, owing to its short growing season, it is ready for harvesting earlier than the wheat. Flax seed in a wet spring can be the farmer's salvation: it can be sown as late as mid-June, and can be left standing until after the wheat has been gathered in. The peas and beans are for canning in eastern Canada: they are valuable in that they add nitrogen to the soil.

The farmer has a whole range of machinery at his disposal. It includes eight tractors of various kinds, five ploughs, cultivators, drills, swathers, combines, elevators, and grain-cleaning equipment. Mechanization has allowed a great increase in the output of the prairies without the need for a corresponding increase in the labour supply. Today one man with a combine does as much work as 72 men with scythes and flails a century ago. The work of this farm, with its outlying portions, is carried out by the farmer, his son, and one hired labourer. During the summer he usually has the help of four Indians from the neighbouring Reserve; but this is not typical of Canadian farming.

A Prairie Township – Portage la Prairie

We may illustrate town life in the prairies from the settlement of Portage la Prairie, on the lowest prairie step, about 60 miles west of Winnipeg. The place was named by French fur-traders who followed the Assiniboine river up-stream as far as this point, and then took the 15-mile trail overland to reach Lake Manitoba. The first building consisted of a log fort, which was erected in 1738; there was no civil settlement till 1854, and as late as 1870 there were still only 130 inhabitants.

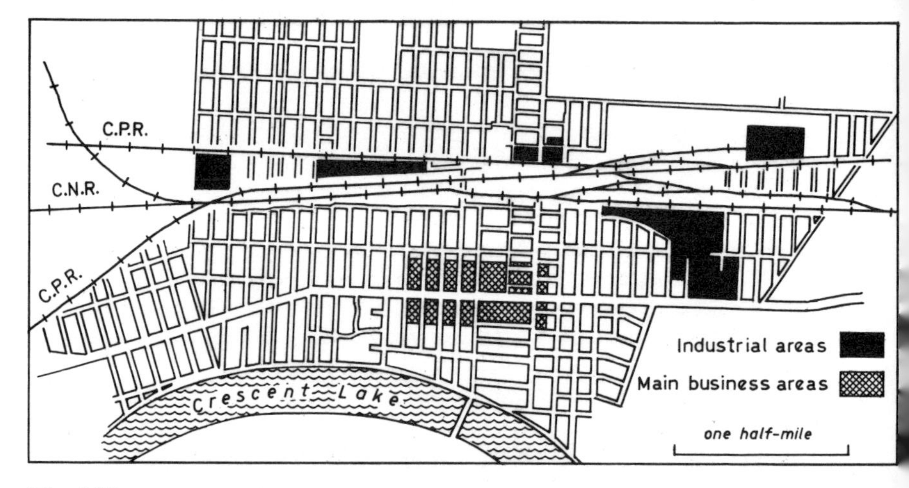

Fig. 101. A PRAIRIE TOWNSHIP

This is Portage la Prairie, which lies on the first prairie step, about 60 miles west of Winnipeg. The town originated as a portage point where fur-traders left the river to cross overland to Lake Manitoba. Its growth was aided by the railway, which opened up the surrounding land for wheat farming. The layout is the work of the land surveyor: the main block of streets north of the railway is precisely a mile wide.

Real expansion took place after the arrival of the railway in 1880, for within a year the population had increased to 800, and for 20 years there was rapid growth. The 1964 population of the town was about 12,900.

Portage la Prairie is the collecting centre for the farm produce within a radius of 30 miles to the west and north-west and 15 miles in other directions: within this area about 20,000 people have their homes, and there are about 1800 farms, with an average size of 350–390 acres. It is a district of deep, stoneless, and fertile black soils; the mean annual precipitation amounts to 17½ inches, and about 70 per cent. of the farm income is derived from crops.

Much of the commerce of the town results from its position between Lake Manitoba to the north and the wide Assiniboine river to the south, for these barriers channel the traffic through the town. The streets are laid out in the normal rectangular grid fashion, and the business centre, with its stores, restaurants, and hotels, lies on either side of the main east–west highway – Saskatchewan Avenue (Fig. 101). A few minutes' walk to the south brings the visitor to the steep banks of an earlier meander of the river – now abandoned and forming a lake. North of the business centre, and parallel to Saskatchewan Avenue, are the main lines of the Canadian Pacific and Canadian National railways, with their acres of sidings.

The industrial and commercial activities of the town are concentrated on land adjoining the railways, and are closely linked with the local farming. They include four sets of grain elevators, two pea- and seed-cleaning plants, an egg-packing plant, a creamery, a factory for the processing of animal feeding-stuffs, and a works for the manufacture of agricultural machinery. There are 24 garages, 17 restaurants, and 4 banks. The 15 churches reflect to some extent the mixture of races in the town: British, 66 per cent.; Ukrainian, 10·6 per cent.; French, 7; Polish, 4·6; German, 2·5; Dutch, 2·5; Scandinavian, 1·9. Through this small town there run 75 freight trains a day; and passengers have the choice of 26 trains a day in various directions.

Transport

The prairie railway system was designed to be served by local wagons drawn by horses or oxen. The advent of the lorry has meant that some stations are redundant, and a few of the local lines have been closed. Nevertheless, the railway still plays a vital part in the transport of grain, and it is generally accepted that it would be uneconomical to transport a crop by road to a railway station more than about 20 miles distant. Many farmers, as in the Home Farm, are served directly by the railway: they load their grain on private sidings into railway trucks, which join the next convenient train. Others deliver their crop to the elevator at the nearest station.

In the Canadian prairies there are more than 5000 country elevators at over 2000 railway stations, and their total storage capacity is more than 400 million bushels. This is not far short of the entire prairie crop (about 530 million bushels). The essential functions of the elevator are to receive grain from lorries, to raise it above the level of the railway trucks, and to load these by gravity. The grain is stored in 20 or more bins, each of which can be allocated to a particular type and grade. The raising mechanism consists of a row of buckets mounted on an endless belt: in addition there are weighing and sampling devices, and perhaps grain-cleaning and dust-collecting systems.

A prairie railway truck carries about 1900 bushels – nearly 60 tons. At the main-line stations the trucks are combined into enormously long trains, containing about 100 trucks and about one mile long: they now have a journey of 500–800 miles to the terminal elevators on the Great Lakes, or on the Pacific coast, or on Hudson bay.

The newest of these routes is the Hudson Bay railway, which was opened in 1929. It runs for about 500 miles through virtually uninhabited forest and tundra to an ocean gulf which is frozen for most of the year. But for prairie centres such as Regina and Saskatoon, Liverpool is brought a thousand miles nearer in comparison with the Great Lakes route, and there has been a steady increase in the quantity shipped. In the last few years this has become stabilized at about 20 million bushels, handled by about 50 vessels during the short eleven-

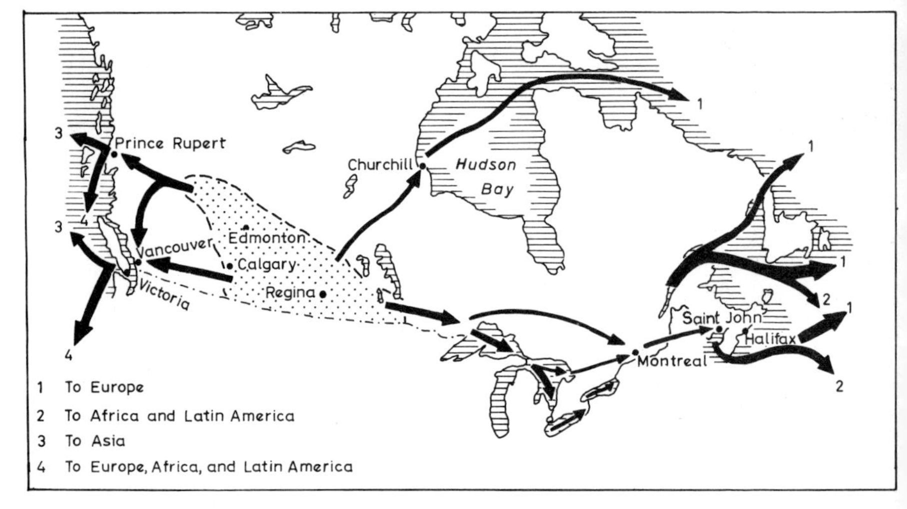

Fig. 102. EXPORT ROUTES FOR CANADIAN WHEAT

week shipping season between the end of July and the middle of October. The single large elevator at Churchill has a capacity of 5 million bushels.

The movement of wheat westward to the Pacific has during the last 15 or so years grown rapidly to reach about 160 million bushels annually: this in fact has now become the chief outlet for Canadian wheat. Most of this grain passes through the seven elevators at Vancouver–New Westminster, but there are in addition one each at Victoria and Prince Rupert. Exports are mainly to China and Japan, which are at present Canada's best customers after the United Kingdom. In contrast to Hudson bay, the Pacific ports are open the whole year round.

Most of the eastward-moving grain is channelled through Winnipeg, and continues to reach the elevators at Fort William–Port Arthur (Fig. 102). Here are 26 elevators with a combined capacity of 102 million bushels – the greatest concentration of elevators on the continent. These discharge into the specially designed lake vessels which with their numerous hatches and unobstructed holds can carry a greater cargo for their size than any other vessel in the world. The largest are 730 feet long, and hold the equivalent of a crop grown over 50 square miles of prairie.

Ice interrupts navigation on the Great Lakes, and the first vessels in mid-April follow in the wake of icebreakers. There is a brisk traffic, with vessels queueing to pass through the locks, and the season closes in mid-December. Since the opening of the St Lawrence Seaway direct shipments to overseas markets have increased to about 16 million bushels annually; but transport by lake freighters is so cheap that the great bulk of the grain is still transferred to ocean vessels at the eastern terminals.

There are five elevators at Montreal and one each at Sorel, Three Rivers, Quebec, and Baie Comeau, with a combined capacity of 45·7 million bushels, so that this group is second only to that at the head of the lakes. These ports handle the greater part of the Atlantic traffic, most of which is destined for Europe; but a small proportion (about one-eleventh of the total exports) moves through the ports of Saint John, with three elevators, and Halifax, with one. These two ports are served by rail.

There are in addition many elevators at the lower lake ports and along the upper St Lawrence river. These fulfil various functions. The Lake Huron ports (Port McNicoll, Midland, Collingwood, Owen Sound, Goderich, Sarnia, and Walkerville) forward their grain eastward by rail. Others at Port Colborne, Toronto, Kingston, and Prescott tranship some of the grain to the ocean ports. All distribute large quantities locally for processing and for domestic use in this, the most densely peopled part of Canada.

Oil and Natural Gas

Petroleum is now by far the leading mineral product of Canada, and almost the entire output is derived from the prairies, with over 80 per cent. of the total production from Alberta. Oil occurs, however, in other parts of the Dominion. The Petrolia field in Ontario has been producing since 1865. In the Northwest Territories oil was discovered at Norman Wells in 1920, and the output was expanded to meet the needs of the Second World War. The Athabaska tar sands of northern Alberta have been known since the eighteenth century, and represent a vast reserve for the future – probably the largest single concentration of oil in the world. Commercial exploitation of this field began in 1967, with a target of 45,000 barrels of synthetic crude oil a day. For long the chief producing area in Canada was the Turner Valley field, on the prairie margins near Calgary: here oil was discovered in 1914, and reached a peak output of 1·4 million tons in 1942.

The situation was radically altered on February 13th, 1947, when Imperial Oil, after spending nearly 8 million pounds on 123 dry holes, struck oil at Leduc, about 20 miles south-west of Edmonton. The field so discovered remains one of the most prolific in Canada. The following year oil was discovered at Redwater, 25 miles north-east of Edmonton, and an oil boom was in being. Redwater too is still an important source, but now the leading producer is the more recently discovered Pembina field, just south of Leduc (Fig. 103). In all about 130 oilfields are listed in Alberta, though about half the output is concentrated in the leading four.

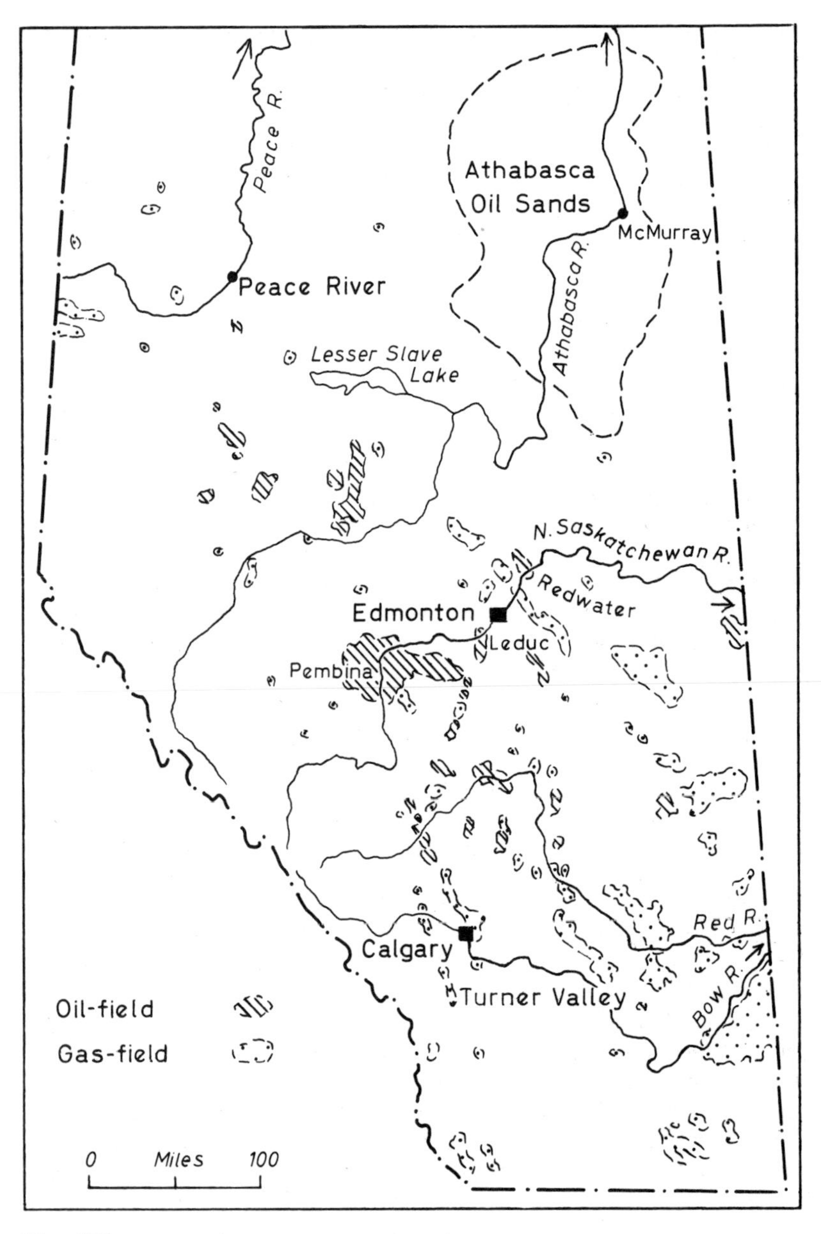

Fig. 103. ALBERTA: OILFIELDS AND GASFIELDS

The chief oilfields lie in a wide belt in the western prairies, bounded to the west by the foothills of the Rockies, to the north by the Peace river, and to the south by the latitude of Calgary. They extend to the south-east into Saskatchewan and beyond its eastern border into Manitoba. There are estimated to be 770,000 square miles of potential oil-bearing land in Canada, of which vast areas remain to be explored.

Since the Leduc discovery prospecting has been active and continuous. It reached a peak during the period 1950–55, when there were over a hundred geophysical teams in the field; the pace has since slackened, and there are now about 40 teams in operation. There are still, however, more than a hundred drilling teams at work, and the known reserves of oil are increasing annually.

The oil-bearing strata are of various ages: the Leduc field draws its supplies from Devonian strata; the Pembina, Cretaceous; the south-east Saskatchewan, Mississippian (Carboniferous); and the field of north-west British Columbia, Triassic. The oil lies at depths of up to 6000 feet.

It is unfortunate that the major supplies of oil lie far from the areas of dense population, for this has entailed the construction of immensely long pipelines. By 1950 the prairie provinces were self-sufficient in oil, and ready to supply more distant markets. By the end of the year the Interprovincial pipeline was constructed, from Edmonton through Regina to Superior, at the head of the Great Lakes. In 1953 it was extended to Sarnia, an important refining centre at the southern tip of Lake Huron. With a length of 1750 miles it was even then the world's longest pipeline: by 1957 it had been extended a further 150 miles to Toronto, and the latest development has been the doubling of its capacity by the duplication of the pipeline over its entire length (Fig. 104).

A second major pipeline – the Transmountain – was completed in 1953 across the Rocky Mountains. This line, 718 miles long, links the Edmonton oilfields to the refineries at Vancouver. Prairie oil is exported in large quantities to the United States: the Puget Sound region in the north-west and the Great Lakes region together have in the past used as much as the prairies themselves, and Canadian oil has been used even in California. The export situation in any particular year, however, depends on market influences, and at present the Montreal area is supplied by imported oil.

On the northern, eastern, and southern margins of the oil-bearing region are important fields of natural gas (Fig. 103). Gas was first discovered in Canada at Medicine Hat in south-eastern Alberta about 90 years ago; but the rise of the modern industry has been largely the result of prospecting for oil. The proved reserves of natural gas in Canada are estimated at 27 million million cubic feet, of which 20

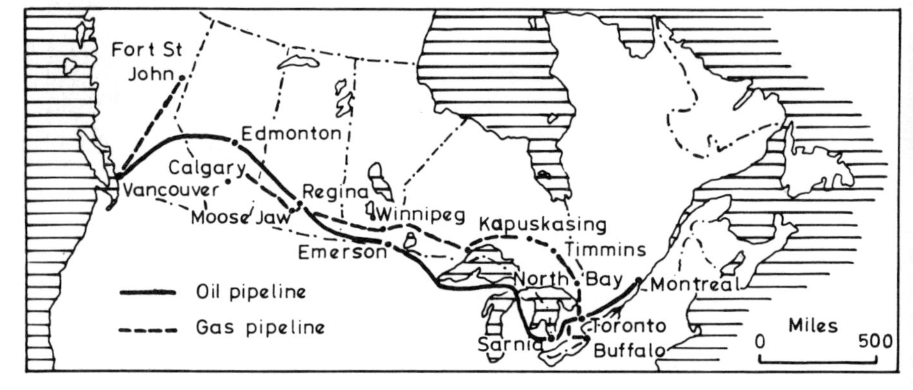

Fig. 104. THE TRANSCONTINENTAL OIL AND GAS PIPELINES

Owing to limitations of scale it has been necessary to simplify the section linking Toronto and Montreal. Note: (*a*) the crude-oil pipeline from the prairies terminates at Toronto, but there is a line from Toronto to Montreal carrying refined products; (*b*) the gas line continues from Toronto to Montreal.

million million are in Alberta; and these reserves, as a result of continuing discoveries, are increasing by 2·3 million million cubic feet annually. The size of the reserves may be appreciated from the fact that one million million cubic feet of gas would supply the needs of a city of a million people for 25 years. Only insignificant quantities of gas are known in Saskatchewan and Manitoba, but the most prolific single field at present known in Canada is that at Fort St John, on the Peace river, within the borders of British Columbia.

As in the case of oil, two major pipelines distribute the gas to the east and to the Pacific, and both were completed by 1958. Westcoast Transmission, 650 miles long, pipes the gas to Vancouver and the American North-west, and is supplied mainly from the Fort St John field; the Trans-Canada pipeline, 2290 miles long, transmits gas through Regina and Winnipeg to Toronto. Both pipelines export gas to the neighbouring parts of the United States.

The effects of abundant supplies of oil and gas in the prairies have been striking. Natural gas is used extensively for domestic purposes, for town lighting, and as a fuel in industry. Winnipeg and Regina have installed distribution systems in their districts, so that there is now a new weapon to combat the long prairie winter. The oil-refineries at Regina, Edmonton, and Calgary are expanding, and a whole range of refinery by-products are at the disposal of petrochemical industries. Natural gas is the fuel for a large fertilizer plant at Calgary and a vast cellulose factory at Edmonton. Much of the oil and gas contains hydrogen sulphide, whose extraction makes available large quantities of sulphur for the chemical industries, and in this raw material Canada is now self-sufficient.

Coal

Before the advent of the prairie oil industry the only local fuel was coal. Though the reserves are great, actual production is relatively small. The entire Canadian output is 10–15 million tons, comparable with that of the South Lancashire coalfield in the United Kingdom. Of this total, about half is derived from the prairies and the neighbouring parts of British Columbia.

The competition of oil and natural gas is reducing the market for house coal, and it is likely that in future this will be used only in districts without gas-mains or power-lines. The good-quality steam coals of western Alberta and the Crows-Nest district of British Columbia have in the past been utilized for locomotive fuel; but during the last few years the demand for this has declined drastically owing to the change to diesel and oil-burning steam locomotion. On the other hand, there are large resources of lignite in Saskatchewan and of sub-bituminous coal in Alberta, and these are suitable for the generation of electricity.

The lignite of south-eastern Saskatchewan is worked by three companies in the Estevan district, about a dozen miles from the international border. It is extracted in open-cast workings with the aid of large-scale machinery, so that the cost at the pit is low, though it is not economic to transport the fuel over any appreciable distance. The sub-bituminous coal of Alberta is worked in four districts by ten different companies. There are pits 20 miles west of Edmonton; at Stettler and Drumheller (both south of Edmonton); and at Lethbridge in the south of the province. Both the lignite and sub-bituminous coals are of Cretaceous age.

There is an expanding demand for electricity in the western prairies, and it is likely that increasing quantities of coal will be mined to supply the power-stations.

SOME PRAIRIE TOWNS

A few prairie settlements have, owing to their favourable locations, developed into major cities. We examine here Edmonton, Calgary, Regina, and Winnipeg. No comparable centre has developed in the wheatlands beyond the American border.

Edmonton (1965 population: 372,000)

Edmonton (Fig. 105a), the provincial capital of Alberta, is probably growing faster than any other city of North America. Its population makes it the fourth city of Canada.

In 1821 the fur-traders chose this site on the north bank of the North Saskatchewan river for the building of a fortified trading-post. The river formed the boundary between the Cree and Blackfoot Indians, so

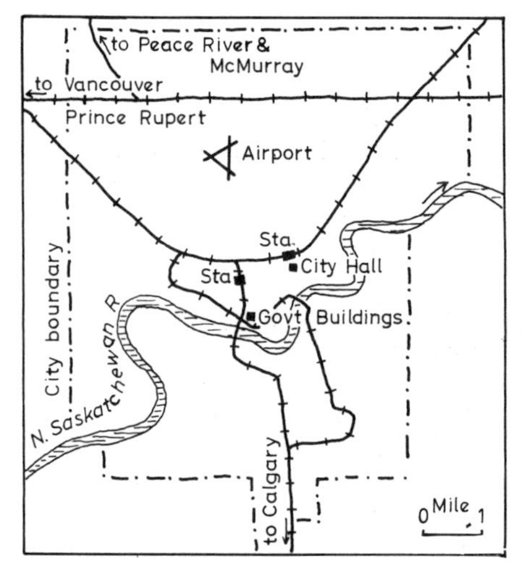

Fig. 105a. THE SETTING OF EDMONTON

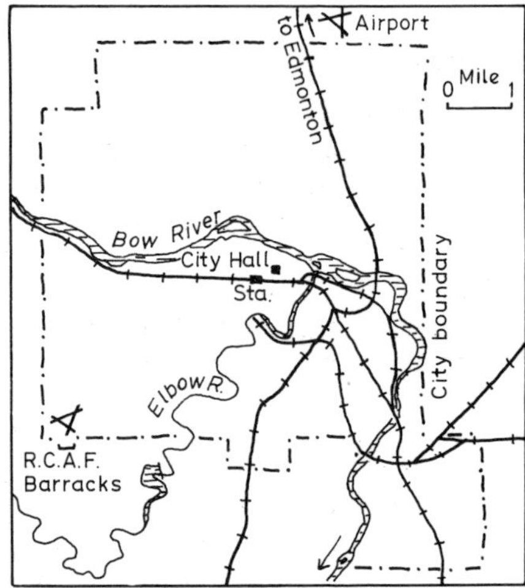

Fig. 105b. THE SETTING OF CALGARY

that the post was accessible to both tribes; the North Saskatchewan was navigable for canoes and small boats, and provided an ample water-supply. Not till 1871 were the first land claims made in this remote district, and until the railways were built it was a three or four months' journey by cart to the nearest large town – Winnipeg.

By the early twentieth century Edmonton had emerged as the commercial centre for the north-western corner of the prairies, and was the focus of ten railway lines. It had been chosen in 1905 as the capital of the newly instituted province of Alberta, and almost automatically became the seat of a university. Its location close to the north-western portion of the Laurentian Shield has more recently made it a useful base for the exploration of the north.

The traditional (and still the largest) industries of Edmonton are related to farming: they include slaughtering and meat-packing, milling and dairying. In 1947, however, the city was transformed by the discovery of the Leduc oilfield, and now it is almost surrounded by oilfields. Refineries and petrochemical industries have been established on the eastern outskirts in 'Chemical Valley', and this expansion has been reflected in new blocks of offices in the commercial area and in substantial suburban houses on the outskirts.

The city owes much of its growth to the railway, for here the trunk route of the Canadian National Railway from Winnipeg to the Pacific is joined by lines from Fort McMurray and the Peace river in the north and from Calgary in the south. Edmonton has almost doubled its population during the last 10 years, and is safeguarding its future by the opening of 50 new schools.

Calgary (1965 population: 311,116)

Calgary was founded in 1875 when an inspector of the Royal North-West Mounted Police chose a site for a fort at the junction of the Elbow with the Bow river (Fig. 105b). It remained a small outpost until 1883, when the Canadian Pacific Railway reached the spot: this heralded an influx of farmers and traders. The city stands in the foothills of the Rocky Mountains, and with an altitude of 3450 feet it is almost at the same height as the summit of Snowdon! Its interests lie therefore in ranching equally with the cultivation of grain, and the early cowboy traditions are revived in the annual summer 'stampede', with its rodeo displays and wagon races. Calgary has grain elevators and flour-mills, but its major activities are the slaughtering and processing of cattle and pigs.

When in 1914 the Turner Valley oilfield was discovered, 30 miles south of the city, Calgary became the headquarters of the new industry, and so it remains, in spite of the later discoveries to the north. Today 285 oil companies have their head offices in the town, and oil-refineries and chemical-works have been added to the older railway workshops and farming enterprises. By population Calgary is the ninth city of Canada.

Regina (estimated population, 1966: 131,127)

Eighty years ago the site of Regina was a desolate, windswept prairie where a pile of bleached buffalo bones overlooked a series of stagnant pools – the Wascana creek. Hence the Indian name of this spot, 'Pile of Bones'. In 1882 the Canadian Pacific Railway reached Pile of Bones, and a settlement consisting of little more than shacks and tents was chosen as the capital of the Northwest Territories and the headquarters of the Mounted Police, and named Regina in honour of Queen Victoria. When the new province of Saskatchewan was created in 1905 Regina became its capital city.

Though the precise locality had little to recommend it (it had no water-supply, little drainage, and no trees), there were great potential advantages in its general position. Today Regina is the most central of the prairie towns, and is the largest settlement between Calgary and Winnipeg. Its fortunes are bound up with the prosperity of farming (Fig. 106), and during the depression and unemployment of the 1930's 'grass-hoppers, the camp followers of drought, ruined gardens and stripped the bark from trees'.[1] With the discovery of oil to the south and potash to the east in the Esterhazy district, Regina has a more balanced economy: in addition to its elevators, creameries, and meat-packing plants it now

[1] Christopher Higginbotham, *The Times*, February 25th, 1963.

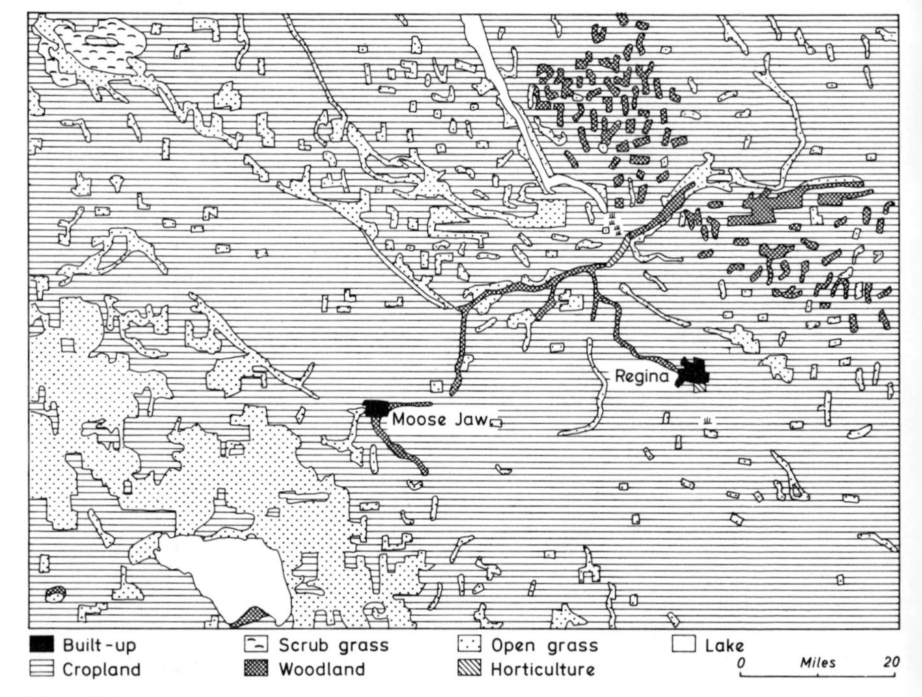

Fig. 106. THE REGINA DISTRICT: LAND USE

Regina is situated in a district of rich glacial loams which forms the heart of the specialist wheat-producing area of the prairies. There are few other districts in North America where so high a proportion of the land is devoted to wheat.

has two oil-refineries and a large new steel-works, and it manufactures soaps, clothing, and cement. Regina is a university centre, and is building an imaginative new civic centre.

Winnipeg (estimated population, 1966: 509,000)

Winnipeg, the largest of the prairie towns, is a sprawling metropolis. Its essential function is to receive and forward the easterly moving flood of prairie grain, cattle, dairy and poultry produce, and pigs; and its railway marshalling yards are among the world's largest.

The district was settled by the French in the eighteenth century, and by the Scots in the nineteenth. Since the rivers formed the chief means of access, the settlements were usually on their banks, and Winnipeg was established at the junction of the Assiniboine with the Red River (Fig. 107). Both rivers have acted as barriers to communication, and the lakes to the north have helped to channel roads and railways towards the river crossing at Winnipeg. But the site is liable to flooding, and the city is having to spend 25 million pounds on protective works.

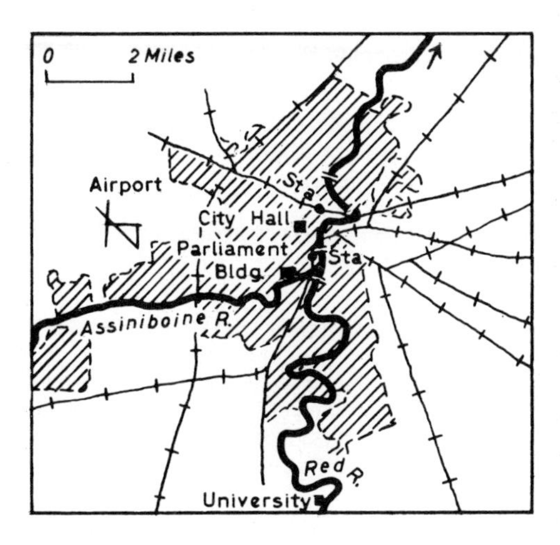

Fig. 107. THE SETTING OF WINNIPEG

The real growth of Winnipeg has taken place only since the development of the railway network on the prairies, and as late as 1878 it was still virtually a village. The speed of its expansion implies a great influx of population, and Winnipeg includes an extraordinary mixture of races and languages, with many of Ukrainian, Baltic, Polish, and Scottish extraction.

Lakes Winnipeg and Manitoba form valuable sources of fish, but fuel was scarce until the arrival in recent years of natural gas from Alberta. Like Edmonton, Winnipeg has close connections with the Laurentian Shield. The city is the supply base for the new mining activities at Moak Lake and Chisel and Stall lakes, and remains the headquarters of the Hudson's Bay Company and the centre of its fur trade.

The chief industries of Winnipeg are associated with prairie products, and include meat-packing, food-processing and -canning, and brewing. The city is a major railway centre, the focus of 17 lines, and has been chosen by the Canadian Pacific Company as a site for repair workshops. In addition Winnipeg is the chief centre in Canada of the clothing industry.

With its cathedral, university, symphony orchestra, and Royal Ballet, Winnipeg is a considerable cultural centre for the prairies. Unfortunately, its rapid extension in area has taken place without town planning, and this will be one of the concerns of the new metropolitan council.

To conclude, the prairies still show something of the frontier spirit. In spite of a few bustling cities, most of the region remains thinly peopled. Cultivated fields are very clearly in evidence, but the homesteads are difficult to spot, both on the map and on the ground. There are still distinctive national enclaves, who preserve their own language and customs, such as the Doukhobors from southern Russia, who resent organized government. Members of one of the sects (known as the Sons of Freedom) sometimes protest by undressing in the streets!

CHAPTER TEN

BRITISH COLUMBIA

British Columbia, the Cordilleran province of Canada, covers an area of 366,255 square miles, and has a population of nearly 1·8 million (estimate, 1965). About three-quarters of the inhabitants live within 100 miles of Vancouver, and most of the remainder live in the mountain valleys of the south. This, then, is a small population, and one that is unevenly distributed. Yet British Columbia has great potential wealth: its timber, minerals, and water-power resources are attracting increasing attention, and its fishing industry is well established. The province is far from the markets of eastern North America, but its resources are in great demand, and figure largely in Canadian and international trade. The exploitation of these resources is likely to increase, but it does not give rise to areas of dense population or to many large permanent settlements.

Southern British Columbia, together with the American North-west, first attracted the attention of the white man because of its fur-bearing animals. Explorers such as Vancouver, Mackenzie, and Fraser were sponsored by the Hudson's Bay Company and the Northwest Company in the eighteenth century. They followed the great rivers westward, and charted the sources of the Fraser and Columbia. In their wake came the fur-traders, who set up posts at Prince George (1807), Kamloops (1812), Vancouver Island (1843), and elsewhere. For their sites they chose either coastal areas or river junctions, for the mountain country was impenetrable.

But the fur trade brought little real settlement, and, as so often in western North America, it was the discovery of gold that brought people into the region. In 1858 gold was found in the Coast Ranges and in the gravels of the Columbia river. Many small mining settlements were founded; but most of them declined. The survivors were those in districts where farming or fishing could support the mining community, such as in the Okanagan valley, the lower Fraser valley, and on Vancouver Island. Eventually the vague holdings of the Hudson's Bay Company were crystallized into two small colonies of Vancouver Island and the mainland; and these in turn were combined in 1866 to form a single province. This became part of Canada in 1871.

In 1855 the first railway reached Vancouver: the province was now effectively linked with the rest of Canada and the eastern markets. The modern era had begun. Progress was accelerated in mining, lumbering, and fishing, and as the population grew it formed a larger market for farm products. The areas of dense settlement are still small and isolated, and the relief of the province still exercises a decisive influence on its human geography. To this we therefore turn.

Physical Basis

A journey across British Columbia by air takes only an hour; but a train takes a whole day to pick its way through the ridges of the western Cordillera. In this raw mountainous terrain, surface travel is difficult, and it is only on the west coast that the big city flourishes and man's occupation of the land seems secure. Yet the width of the Cordillera in British Columbia is not great – only about 400 miles, and far less than in the United States. Within this tract lie several distinct mountain ranges, plateaux and deep troughs, all of which have been trimmed by the recent work of glaciers (Fig. 108).

The physiographic provinces of British Columbia form continuations of those across the American border, but they carry different names. Thus the Coast Ranges of Oregon and Washington states terminate as land ranges in the Olympic peninsula: farther north, in Canada, they are partially drowned and appear in the form of Vancouver Island and the Queen Charlotte island group; similarly the lowland trough of the Puget–Willamette area has been submerged to form the Strait of Georgia. It will be seen, then, that the Coast Range of British Columbia has no structural link with the ranges of the same name in the United States, but forms the continuation of the Cascade Ranges. The two other major elements – the interior plateaux and the Rocky Mountain Trench – continue unchanged across the border.

As in the United States, the term Rocky Mountains is properly applied only to the easternmost range of the system: it forms a real barrier to communications, and is crossed by only three passes. These are the Yellowhead, the Kicking Horse, and the Crow's Nest, and all are utilized by railways.

Immediately west of the main range of the Rockies is the deep and persistent Rocky Mountain Trench. It is clearly not a river valley, but is a tectonic (that is, structural) feature resulting from the weakening of the rocks along a line of faulting: on a smaller scale, it may be compared with the Great Glen in Scotland. The trench is occupied by parts of several rivers, in particular the Kootenay, the Columbia, and the Fraser. It separates the Rockies from the Selkirk mountains in the south and the lower Cassiar Range farther north, near the Yukon. Since their formation at the close of the Cretaceous these 'young' folded mountains have been subjected to severe erosion, so that what we now see are the crystalline denuded stumps of the former mountain ranges.

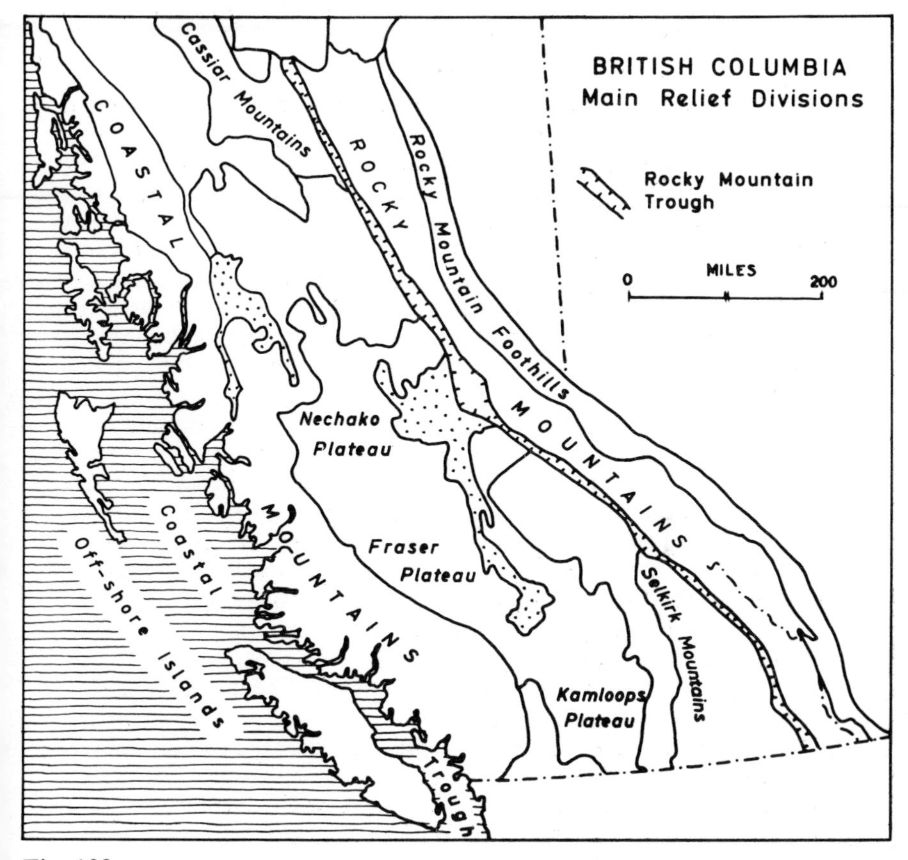

Fig. 108. BRITISH COLUMBIA: MAIN RELIEF REGIONS

In British Columbia the western Cordillera are only 400 miles wide but are still of considerable complexity. The persistent fault-guided Rocky Mountain Trench is prominent in the east. Major valley zones are stippled. The horizontal lines represent the Pacific Ocean.

West of the Selkirks and the Cassiar Ranges are the interior plateaux. They exhibit a variety of surface form resulting from uplift, faulting, volcanic activity, and glaciation. In the south is the Fraser Plateau, whose general surface is of moderate height, but is deeply dissected by the troughs containing the Kootenay, Arrow, and Okanagan lakes. Farther north lies another area of subdued relief – the Nechako Plateau.

Like the Rockies, the Coast Ranges represent only the granitic cores of folded mountain systems. Their average height is about 4000–5000 feet; in the south, however, there are peaks rising to the 7000 or 8000 level, and the ranges extend northward into Alaska, where they culminate in Mt McKinley (20,300 feet), the highest mountain in the continent. On their eastern flank the ranges are complicated by faulting; westward they fall sharply to the sea, so that there is no real coastal plain, but instead a row of deep fiords.

The most westerly element in the pattern of relief comprises the row of offshore islands. The most mountainous of them is Vancouver Island, whose spine in Mt Victoria reaches more than 7000 feet. Its southern portion, however, together with the adjacent part of the mainland, forms the largest extent of coastal lowland in the province.

Very little of British Columbia falls outside the western Cordillera; but in the far north-east is a relatively low region drained in the north to the Peace river and in the south to the Liard: it forms part of the interior lowlands of Canada.

In spite of a relatively long history of erosion, we can only describe the landforms of British Columbia as immature. It has strong relief features that have resulted from geologically recent events; its rivers run in ungraded channels, with falls and rapids, gorges and tortuous courses, that follow the weaknesses in the rocks; moreover, they have been deranged by the ice sheets. In the south a characteristic pattern is formed by the long and narrow lakes, which occupy over-deepened valleys that have been partially blocked by moraines.

The climate of British Columbia is as diverse as its structure and relief, but we can detect a measure of symmetry. The major features of relief range north and south, at right angles to the westerly airstream, with its depressions and anticyclones. Maritime influences are felt strongly on the coast, but do not penetrate much more than 150 miles inland. Everywhere altitude and aspect are decisive elements in the detail of local climate.

Coastal areas, as one might expect, show low ranges of temperature, which rarely exceed 30 degrees Fahrenheit annually (Fig. 109). Inland, however, the range rises to about 50 degrees, as at Kamloops. The growing season decreases both inland and northward. In the extreme south it is as high as 200 days in favoured areas – that is, it compares with the northern boundary of the Cotton Belt. In the middle Fraser area it is only 90–100 days long; and in the northern interior as short as 50 days.

Annual totals of precipitation show an equal variety. On parts of the coast as much as 200 inches is experienced, on exposed west-facing slopes. In contrast, some of the sheltered inland valleys receive less than 10 inches per annum, and can be farmed only with the aid of irrigation. Snow is rarely experienced on the coastal lowlands; but on the mountain-sides and in the interior plateaux it accounts for much of the winter precipitation. Okanagan receives about 10 inches of snow; farther east, near Nelson, the figure rises to as much as 80 inches. As one moves east not only does the total of precipitation alter, but also its

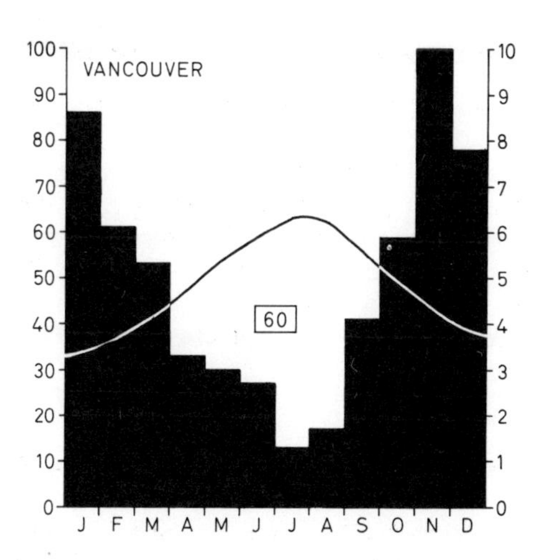

Fig. 109. VANCOUVER: TEMPERATURE AND PRECIPITATION
For key see Fig. 46 (p. 117).

distribution. In common with regions farther south, the coast receives most of its rainfall in winter, when the stream of depressions is at its peak. Farther inland the distribution becomes more even, and in the east it tends to the summer maximum that is characteristic of continental interiors.

In every way, the physical geography of British Columbia intrudes itself on human activities. The climate, acting through vegetation, offers the possibilities of forest industry, or more directly sets the limits of farming. The abundance of igneous intrusions aids the concentration of mineral deposits. The great troughs and zones of weakness have facilitated the construction of through routeways.

The sea too is a potent magnet, and the coastlands are appreciated all the more after the traveller has crossed the inhospitable interior. The coastal waters are not only rich in salmon, but afford important shipping lanes and allow access to commercial timber.

Three coastal cities compete for importance. Victoria, the provincial capital, lies in lowland country on Vancouver Island, and has ready access to the sea, but is handicapped by its separation from the mainland. New Westminster, the earliest urban centre, was both seaport and river port, and commanded a significant route into the interior; but it could not keep pace with the increase in the size of ships. Vancouver not only benefits from the mountain routes to the east but stands alongside the deep and sheltered waters of Burrard Inlet, and its port is far superior to the delta of the Fraser river.

The white man has built on the experience of the Indians who fished the salmon and exploited the forests. It was they who first carved and erected the totem pole, symbol of the gods of the air, the forest, and the sea.

In British Columbia there are four primary fields of economic activity: they comprise forestry, farming, fishing, and mining. There are manufactures, it is true; but most of these can be mentioned conveniently under the heading of forestry or mining. To serve these activities the province is developing its water-power resources and improving its transport facilities: and in all these spheres British Columbia expresses itself in its own distinctive manner.

Forestry

Forestry and its related industries form the very basis of the economic life of the province. They include not only the management of the forests, but also the sawmilling industry and the shipment of sawn timber, the production of woodpulp, and the manufacture of paper, of plywood, and of veneers. This group of industries is not only already immensely important – however measured – but it is prosperous and is rapidly expanding.

We may regard Canada as a vast reserve of timber, for almost half of its surface (48 per cent.) is classed as forest. Much of this, however, is not commercially useful owing to its inaccessibility, and if we consider the *accessible* standing timber of all kinds – large and small, coniferous and deciduous – we find that more than half of this (54·5 per cent.) is estimated to be within British Columbia, which possesses nearly four times as much as its nearest rival province, Ontario.

If we now narrow our vision to the stands of large coniferous timber – which form the basis of the lumber or sawmilling industry – we find that British Columbia dominates the whole of Canada, with 83·8 per cent. of the total volume, and 15 times as much as Ontario. The quantities of timber actually cut do not form quite so impressive a proportion, but are still outstanding, for British Columbia supplies 70 per cent. of all the sawn timber shipped from Canada.

Three-quarters of this timber is shipped to the United States and about 11 per cent. to the United Kingdom; but British Columbian timber is sent all over the world. Japan, Australia, the Common Market countries, and South Africa are important customers, but regular supplies are also sent to more remote lands such as New Zealand, Israel, Hong Kong, Formosa, and the South Sea Islands. A single ocean freighter at the wharf of a sawmill may be loading sufficient timber to build 700 bungalows.

We may illustrate the timber resources of the province in another way. The commercial forests of British Columbia total 118 million acres. This is equal to the combined forest resources of the entire American West, including the states of Washington, Oregon, and

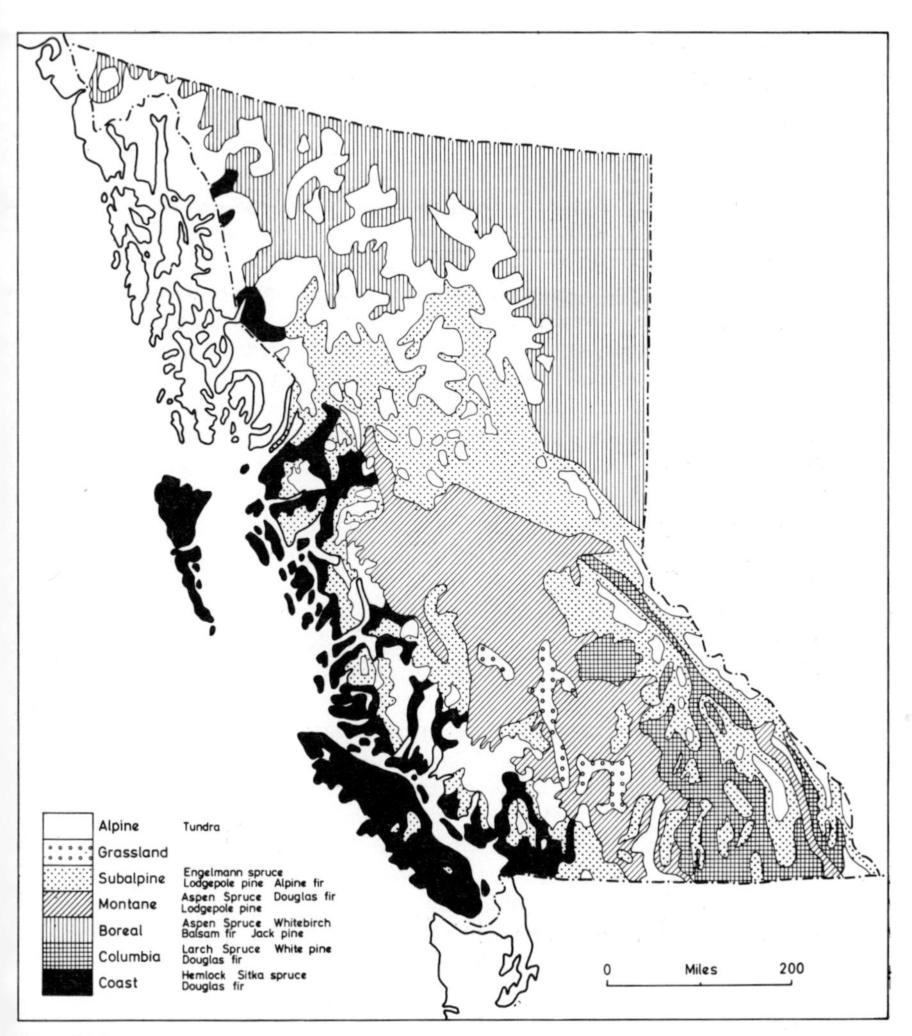

Fig. 110. BRITISH COLUMBIA: VEGETATION

The map pays special attention to the classification of the forests. *Based on 'Forest Conservation', Department of Forestry, Canada, 1957.*

California, Idaho, Nevada, and Utah, Arizona, Montana, and Wyoming, Colorado and New Mexico.

It is in the cutting and sawmilling branches that British Columbia dominates; nevertheless, the province has important shares of the associated manufactures; she accounts for 19 per cent. of the Canadian output of woodpulp and 13 per cent. of its production of paper.

Almost the whole of British Columbia is forested (Fig. 110); only the higher plateaux in the north and the highest summits in the south are too cold for trees. But the forest cover ranges widely in its value for commercial exploitation, and the largest areas are not in fact the greatest producers.

Five forest regions may be distinguished in British Columbia, and only one of these extends far beyond the boundaries of the province: this is the *Boreal region* of the north and north-east. It forms part of the great forest belt which stretches across Canada from Newfoundland to the Alaskan border. The Boreal region covers 1·9 million square miles in Canada, and represents 82 per cent. of all the Canadian forests by area, though its actual yield of timber is relatively small. The main species consist of black and white spruce, balsam fir, tamarack, jack pine, white birch, and aspen: these are typically pulp trees, and in British Columbia the region is too remote to contribute very much to the economy.

The *sub-alpine forests* are almost confined to British Columbia but extend beyond its south-eastern border in a belt 50–60 miles wide flanking the Rocky Mountains. They reach their greatest extent just to the south of the Boreal forest, and here too the timber is largely inaccessible. Indeed, the steep and high mountain slopes which characterize much of the region make it almost inevitable that these forests will be of little commercial value. In places along the west coast, however, the sub-alpine forests reach down to tidewater, and there it becomes feasible to exploit them.

The chief species comprise the Engelmann spruce, alpine fir, and lodgepole pine. The Engelmann spruce, reaching a height of about 100 feet, is larger than the white spruce but less lofty than the Sitka spruce. It forms a valuable timber tree. The alpine fir is smaller, and is mainly used for pulping. The lodgepole pine is a straight, vigorous, and hardy tree which grows throughout British Columbia except in the extreme north-east, though its exploitation is largely confined to the interior. The timber is used for light constructional purposes, pitprops, and telegraph poles, and also finds an important outlet in the pulping industry.

The *montane forests* occupy most of the interior plateau region of the centre and south of the province, where the rainfall is rather low. A characteristic tree is the lodgepole pine; prominent too is the Douglas fir, though here it does not attain the stature that it reaches on the coast. The montane forests are open in character and contain considerable stretches of pasture-land suitable for sheep and cattle. The small sawmills supply local constructional needs and provide timber for the manufacture of fruit boxes.

The *Columbia forest* region, covering only 18,000 square miles, is the smallest of all. It occupies most of the lower ground of south-eastern British Columbia, and sends a long tongue northward along the

Rocky Mountain Trench. The timber species are similar to those of the coastal forests (noticed below), but include in addition white pine and larch.

Western white pine produces a soft but strong timber, with a lively pattern and a low shrinkage rate, so that it is particularly suitable where dimensional stability is required, as in cabinet work, pattern-making, and the construction of window-frames. Larch is limited to this corner of British Columbia. It produces a heavy, strong, and durable timber, suitable for flooring, piling, and heavy constructional work, and it forms an important commercial timber.

The coast forest region occupies about 50,000 square miles. It is thus a comparatively small region, representing only 2·2 per cent. of Canada's forests by area, but it is by far the most productive of all the forest regions, and it yields almost one-third of the entire Canadian output of lumber. It extends in a long and narrow belt along the coast, including Vancouver Island, the Queen Charlotte and smaller islands, and the lower parts of the mainland coast, and it sends tongues inland along the valleys for a distance of about seven miles.

This is a region of mild and equable temperatures and generous rainfall, so that trees grow tall and fast. It is also the most accessible of all the forest regions, for it is intersected by deep, natural waterways and by many valleys with easy gradients and level floors.

One of the most valuable species is the Douglas fir, which provides the tallest trees in Canada. This species, more than any other, has established the reputation of British Columbia timber throughout the world. As we have seen, the Douglas fir grows well also in the drier conditions of the montane forest; but it is on the moist soils of the southern coastlands that the tree reaches its finest development, and here it attains a height of 120–180 feet and a diameter of 2–6 feet. Occasionally it grows to 300 feet and has a diameter of 15 feet. It lives to a great age, commonly to 600 or 700 years and occasionally even to 1000 years. Its timber is one of the hardest and heaviest of all the softwoods, and is immensely strong and durable: pound for pound it is stronger than concrete or steel. Douglas fir is ideal for heavy structural work – for sills, posts, joists and beams, rafters, mine and railway timber, flagpoles and ships' masts. It accounts for about one-third of all the timber produced in British Columbia.

In output ranking about equal to Douglas fir is the western hemlock, which grows throughout the coastal forests and is found also in the south-eastern interior. Its average height is about the same as the Douglas fir, and its timber is almost as durable. It wears evenly and hardens with age, so that it is useful in framework and general construction purposes, and in the construction of wood-block floors for ballrooms and gymnasia. Western hemlock is also widely used for pulp.

It accounts for more than 20 per cent. of the annual cut of the province.

Third in importance in the coast forests is the Sitka spruce, named after the Alaskan port farther north. It clings to the coast in a belt rarely more than 50 miles wide, and reaches its greatest development in the Queen Charlotte islands, where it often attains heights of 250 feet. The timber is unusual in that it combines lightness with strength, so that it is valuable in the manufacture of the frames for light aircraft. In addition, it glues and stains well and possesses resonance, so that it is used in the construction of musical instruments, including pianos and organs. Two related species – the Engelmann spruce of the interior of the province and the white spruce of the north – are of smaller stature. All spruce timber is tasteless and odourless, so that it is favoured for the manufacture of fruit-boxes; it is also valued for pulping.

Forest Management

Virtually the whole of the forest-land of British Columbia is owned by the provincial Government, but much of it is managed and harvested under licence by private companies, with safeguards for minerals, recreation, and the development of hydro-electricity. The forests are operated on a basis of sustained yield, so that cutting is accompanied by replanting or natural regeneration. It is estimated that three times the present yield could be maintained indefinitely, assuming wise administration.

The two major menaces to the forestry industry are uncontrolled fire and insect pests. About 80 per cent. of the forest fires are started by man, and most of the remainder by lightning. The risk of fire is highest where warm weather follows a prolonged spell of drought. To combat the danger an elaborate fire-fighting organization is maintained by the forestry department. Hundreds of look-out towers are manned, and these are supported by aircraft; fire-fighting parties are supplied by helicopters, and the fire itself may be attacked by flying-boats fitted with 6000-gallon water-tanks.

Less spectacular than fire but equally destructive are the many pests which attack growing trees. They include bark beetles, wood-boring beetles, fungi, bacteria, and plant viruses. They can often be controlled by the introduction of suitable parasites or insect diseases or by spraying with chemical insecticides: this is sometimes carried out from aircraft.

Several methods are in use with the object of maintaining a sustained yield. The timber may be logged in patches which are separated by considerable belts of standing timber, so that perhaps only half the potential harvest is reaped; this is done in the expectation that the remaining trees will reproduce themselves in the logged areas. Reforesting of logged areas has also been attempted by direct seeding, either by hand machines on the ground or from the air. This is not always successful, for the moisture content of the soil must be sufficient for germination, the species must be appropriate to the district, and the seeds are liable to be devoured in large quantities by mice and squirrels.

The most expensive, but at the same time the most reliable, method is by replanting from a nursery, such as that established at Duncan, in the south-east of Vancouver Island. In the coastal districts, where growth is rapid, trees are replanted successfully after only two or even one year in the nursery. Most coastal replanting is with Douglas fir; in the interior the species used include ponderosa pine, white spruce, and Douglas fir.

A Timber Enterprise in Vancouver Island

We may illustrate the lumber industry from an actual company which operates in Vancouver Island. Its timber holding consists of over 400 square miles of hilly, wooded land to the north and east of Nootka Sound, which is a little to the north-west of the centre of the island (Fig. 111).

The main logging camp is at Gold River, and this houses about 200 men, some of them with their families. It is a self-contained community with its own post-office, school, recreation hall and sports grounds, and repair workshops. A second, smaller camp has been established at Fair Harbour to serve the outlier of forest-land to the west of Tahsis. When a new camp is being built the first homes are constructed on rafts of logs, and are quite serviceable afloat until a permanent site can be cleared for them. In addition, many smaller floating camps are maintained: accommodating from 20 to 40 men, they are moved from place to place as new logging sites come into use, and in this way travelling time is greatly reduced.

When an area has been selected for logging, first the smaller trees are removed, and their timber is collected for the pulp and paper mills. The mature trees are then felled, cut into 40-foot lengths for handling, girdled by steel cables, and hauled by tractor to a central point. Here hauling and loading is accomplished with the help of cables and tackle supported by a tall, mobile steel spar and powered by an engine mounted on a truck. Loads of up to 50 tons of timber are carried by trailers 60 feet long over steep roads and across bridges, and so down to the coast to meet ocean freighters. One of the first tasks of a timber company is thus to build roads and bridges through the virgin forest; and during six years the engineers of the Tahsis company have constructed 125 miles of roads in the Gold River district.

Near Gold River is a shore dumping ground at Muchalat, where the logs are formed into floating booms – great circular or elliptical rafts

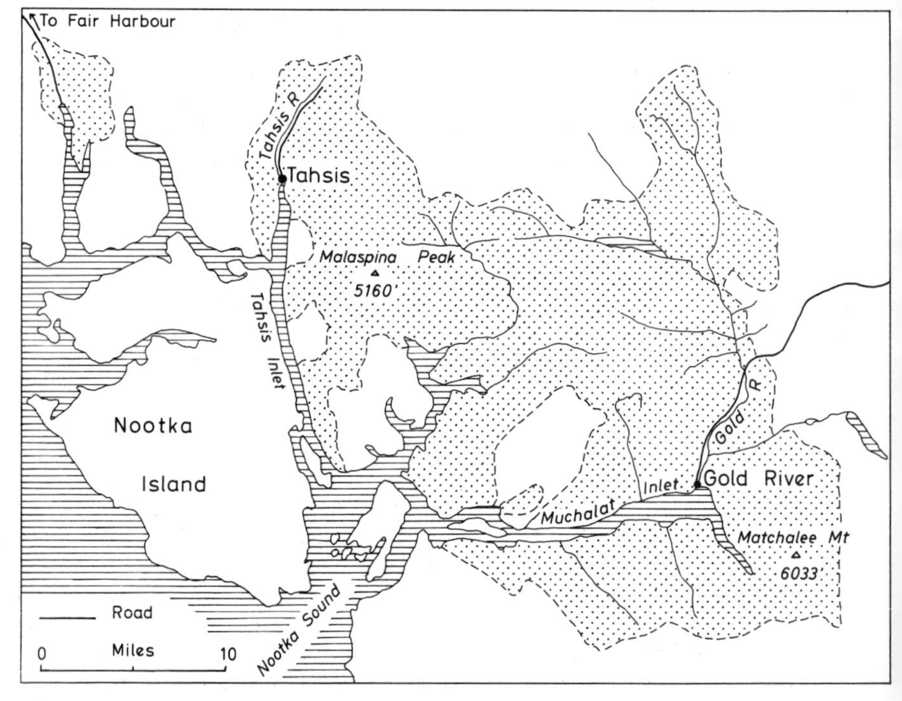

Fig. 111. THE TAHSIS TIMBER COMPANY

The timber holding of this company is in the north-west of Vancouver Island. The company operates in the stippled areas. See also Fig. 112.

of loose logs. These are towed by powerful tugs to the sawmill at Tahsis. Other logs are loaded on to 6000-ton self-propelled barges for transport to the mill.

The Tahsis sawmill lies at the head of the 16-mile-long Tahsis inlet, a deep, navigable, and sheltered waterway which branches north from Nootka Sound. Sawmills occupy wide areas owing to the need for extensive storage space for logs, for sawn timber, and for the waste. The raw logs are stored afloat in the mill-pond and are guided by boom men to a conveyer which takes them to the barker house: here in a matter of seconds the log is stripped of its bark. Henceforth all the waste is clean, so that it can be converted into chips for the pulp industry. The logs are passed four times through a band saw to reduce them to square sections; these are then cut to smaller sizes by a multi-bladed gang saw. The lumber is then trimmed, sorted, graded, and placed ready on the wharf for shipment.

No road or railway links the mill to civilization, so it must provide all its own services. The employees live in well-designed houses built on the

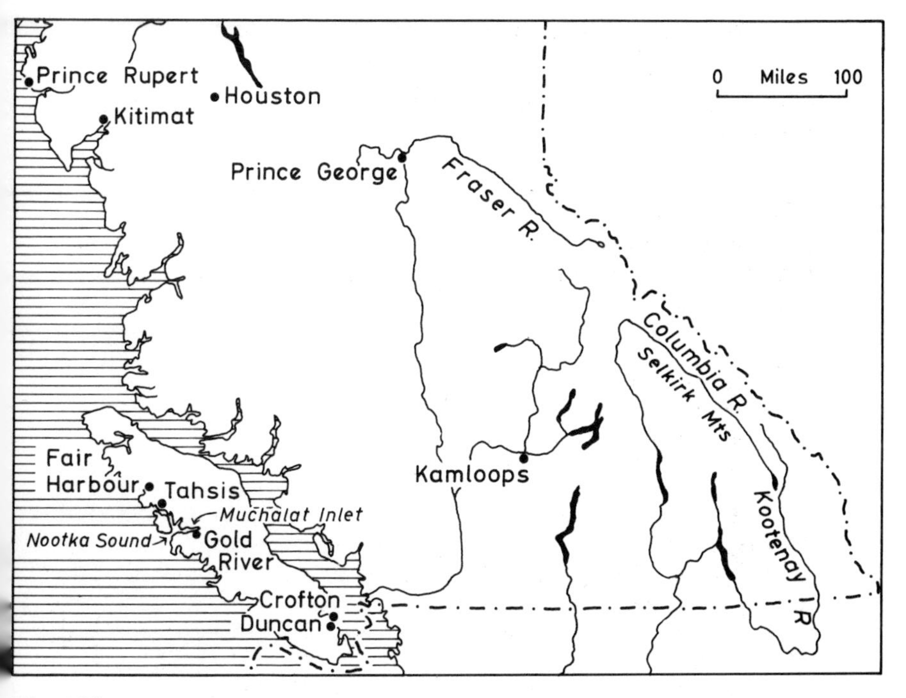

Fig. 112. BRITISH COLUMBIA: NEW FORESTRY PROJECTS

lower hill slopes close to the mill. The wharf is in regular use, and handles about 100 vessels a year.

While timber, clearly, is the major product of the forests, there are several important secondary products. The pulp and paper industries utilize 17 per cent. of the timber and much of the mill waste. British Columbia produces half of all the Canadian woodpulp, 15 per cent. of its paper, and almost the whole of its softwood plywood and its red cedar roofing shingles.

The forestry industries of the province are expanding rapidly. Two 30–40 million dollar projects have been completed in the south-east of Vancouver Island – namely, the construction of a new paper-mill at Crofton and the expansion of an existing mill at Duncan bay (Fig. 112). Three more new mills are under construction on the mainland – one at Kamloops and two at Prince George – and represent a combined investment of 155 million dollars. In 1965 construction began of a large new mill for the production of kraft pulp at a cost of 60 million dollars; its location is at Gold River, in the district we have already examined. Timber rights have been granted in five other districts of the mainland, two of them in the Rocky Mountain Trench north of Prince George, the others at Houston, Prince Rupert, and Kitimat. These are healthy signs, and it is clear that the British Columbia forestry industry has an assured future.

Mineral Industries

The following estimates for 1964 are not strictly comparable with one another but give some indication of the relative significance of the four primary industries of British Columbia:

	Canadian dollars (millions)
Net value of all forest products	900
Value of all minerals	262
Income from all farm products	148
Landed value of all fish	45

The total value of all the minerals raised in the province (including oil and natural gas) is thus rather less than one-third of that of the forest products but nearly double that of all the farm products. Like forestry, the mineral industry is expanding rapidly. New ore bodies are being prospected, new mines are opening, new smelters are being established.

The first mineral to be exploited in British Columbia was gold, and in 1860 gold accounted for 98 per cent. of the value of all the mineral products; it has since declined to about only 8 per cent. of the total, but there are still flourishing gold-mines in the province. On the eastern flank of the Coast Range there are gold-workings in the neighbourhood of Bridge river, where there are the appropriately named Minto Mine, Pioneer Mine, and Gold Bridge. In addition to several other localities, gold is recovered at Sheep creek, near Nelson, in the south-central part of the province.

Here, indeed, is the most active mineral-producing district in British Columbia; but gold has now yielded place to the base metals zinc, lead, and copper. These three, together with oil and natural gas, account for two-thirds of the total mineral output of the province by value (Fig. 113). Significant changes have taken place recently in the relative importance of the minerals produced in British Columbia. Copper has reached an important place only since 1961, and oil and gas only since 1958; the two latter are more conveniently considered in connection with the prairies (p. 275).

The mineral-bearing region has its own character. Lofty parallel mountain ranges are capped by icefields and separated by long and deep trenches, most of which are occupied by lakes. Roads and railways cling mainly to the trenches, but there are sufficient transverse routes to allow communication from valley to valley. The Crow's Nest Pass

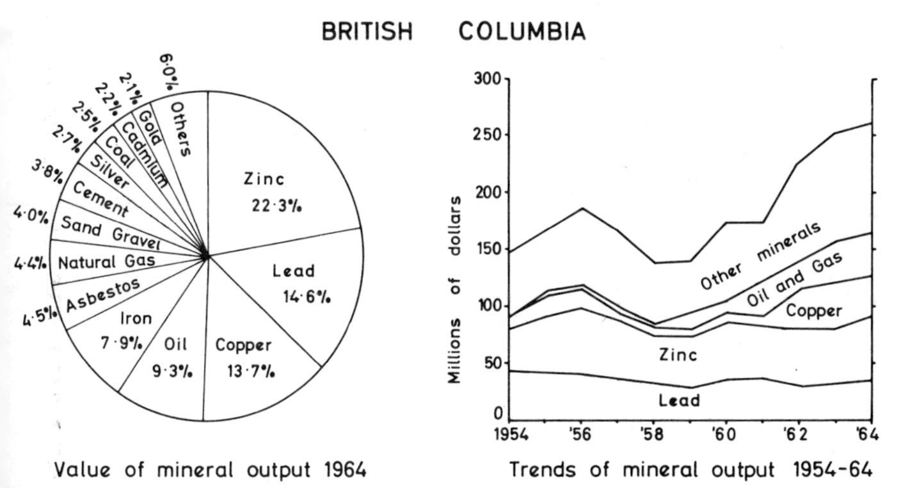

Fig. 113. BRITISH COLUMBIA: THE MINERAL INDUSTRY

Diagram (*a*) indicates the relative shares of the individual minerals in relation to the total output of the province by value in 1964. The total output amounted to 262·2 million Canadian dollars. Diagram (*b*) illustrates the increasing value of the mineral output since 1960, largely a result of greater outputs of oil, gas, and copper.

provides a routeway for both the road and the railway from Alberta into British Columbia. They forge westward by zigzag paths, never far from the American border, and terminate at Vancouver.

Practically all the settlements of the region originated as mining camps, but many of them have degenerated into 'ghost' towns. Among the remaining centres of importance are Salmo (20 miles south of Nelson), with two lead–zinc mines; Remac (20 miles east-south-east of Trail), with another lead–zinc mine; and, most famous of all, Kimberley, on the east side of the Purcell mountains, one of the largest lead–zinc producers in the world.

The commercial and financial focus for this mineral district is the small town of Nelson; this is a route centre on the trans-continental railway, the junction of three main roads, and was formerly served by steamers on Kootenay lake.

At Trail and more recently at Kimberley smelting and chemical industries have been established. Trail is built on a series of gravel terraces overlooking the Columbia river a few miles after it emerges from the Arrow lakes. This is the largest inland centre of the province and its whole existence depends on the great smelting plants – the largest in Canada and among the largest in the world.

Concentrates are received here from all parts of the province, from the Yukon, and from overseas. The chief metals produced are lead and zinc, and the daily output is of the order of 600 tons of lead and 450 tons

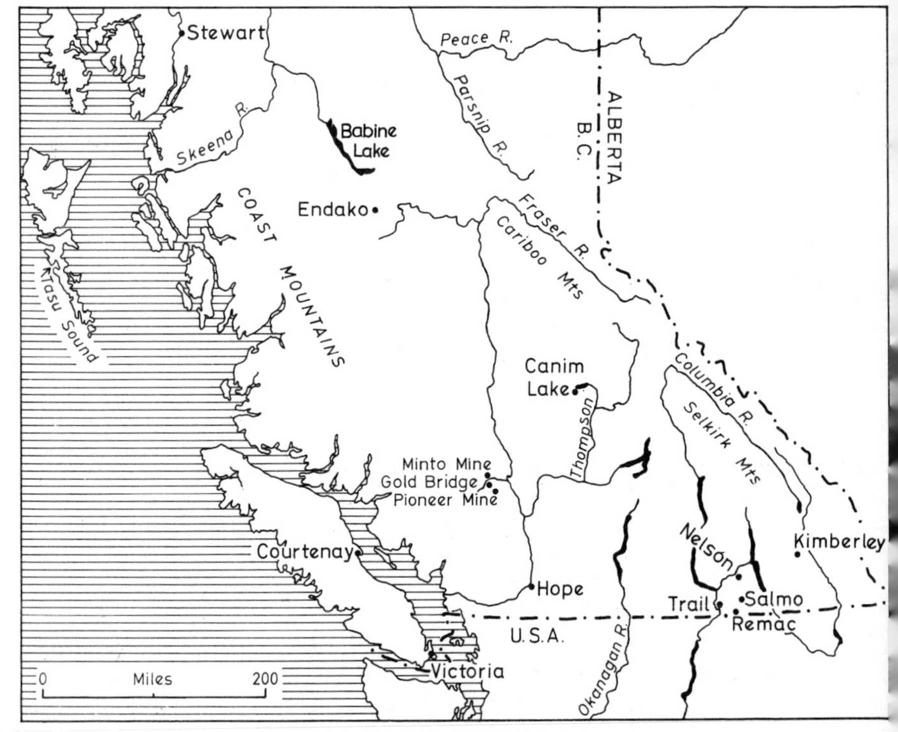

Fig. 114. BRITISH COLUMBIA: MINING AND SMELTING SITES
The map indicates the location of the sites mentioned in the text.

of zinc. The same ores contain smaller proportions of other metals: they have a significant silver content, so that Trail is the largest producer of silver in Canada. In addition the smelters refine copper, cadmium, bismuth, antimony, tungsten, and sulphur. Associated with the refineries are chemical industries based on some of the products: here are manufactured chlorine, caustic soda, sulphuric acid, ammonia, and fertilizers.

The refineries and these associated plants have been recently enlarged, and employ about 7000 people – nearly half the total population of the town and its suburb, Rossland. So important an industry requires large quantities of power, and this is supplied by hydro-electric plants on Kootenay river.

Most of the lead–zinc ore smelted at Trail is derived from the Sullivan mine at Kimberley – the source of 80 per cent. of Canada's lead; but Kimberley too is growing as an industrial centre. Its mine tailings contain appreciable quantities of iron, and this is now being recovered for the production of pig-iron. Associated activities include the production of phosphoric and sulphuric acids and the manufacture of fertilizers. All these plants were expanded during 1964.

There are many other mineral-producing areas in the province: they include several recently opened copper-mines in the Vancouver area and elsewhere. Much of the output is to be shipped in the form of concentrates to Japan. Six new concentrators are in various stages of progress; they are not confined to any one district but are scattered throughout the province.

In order of importance they are as follows (Fig. 114). A molybdenum plant with a daily capacity of 10,000 tons is situated at Endako, on the upper Fraser river system, about 20 miles above the junction of the Nechako river. A 7000-ton-capacity copper concentrator has been built in the north-west of the province, right against the Alaska border, 25 miles north of Stewart. In the far west, on Moresby Island of the Queen Charlotte group, a 6000-ton concentrator of iron ore has been constructed at Tasu Harbour. In the centre of the province, between Prince Rupert and Prince George, a 5000-ton plant is concentrating the copper ores of Babine lake; on the east coast of Vancouver Island a 1000-ton concentrator is treating copper ores 15 miles north of Courtenay; and in the south-centre of British Columbia a molybdenum plant of the same capacity is operating at Canim lake, 85 miles north-north-west of Kamloops.

These are hopeful signs, and they point to a steady expansion in the mineral industries of British Columbia.

Farming

Only 2 per cent. of the area of British Columbia is occupied as farm-land and the total of actually improved land is only a half of one per cent. In spite of this very small proportion of the area, farming occupies an important place in the life of the people, and its products are well known throughout Canada and in many other parts of the world. Farming in the province is prosperous and expanding. During the decade 1951–61 the commercial farming area increased by 19 per cent., the number of cattle by 44 per cent., the number of poultry by 65 per cent., and the capital invested by 100 per cent. Within the last two decades (1941–61) the total cash income of all farmers has trebled.

In this predominantly mountain province the farm-land is necessarily scattered and localized in a few favoured tracts. Its chief feature is its specialized character. Of the grain, 70 per cent. is grown in the Peace River district, whose major portion lies within the borders of Alberta. Eighty-five per cent. of the small fruit and 70 per cent. of the milk, eggs, and poultry are derived from the Fraser valley; on the other hand, 92 per cent. of the tree fruits are grown in the Okanagan valley. Half the

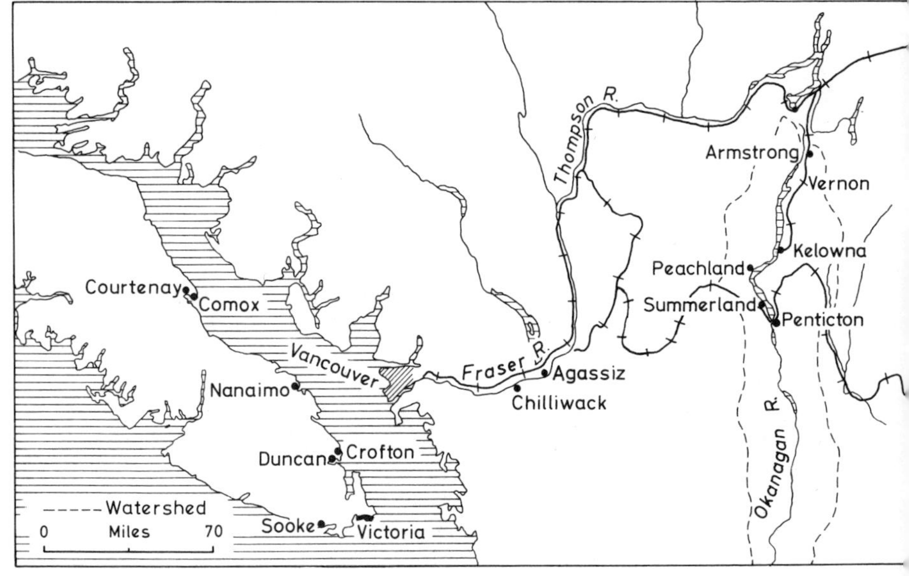

Fig. 115. BRITISH COLUMBIA: FARMING CENTRES

sheep and four-fifths of the beef cattle are reared in the pastures of the southern and central interior regions of the province.

We examine particularly three farm districts: these are the lower Fraser valley, the Okanagan valley, and the south-east of Vancouver Island (Fig. 115).

The Lower Fraser Valley

The Fraser is one of the major rivers of North America. It rises in the heart of the Rocky Mountains near the Yellowhead Pass, makes a great bend to the south near Prince George, and reaches the sea in a broad delta at Vancouver – a total length of 790 miles. Only the lowest 65 miles, however, comprise the farming district of the Lower Fraser.

The delta and the neighbouring floor-plains of the river lie below the 25-foot contour line and the farming-land must be protected by banks against flooding, both from the river and from the sea. Formerly there was much waterlogged and peaty land; but the construction of drains and pumping stations has converted most of this into valuable pasture. Farther from the river the land rises to 400 feet in the south and to over 1000 feet in the east, near Agassiz and Chilliwack. Here the soils are of glacial origin.

The rainfall is normally over 50 inches per annum, but even so tends to be deficient in the three summer months, when it is often supplemented by sprinkler irrigation. The farmers concentrate largely on dairying, and the land use reflects this tendency. Nearly two-thirds of the improved land is devoted to hay and pasture, and the main cereal crop – oats – is fed mainly to cattle either as hay or in the form of silage, or as feed grain.

Dairy farming here is the result of several factors. In part it is a response to the damp, equable climate and the alluvial soils; but there are also compelling economic forces, for within a relatively short distance is the Vancouver metropolitan district, which contains almost half the population of the entire province. The Fraser valley thus helps to satisfy a lively demand for daily fresh milk. In the quite small area between Vancouver and Hope (about 100 miles from the sea) are half the dairy cows of the province; these produce about 60 per cent. of the total milk of British Columbia, which is collected in some 35 dairies. In the valley the familiar brown-and-white Ayrshire breed is seen together with the rich fawn of the Guernsey and Jersey, and the Holstein, of Danish ancestry.

The industry is organized on a co-operative basis, and there are large milk, butter, and ice-cream plants in Vancouver, while in the valley itself there are powdered- and condensed-milk factories and butter and cheese factories.

In addition to its dairy industry, the lower Fraser supplies poultry and eggs, small fruit, vegetables, and flowers to the Vancouver market. In the valley there is an estimated 80 per cent. of the provincial production of poultry. All branches of the industry are represented: there are commercial egg farms, breeding farms and poultry-meat farms, and hatching-egg producers; in addition, turkeys, ducks, and geese are reared. The industry spreads throughout the district, but the heaviest concentration – the heaviest, probably, in the whole of Canada – is within a range of 15 miles of Cloverdale, to the south-east of Vancouver.

There is little commercial production of tree fruits here, but the lower Fraser is noted for its small fruits and its vegetables (Plate 12). Towards the end of May the strawberries are beginning to ripen, and later varieties continue to fruit until the early autumn. Raspberries, loganberries, boysenberries, blueberries, and cranberries are also grown. The first rhubarb is raised under glass, and is on sale from January to March, when it is followed by field rhubarb. In April the spinach is ripe, and in May the first lettuces appear. About the middle of May these are joined by turnips, radishes, onions, parsley, cabbages, cress, and asparagus. Towards the end of May the first early potatoes reach the Vancouver market; they continue into mid-June, and are followed by a second crop in July.

In the district there are several other specializations in horticulture and related pursuits (Fig. 116). All are forms of intensive production where skill is concentrated upon a small area of land, and where the nearness to the market is a primary economic control. Daffodil, narcissus, and tulip bulbs are grown, along with other spring plants, and there is a growing production of cut flowers. There are 2 million square feet of glasshouses in which tomatoes, cucumbers, flowers, and bedding plants are raised. In specially constructed 'houses' 4000 tons of mushrooms are produced annually, and 3200 colonies of bees produce about 225,000 lb of honey. Other products of this fruitful district include nuts, hops, and even tobacco and table grapes.

The Okanagan Valley

Second in importance to the lower Fraser is the Okanagan valley. This is a long, narrow, and deep trench, extending for more than 130 miles from the neighbourhood of Salmon Arm in the north to the American border. At Armstrong in the north it is 12 miles wide; but southward its width decreases to about 3 miles, and at the same time its elevation becomes lower. Much of its floor is occupied by the 70-mile-long moraine-dammed Okanagan lake; this has considerable climatic influence on the district, for its large body of water has a moderating effect and reduces the danger of frost.

The drainage system has been rejuvenated, and this has had important human consequences. The bench and terrace lands along the valley sides are often covered by light gravelly and sandy alluvial fans and glacial soils which warm up quickly in summer and provide attractive sites for orchards. The fruit-trees rarely suffer from late frosts because the cold air can drain away into the valley bottoms.

The district is sheltered from strong winds and enjoys a sunny climate; precipitation decreases southward from about 13 inches per annum in the north to as little as 7 inches in the south, so that fruit can grow successfully only with the aid of irrigation. Fortunately, the physical conditions for irrigation are favourable, for the winter snows on the mountain heights provide a reliable source, and there are many small lakes to act as natural reservoirs. Water is easily led by gravity from the small streams descending the steep valley walls, to irrigate the benches and terraces, and no major works are needed. The total area so supplied amounts to over 50,000 acres.

Although the Okanagan valley is far from major settlements it is well served by road and rail, and is oriented towards Vancouver, which is

---

Plate 12. PART OF THE LOWER FRASER VALLEY OF BRITISH COLUMBIA

The photograph illustrates a stretch of the Fraser river close to its mouth and part of the built-up area of Vancouver, together with the neighbouring farm-land. The mild climate, with a growing season of up to 260 days, allows the production of a wide range of farm crops, including grain, small fruits, vegetables, hops, and grapes. Dairying too is important, with a concentration on fresh milk. Farming is stimulated by the brisk demand for milk, fruit, and vegetables from the neighbouring population. The regular rows of market-garden crops are apparent in many of the fields in the area.

Photo Royal Canadian Air Force. Crown copyright reserved

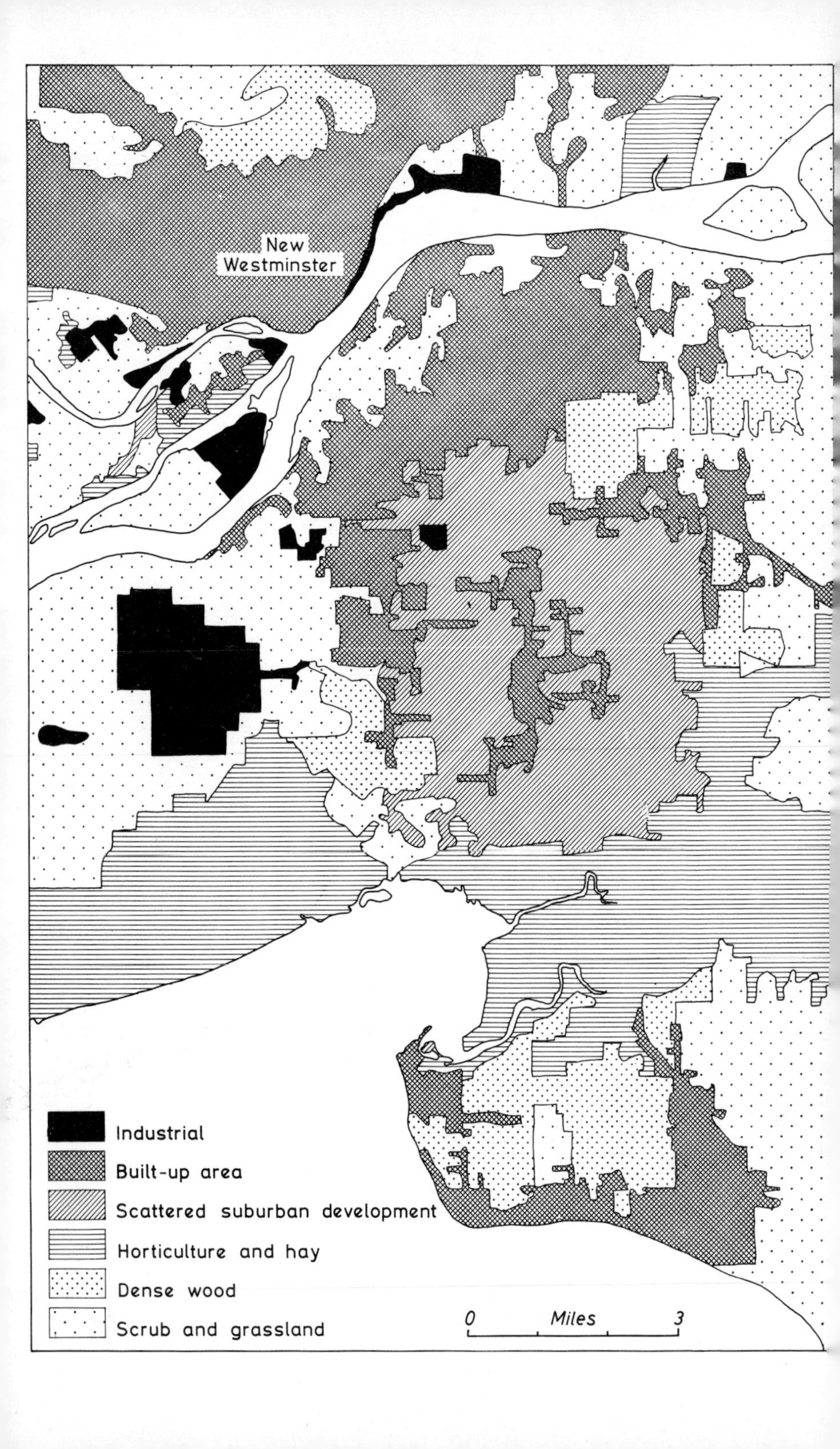
New Westminster
Industrial
Built-up area
Scattered suburban development
Horticulture and hay
Dense wood
Scrub and grassland
0 Miles 3

254 miles away by road from Penticton, or about 12 hours by rail. The economic life of the valley centres on about two dozen villages and three larger commercial towns of 9000 to 12,000 inhabitants: these are Vernon, Kelowna, and Penticton. All three have developed where side valleys open into the main trench, so that they have become route centres with links to the outside world.

Vernon (population, 1961: 10,250) is the commercial focus for the northern part of the valley, which contains the oldest-established orchards of the Okanagan. Farther north, around Armstrong, the rainfall is generally sufficient for crop-growing without the need for irrigation; here the specialization is on peas for drying, and there are nearly 2000 acres under this crop. In addition the fertile bottom lands grow celery, cauliflowers, and cabbages. Armstrong has a pea-processing plant and a cheese factory.

Round Vernon itself are 45,000 acres of tree fruits, particularly the hardy varieties of apples, pears, plums, and prunes. Here irrigation is necessary, and 6000 acres are irrigated. Vegetables, cereals, dairying, and ranching add variety to the district. The industries of the town reflect the local needs: Vernon has a modern creamery, milk and ice-cream factories, and fruit-storing, -packing, and -processing plants.

Kelowna (population, 1961: 13,188) is the commercial centre for the productive middle portion of the valley, where the largest quantities of fruit are grown. There are 8000 acres of orchards in the district, particularly growing apples and pears, but also sweet cherries, plums, and prunes. Specialization on peaches takes place on the western shores of Okanagan lake (where one of the villages is named Peachland), and the town is linked with these settlements by a vehicular ferry. Local sawmills satisfy the demand for timber to make irrigation flumes and fruit-boxes. Kelowna fulfils certain other functions for the valley as a whole: there are a resident dairy inspector and a horticultural supervisor, an office of the Soil Survey, and the library headquarters of the valley.

Penticton serves the southern part of the valley. It has been growing rapidly, having doubled its population since 1941 to reach 13,859 people in 1961. Here the climate is warmer and drier, and irrigation is essential. With its aid, however, the fruit and vegetables grow well and

---

Fig. 116. THE LOWER FRASER VALLEY: LAND USE

The area represented lies immediately south-east of Vancouver, which is now joined by urban development to New Westminster. The latter was the original settlement: it grew as the port for the goldfields up-stream, and was at first the capital of the province. In a state of nature the heavy rainfall and equable temperatures encouraged the growth of dense forests (see the climate graphs, Fig. 109, p. 289, and portions of these remain. The characteristic feature of this area, however, is the large extent of land under 'horticulture and hay' – that is, providing vegetables and dairy products for the greatest urban population of western Canada.

ripen early. The district produces apples, pears, apricots and peaches, cherries, and tomatoes (Plate 13).

The benchlands at Penticton are irrigated from creeks draining from the east. A few miles to the north, at Summerland, are the Federal laboratories and field plots where varieties are tested, orchard problems are investigated, and research is pursued relating to plants, pests, and diseases. Penticton is served by all forms of transport: by barges on the lake, by railway to the east, west, and south, and by a new all-weather road linking with Vancouver. In addition the town has an airport on the Canadian Pacific airline between Vancouver and Calgary.

Since the Second World War the marketing trend has been to increase sales in the home area and reduce shipments abroad. In this remote valley marketing would be virtually impossible by the individual growers, and there is a powerful incentive towards co-operative trading. The same spirit is also seen in the control of water resources, and these are often municipally owned.

South-eastern Vancouver Island

The third farming district of British Columbia consists of the several areas of comparatively low and level land on the southern and eastern shores of Vancouver Island. The winter climate is exceptionally mild, and frosts are rare. Though the island is on the average only 50 miles wide, there are remarkable climatic differences between its eastern and western fringes. The west coast, facing the rain-bearing winds, receives between 70 and 120 inches of rain per annum, while in the sheltered east the corresponding figure – at Victoria, for example – is only 27 inches. Since two-thirds or more of this occurs in the winter half of the year, it must usually be supplemented by irrigation.

South-eastern Vancouver Island enjoys the highest totals of sunshine in British Columbia. Victoria holds the record, with 2207 sunny hours in the year – a figure which approaches Mediterranean conditions. Nanaimo has almost, and Sidney just over, 2000 hours of sunshine, while for comparison the sunniest place in the United Kingdom (Eastbourne) has a computed average of 1811 hours during the year.

The farming districts extend from the Sooke area (about 20 miles

---

Plate 13. ORCHARDS IN THE OKANAGAN VALLEY OF BRITISH COLUMBIA

The photograph shows part of the deep Okanagan Trench, with the town of Penticton, situated at the southern end of Okanagan lake. North is at the top of the picture. To the east the land rises to lofty plateaux whose summits rise above 6000 feet. The scanty cover of trees is an indication of the low rainfall – as little as 9 inches annually. Between the steep, barren hillside and the shore of the lake is an irrigated bench that is devoted to orchards. In this sheltered valley the lake waters moderate the temperatures, and the growing season lasts 200 days. The Okanagan valley produces over 90 per cent. of the apples, pears, and peaches of British Columbia. There are canning factories in Penticton.

Photo Royal Canadian Air Force. Crown copyright reserved

west of Victoria) eastward and northward, into the Saanich peninsula (north of Victoria) and along the coast through the districts of Duncan, Nanaimo, and as far north as Comox and Courtenay (Fig. 115, p. 302). The last-named, 140 miles north of Victoria, is the terminus of the railway. The Island Highway, however, continues northward for a further 82 miles, and there is much potential farm-land in the valley of the Salmon river awaiting development.

The farming is very similar in character to that in the lower Fraser valley. Dairying is important throughout: there is a brisk demand from Victoria for fresh milk, so that the local supplies must be supplemented by 'imports' from the mainland. The Victoria district is noted for its poultry production, and the nearby Saanich peninsula has an old-established strawberry industry.

Fishing

British Columbia plays a vital part in the commercial fishing industry of Canada. The numbers employed in the provincial fisheries are smaller than those of Newfoundland, and the landings by weight are sometimes below those of Newfoundland and Nova Scotia: nevertheless, the value of the product in British Columbia is usually the highest of all the Canadian provinces, rather higher than that of Nova Scotia and more than twice as great as that of Newfoundland.

The reason for the high value of the British Columbia fisheries products lies in the nature of the catch: the greater part of the Atlantic fisheries is made up of lobsters, cod, haddock, and herring, and these are of comparatively low value; the British Columbia catches, on the other hand, consist of between 65 and 75 per cent. (by value) of salmon, while most of the remainder comprise herring and halibut.

The technique of salmon-fishing is illuminated by a brief reference to the life of the salmon. The Pacific salmon is biologically distinct from the Atlantic salmon, but the habits of both genera have much in common. The Pacific salmon itself comprises five distinct species of commercial importance, whose average weight varies widely, from about 4 lb in pink or humpback salmon to about 25 lb in the king or spring salmon, while individuals of the king salmon have been known to reach the astonishing figure of 80 lb. Intermediate between these weights are the dog salmon, averaging about 9 lb, the sockeye salmon, averaging about 7 lb, and the silver salmon, averaging about 6 lb. It is the smallest species, however, that provides the major proportion of the catch.

The salmon spend most of their life in salt water, where they live up to five years. They feed abundantly and grow rapidly; when they reach maturity the urge to spawn brings them to the river-mouths of western Alaska, of British Columbia, and of the north-west coast of the United States. King salmon penetrate far up-stream, leaping waterfalls and rapids to reach the head-streams of the rivers. They have been found in the headwaters of the Yukon 3000 miles from the sea. Other species travel shorter distances, and the pinks penetrate only a few miles above the river-mouths. All are believed to aim for the particular stretch of water in which they were born, though how they accomplish this is a mystery.

Once in fresh water the salmon ceases to feed, and internal biological changes take place. Thus the violent energy required to combat the up-stream journey cannot be replenished, and the salmon often arrives at the spawning ground in a ragged and emaciated condition. The female prepares a 'nest' in the gravel of the river-bed and deposits the eggs, which are then fertilized by the male. Both adults now apparently lose all interest in life: they drift helplessly down-stream, and within about a fortnight are dead. The life-cycle is completed by the young fry, which remain in the freshwater lakes or rivers for up to a year before migrating to the sea.

It is clear that the fish are in prime condition when, having completed their feeding in salt water, they are crowding into the river-mouths to pass up-stream; and it is on or near this occasion that salmon-fishing takes place. It is a seasonal occurrence; but the timing and duration of the salmon 'run' varies between different species, and even between different rivers for the same species. King salmon enter some rivers in the early spring, and the migration may be continuous until the autumn, or there may be a slack period during the summer; the sockeye 'run' continues from early summer to late autumn.

Salmon may be caught by one of three methods: by trolling, by seining, or by gill-netting. A troller is a small power-driven boat manned by only one or two men, with hooks and lines fastened to two or more long poles: it is merely a refinement over fishing with rod and line. A gill net is rather like a wire-mesh fence floating below the surface of the water: it is placed so that it lies across the path taken by the migrating salmon, and it drifts with the current and the tide. The fish tries to force its way through, but its gill covers become entangled in the mesh.

A seiner is a much larger boat, with sleeping and feeding accommodation for seven to ten men. A school of salmon is encircled by a long net, one end being hauled by a man in a rowing-boat. The net is hauled in by power, and is so constructed that there is no outlet from it.

The salmon fisheries are carefully regulated by the Federal and provincial governments on a sustained yield basis. Stairways are provided to assist the up-stream migration; ways are sought of protecting the young fry; eggs are transplanted from crowded to sparsely inhabited rivers; and a careful watch is kept on river pollution.

The salmon catch varies quite widely from year to year. In 1962 a 32-year record was broken, when 33 million salmon were caught in British Columbian waters. So large was the catch that the canneries could not cope with it, even by working non-stop. All the major rivers and inlets contribute their quota to the salmon catch: among the chief of them are the Rivers inlet (north of Vancouver Island) and the Fraser, Skeena, and Nass rivers.

About 80 per cent. of the catch is canned, and most of the rest is sold fresh or frozen. A modern cannery is almost entirely automatic. A machine cleans the fish and removes the inedible parts in a single operation, at the rate of over 60 a minute. Another cuts the flesh crosswise, and to such a size that it will just fit the tin. A third fills the tin. Other machines add salt for flavouring, loosely cover the tins, and then vacuum-seal them. The cans are steam-cooked for 90 minutes in large retorts which hold 4800 at a time, and after labelling are ready for the market.

The chief customer is the United Kingdom, which takes about a third of the exports; important quantities are also shipped to the United States, France, Belgium, and Australia.

Hydro-electricity

In three areas major hydro-electric schemes are at various stages of development: these are in the Kitimat district and in the Columbia and Peace river basins.

Development in the Kitimat district is linked with the production of aluminium from imported bauxite at Kitimat, on the north coast of the province. In 1950 Kitimat was a small and remote Indian mission station at the head of Douglas Channel, which opens into Hecate Strait and is sheltered by the Queen Charlotte islands (Fig. 117).

To the west the land rises abruptly to more than 7000 feet, and receives an annual precipitation of more than 100 inches. The lofty plateau has been gently tilted down to the east, and the general flow of the drainage is in that direction; in a state of nature the water passed through a chain of lakes. All this has been changed by man. The outlet of the Nechako river has been blocked by Kenney Dam; a reservoir has been created covering 350 square miles at a height of 2600 feet above sea-level, and a ten-mile tunnel has been cut through the Coast Range to allow the water to spill westward. The natural drainage has been reversed in an area equal to almost the whole of Yorkshire.

The water falls to sea-level through a vertical height 16 times as great as Niagara Falls, and in the process it yields 1,050,000 horse-power of electrical energy at the Kemano power-house. The object of this development is the smelting of aluminium, for this is a process requiring abundant and cheap electricity. The power is transmitted for 50 miles through rugged country to the Kitimat smelter, on the shore of Douglas Channel. This sheltered fiord is sufficiently deep to receive the bulk carriers laden with bauxite from Jamaica and Guyana. The smelter at

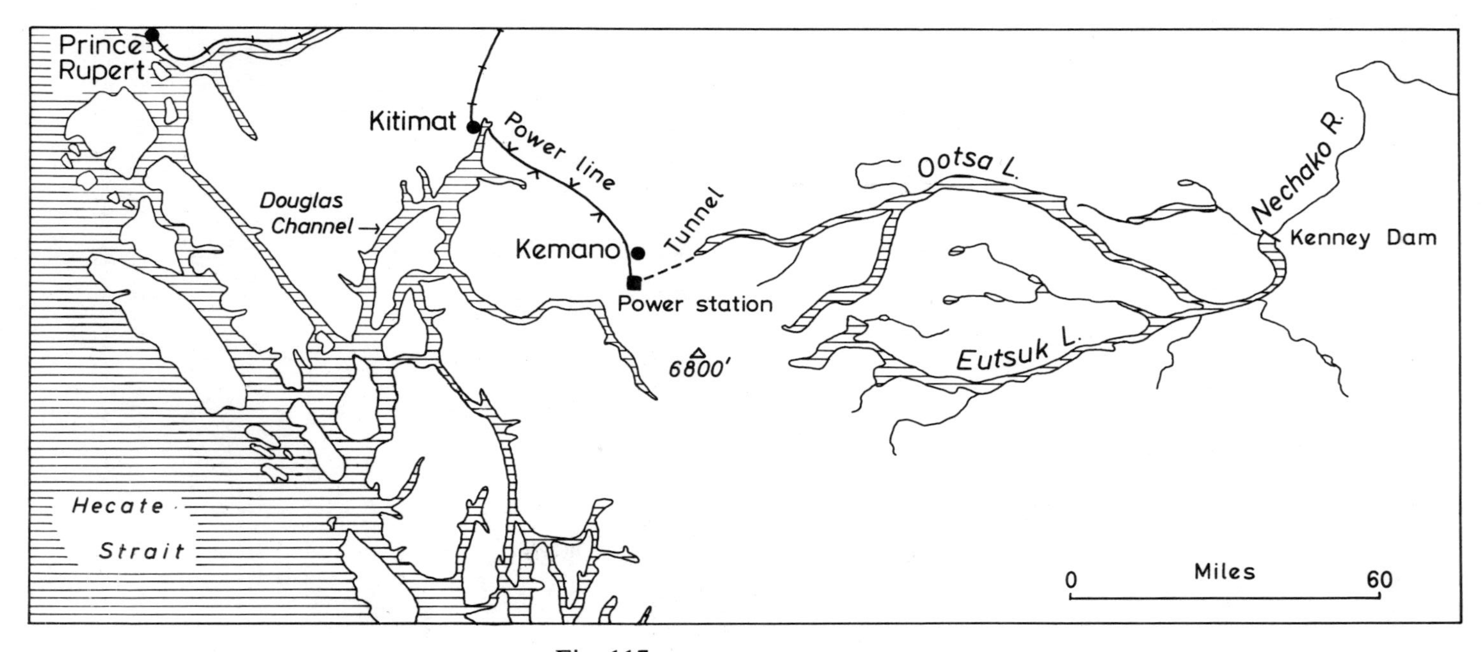

Fig. 117. THE KITIMAT PROJECT

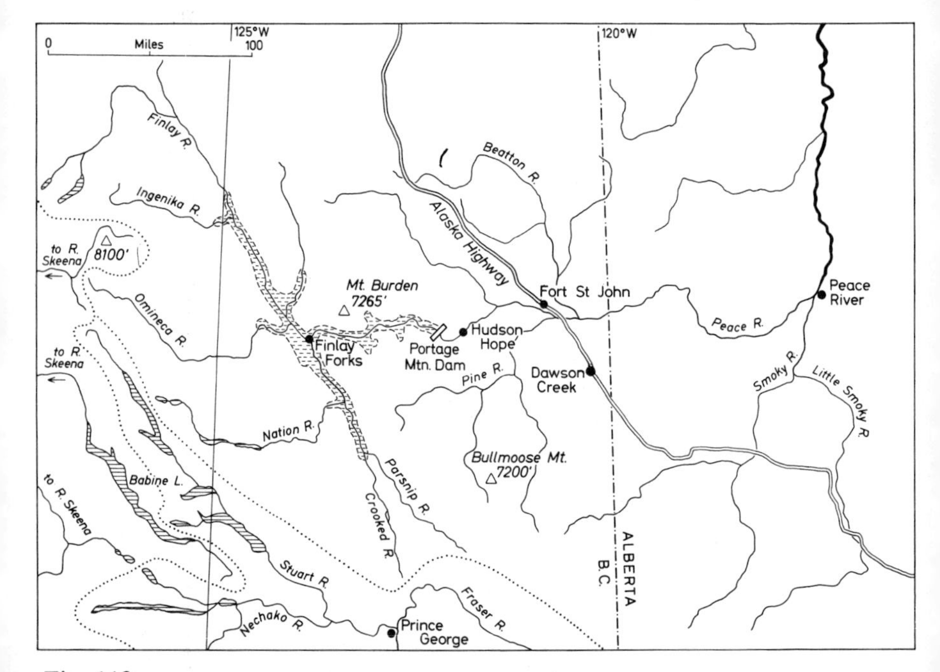

Fig. 118. THE PEACE RIVER PROJECT

The diagram indicates the extensive basin of the upper Peace river, whose waters are being tapped for hydro-electric power by the construction of the Portage Mountain Dam. A vast new reservoir is being impounded, its shore corresponding with the broken line. Ultimately a capacity of 2500 MW will be developed at the dam site. In a small area to the south-west the lakes and streams drain to the Skeena and Fraser rivers.

present has a capacity of 272,000 tons of metal a year; it is designed for an ultimate capacity of 550,000 tons, to make full use of the available power, and will then be among the largest aluminium plants in the world. Close by a new town has been built to house the workmen and their families, and to provide them with the amenities of modern civilized life.

The Peace river originates in a row of eastward-flowing streams which drain into the Rocky Mountain Trench. Their waters are collected by the two chief rivers which occupy this portion of the Trench – the Finlay from the north and the Parsnip from the south. These two join near Mt Selwyn, and their combined water (now known as the Peace) passes eastward into Alberta, and eventually becomes a main affluent of the Slave river – part of the great Mackenzie river system. The upper portion of this river basin, a region of heavy and well-distributed rainfall, is now the scene of one of the world's major hydro-electric projects (Fig. 118).

The main dam, 650 feet high and stretching 1·3 miles across the Peace river valley, is under construction: this is at Portage Mountain, a few miles up-stream of Hudson's Hope. Behind it a great reservoir will gradually form. It will spread 70 miles up-stream to Finlay Forks, then 90 miles north along the Finlay and 110 miles south along the Parsnip and Crooked rivers, thus submerging 200 miles of the floor of the Rocky Mountain Trench. It will take eight years to fill completely, and will then contain nearly three times as much water as Lake Mead, behind the American Boulder Dam. This new vast artificial lake will form the largest body of inland water in British Columbia.

At the foot of the dam is the main power-house, scheduled to begin operating in 1968. During the 1970's 12 generating sets are to be installed, and then with a capacity of more than 2500 MW this will be the largest power-station in the western world, and the second largest in the world. Unfortunately, this site is far from the main centres of population, and power-lines about 600 miles long are to be constructed; these will probably operate at half a million volts.

The Portage Mountain development is envisaged as only the first stage of the utilization of the energy of the Peace river. A second stage of 650 MW is already planned, and there will still remain about 200 MW available for development down-stream, half of it in Alberta.

The third project, in the Columbia river basin, is still in its early stages. The Columbia, the fourth largest river in North America, flows through a region where important advances have been made during the last generation, so that there is a large and growing demand for power.

The river rises in Columbia lake, in British Columbia, and the main-stream runs for 480 miles through Canada, and another 740 miles through the United States, before emptying itself into the Pacific. In the Canadian portion there are estimated to be 5000 MW of potential energy available, of which only 400 kW have been already developed. In the American portion there are estimated resources of 35,000 MW, of which 10,000 are developed or in process of development. Though there are greater resources in the United States, it has been shown to be more economic in the first instance to concentrate the development in the Canadian portion of the river basin.

The Columbia is erratic in volume and disastrous flooding has been experienced in the United States portion. Storage reservoirs in the Canadian section would not only be productive of power, but would also reduce down-stream flooding; thus the Columbia river development has become a matter for negotiation between the two nations.

In 1961 the Columbia River Treaty was signed, and the basic proposals for harnessing the river were agreed. Canada will construct three major dams: these are at Mica creek, where the Columbia leaves the Rocky Mountain Trench; at Duncan, just above Kootenay lake; and at the outlet of Lower Arrow lake, 30–40 miles before the main-stream enters the United States (Fig. 119).

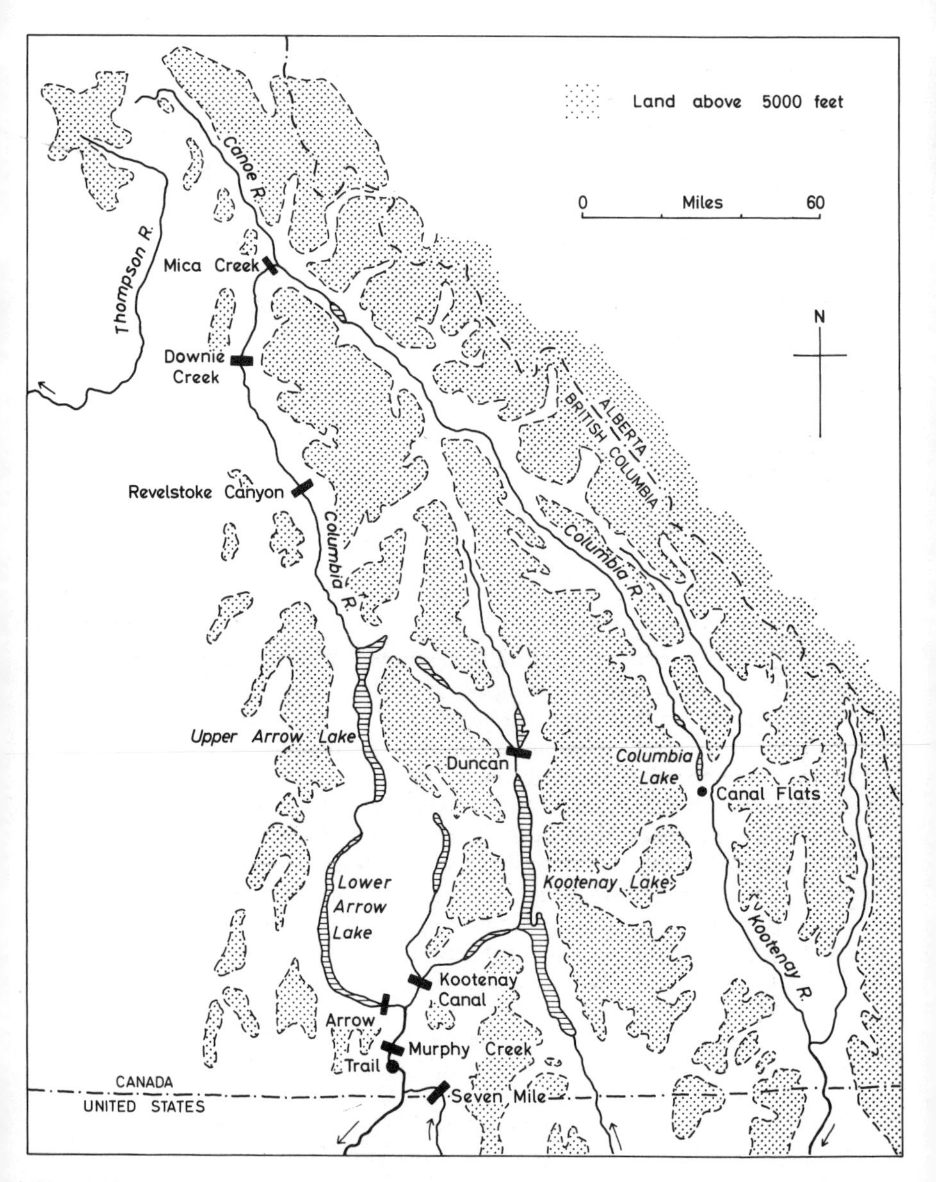

Fig. 119. THE CANADIAN COLUMBIA RIVER

The map shows the sites of the projected dams. There are already 11 dams on tributaries of the river, but these are omitted. The proposed dams will enlarge existing lakes and create new ones. The capacities of the power stations are planned to be as follows: Mica Creek: 1820 MW; Downie Creek: 1000 MW; Revelstoke Canyon: 630 MW; Seven Mile: 350 MW; Murphy Creek: 300 MW; Kootenay Canal: 270 MW.

The United States will make a cash payment in respect of each dam as a recognition of its value in flood-control down-stream. In addition to these three 'treaty' dams, Canada proposes to construct three others on the main-stream and two more on tributaries. At all the dams except Duncan and Arrow there will be power-plants, the largest being at Mica creek (1820 MW) and Downie creek (1000 MW). For purposes of comparison we may notice that the nuclear power stations at present under construction in the United Kingdom are mainly in the range of 500 to 600 MW.

The total energy to be developed in the Canadian section of the Columbia river is planned at about 4400 MW – nearly twice as much as the total capacity of all the plants at present operating in British Columbia. This will be a truly impressive contribution to the energy needs of southern British Columbia and north-western United States.

Vancouver (population, metropolitan area, 1961: 790,165)

Three-quarters of the entire population of British Columbia are concentrated in a small district within 50 miles or so of Vancouver and Victoria, and we must examine this area more closely (Fig. 120).

Vancouver has grown close to the boundary between two very different coastal types. To the north is a region of fiords, where deep and sheltered waterways penetrate far inland and are bordered by the steep wooded slopes of the Canadian Coast Ranges. To the south are shallow, muddy creeks and lagoons, characteristic of deltaic flats recently formed of river silts. The most southerly of the fiords is Burrard Inlet, whose southern shore is occupied by part of the built-up area of Vancouver; the most northerly of the deltas is that of the Fraser, where the earlier New Westminster was founded. Both are now joined in the metropolitan area of Vancouver, which contains half the population of the province.

The main reason for this remarkable concentration of people undoubtedly lies in the deep trench of the Fraser river, which together with its tributary the Thompson provides the only practicable route eastward through the plateaux and lofty ranges of southern British Columbia, across the Selkirks and through the main ranges of the Rockies at the Kicking Horse Pass, and so into the prairies of Alberta.

As in many other districts, it was gold which first brought a population into the lower Fraser district. About 1854 the precious metal was discovered near Hope, about 100 miles from the sea, and 10,000 miners flocked into the district. In pre-railway days, when land transport was slow and shallow-draft vessels were employed, it was natural to utilize the Fraser itself, and a seaport was established at New Westminster. Appropriately named, this town became the capital of the mainland province for several years, until 1866, when its functions were taken over by Victoria.

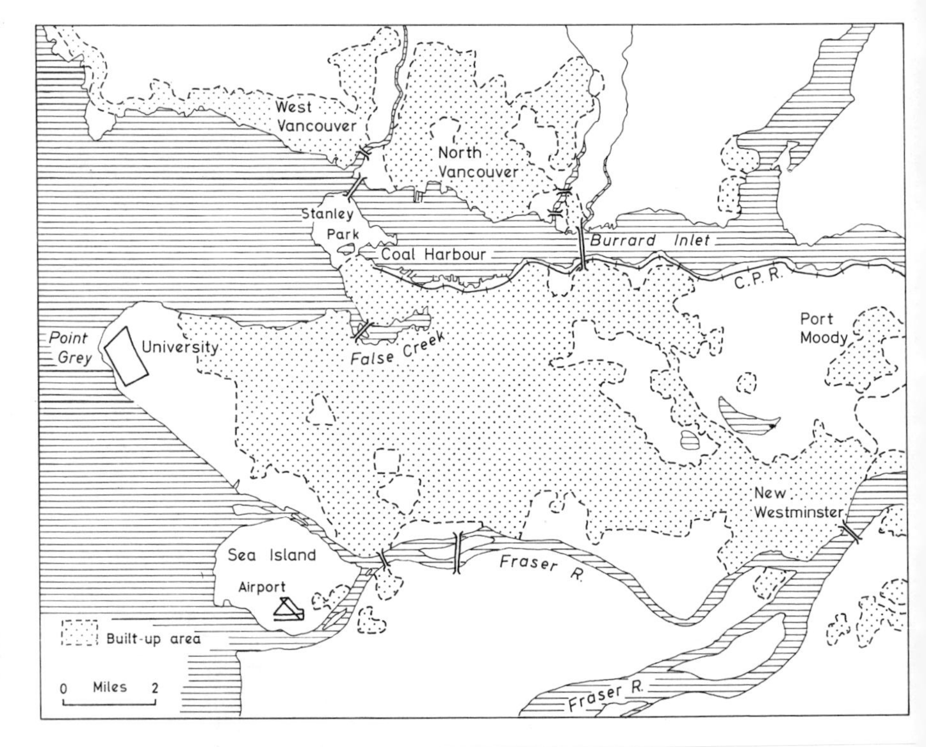

Fig. 120. THE SETTING OF VANCOUVER

The earliest settlement was at New Westminster, when the Fraser river was the chief means of communication. The rise of Vancouver dates from 1885, when the site was selected as the Pacific terminus of the transcontinental Canadian Pacific Railway, whose last few miles are indicated on the map (later railways are omitted). The early city was confined between Burrard Inlet and False Creek; today the built-up area extends to New Westminster.

The magnificent deep water of Burrard Inlet went almost unnoticed until the middle 80's; but in 1857 lignite was discovered on its south shore, and the spot was named Coal Harbour. Five years later the first hut to occupy the site of Vancouver was built, just to the east of Coal Harbour. The effective foundation of the town took place in 1885, when the site was wisely chosen as the terminus of the Canadian Pacific Railway, and named after the British captain who had charted the coasts of the district in 1793.

The new town grew with remarkable speed, for it possessed all the advantages of the Fraser routeway together with a magnificent harbour. In 1886 it contained 600 people, when it was swept by a disastrous fire. The first buildings were soon replaced; the next year the population reached 2000, and in the following year, 6000. By 1905, only 20 years after its foundation, the town numbered 45,000 people; it contained seven banks, eight churches, at least six sawmills, an opera house, and a university college. It was firmly linked to the deep-water wharves along Burrard Inlet, and its commercial core was established on a morainic ridge to the south reaching a height of about 120 feet above sea-level.

The later development of Vancouver has been equally striking. Between 1905 and 1910 it more than doubled its population. With the opening of the Panama Canal in 1914 it was enabled to engage more successfully in the European trade, in addition to its traditional Pacific connections. From the 1920's onward more and more prairie grain found its outlet through Vancouver, and this traffic has so expanded that now the proportions moving to the Atlantic and Pacific are approximately equal. The most recent developments in its hinterland have been the construction of an oil pipeline from Edmonton in 1953 and a gas pipeline from the Peace River district in 1958, so that the region is now blessed with a variety of sources of energy.

The economic growth of southern British Columbia is partly a result of its favourable climate. Abundant sunshine, mild winter temperatures, and a relatively low rainfall have aided the production of fruit in the Okanagan valley, and have allowed a varied agriculture in the lower Fraser valley. Both these districts are tributary to Vancouver, which also shares in the genial climate. Its harbour is ice-free, and, sheltered by the mountains of Vancouver Island, the town has a (relatively) low rainfall of 60 inches per annum. In contrast, North Vancouver, only three miles away, experiences 80 inches, and the lower mountain slopes behind it 120 inches.

Apart from the fertile farmlands of the lower Fraser valley, the chief local resource is timber. In its natural state the region was clothed in magnificent forest, and a sample of this is preserved in the tall stands of Douglas fir and western red cedar in Stanley Park, on the peninsula to the north-west of the city. Little of the original forest remains in the immediate neighbourhood; but there are still important local timber-using industries, particularly on the shores of False Creek and in New Westminster. They comprise about 30 sawmills and shingle mills (shingles are wooden roof 'tiles') and about 60 other timber-based factories.

The commercial core of Vancouver remains on the glacial ridge, and here are the large shops, the department stores, and half a dozen skyscrapers. Fronting Burrard Inlet are the main wharves, with regular shipping connections to about 50 different countries, together with 9 large grain elevators, warehouses, and industrial works. Vancouver is by far the greatest dry-cargo port on the Pacific shores of both the Americas; it is also the largest exporter of grain in the world.

Suburban residences occupy most of the rolling land between Burrard Inlet and the Fraser, while the flatter land at the head of False Creek houses the Japanese and Chinese quarters. The Chinese played an important part in the early days of the province, labouring on the railways, extracting yet more gold from a gravel bed pronounced 'barren', opening cafés and stores in the pioneer towns. The Chinese grocer on the corner survives the competition of the chain store because he remains open until midnight. Chinatown contains some colourful stores and restaurants, but most of the families are being rehoused in new, specially designed flats with a communal flavour about them. The University of British Columbia enjoys a particularly attractive setting near the sea at the western end of Point Grey.

Vancouver passed the quarter-million mark about 1931 and the half-million mark in 1951. With a metropolitan population of 790,165 persons in 1961, it is now well on the way to joining the 'million' cities. It ranks third among the metropolitan areas of Canada, after Montreal (2,110,679 in 1961) and Toronto (1,824,589).

Victoria, Prince George, Prince Rupert

Victoria, lacking any large hinterland, remains very much smaller than Vancouver. It was founded in 1843 as a fortified fur-trading post of the Hudson's Bay Company, on a sheltered cove which possessed a deep-water harbour. Fifteen years later came the discovery of gold on the flanks of the Cariboo mountains, in the upper reaches of the Fraser river system. It was a journey of over 500 miles up-stream, but Victoria was the only seaport in the region, and it became the supply base for the miners. Then in 1866 Vancouver Island was combined with the mainland to form an enlarged British Columbia, and Victoria was proclaimed the new capital. Today Victoria is perhaps primarily a centre of administration; but it is also the commercial centre for the productive farming districts of south-eastern Vancouver Island; its port is of more than local significance; and there is the important naval dockyard of Esquimalt on its western outskirts.

The genial climate and the scenic beauty of its surroundings have attracted many tourists to Victoria. The town enjoys mild winter temperatures and an exceptionally low rainfall, of only 27 inches annually. The population of its metropolitan area in 1961 was 154,152.

Prince George and Prince Rupert lie in the sparsely peopled northern part of the province. Both were planned on a generous scale, and though they are increasing in size, neither has yet justified the imagination of the founders.

Nature has given a striking nodality to the site of Prince George. Near here the Fraser makes its great bend to the south, and at the same spot receives its tributary from the north, the Nechako. The transcontinental C.N.R. line, following the upper Fraser, passes through the spot on its way from Edmonton to the Pacific at Prince Rupert. In recent years this nodality has been strengthened by the construction of railway links southward to Vancouver and northward to the grain-lands of the Peace River district. The land in the angle of the river junction was planned for a large town in 1915; yet by 1941 the population was only about 2000, and only one-sixth of the planned area was occupied. But, as we have seen, rapid progress is taking place in many parts of British Columbia; in the 1961 census the population of Prince George had reached nearly 14,000, and we may expect a further rise.

The site of Prince Rupert is sheltered by an island from the open sea; its harbour is ice-free and possesses deep water; and it lies close to the mouth of the Skeena river, which provides a natural routeway eastward into the interior. Prince Rupert was chosen as the Pacific terminal of the C.N.R. line, and about 1906 the site was planned for a town of 50,000 people. At the 1961 census the population numbered only 12,000. There is a fishing harbour, a cannery, grain elevators, and a cold-storage plant; but there seems little likelihood at present of any rivalry with Vancouver.

CHAPTER ELEVEN

THE NORTHLANDS

A characteristic feature of the Northlands is their lack of close settlement. A glance at the population map will help to indicate their limits. We exclude the Atlantic provinces of Nova Scotia, Prince Edward Island, and New Brunswick, for although the hilly interiors of the two mainland provinces are sparsely inhabited, their lowlands are well peopled. Newfoundland too we exclude, since it possesses a personality which is distinct from that of the rest of the vast region. The St Lawrence Lowlands and the Lake peninsula are closely settled; but Ontario north of the Great Lakes and Quebec north of the valley of the St Lawrence clearly form part of the Northlands. We have already seen that the greater part of the prairie provinces is in fact almost uninhabited; and the southern boundary of the Northlands corresponds fairly well with straight lines joining Winnipeg with Prince Albert in Saskatchewan, thence to the Lesser Slave lake and westward to the Pacific in the region of Prince of Wales Island (Fig. 121). In the north-west we include the American state of Alaska.

A vast area is so delimited – one which probably exceeds that of the 48 conterminous states of the United States. Its largest town is Sudbury, with a population of 111,000 in the metropolitan area, and it is tempting to regard this district as part of 'settled' Canada. But Sudbury owes its very existence to the mineral wealth in its neighbourhood, and in this respect is similar to Schefferville and Yellowknife; it is conceivable that other areas, at present remote, may repeat the experience of Sudbury. We include the many large islands which stretch towards the North Pole. Baffin Island, the largest of them, is almost twice the size of the British Isles.

With only a few exceptions (notably in British Columbia and Alaska), this major portion of the continent shares a dry, cold climate; it lacks roads and railways, and has only limited possibilities for agriculture; but it forms a storehouse of mineral wealth, it is rich in water-power resources, there are valuable salmon fisheries in the west and considerable timber reserves in the south.

Fig. 121. THE NORTHLANDS

The map indicates the vast extent of this region, which includes more than 80 per cent. of the surface of Canada, together with the state of Alaska.

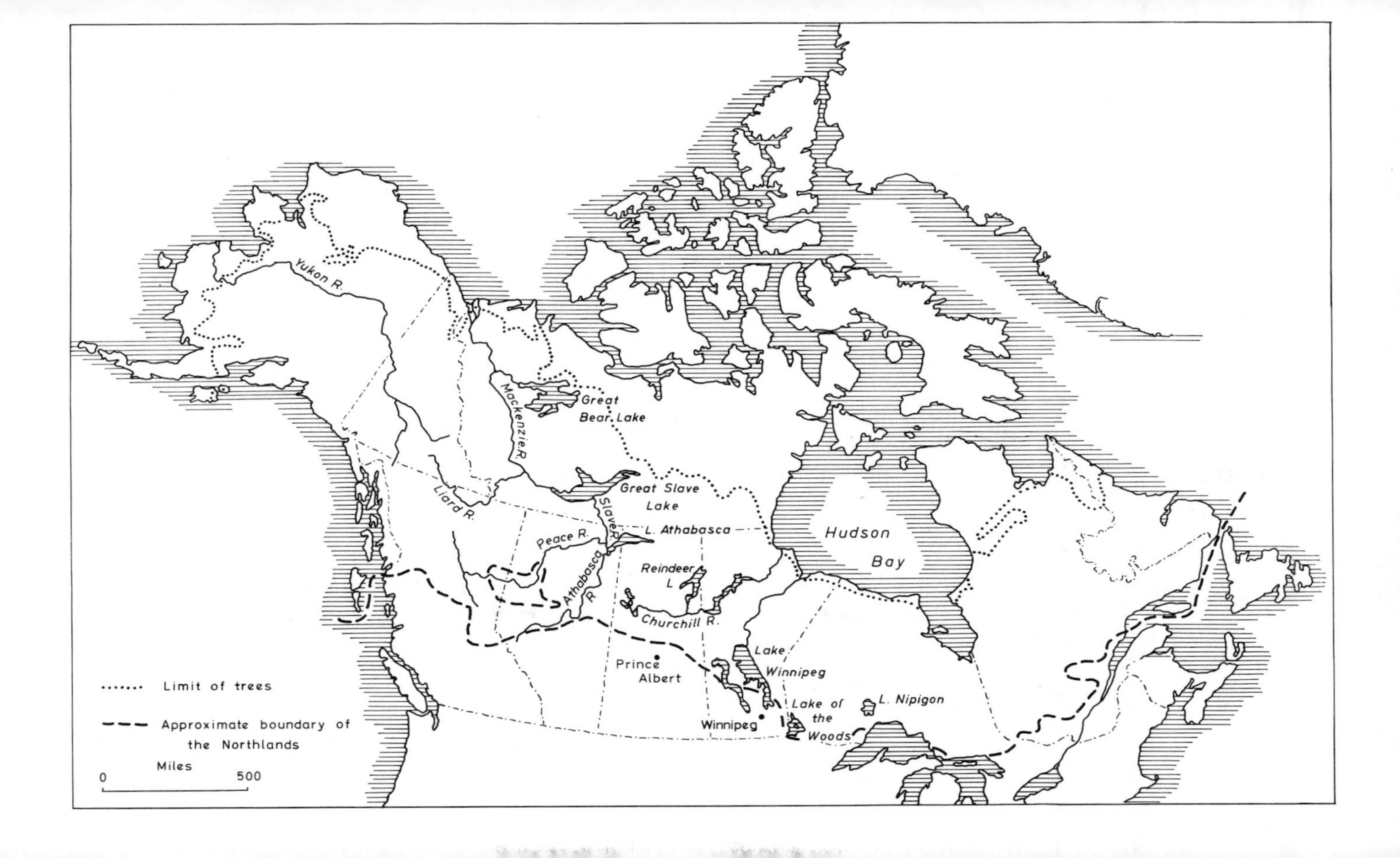
Yukon R.
Mackenzie R.
Great Bear Lake
Liard R.
Great Slave Lake
Slave R.
L. Athabasca
Peace R.
Athabasca R.
Reindeer L.
Churchill R.
Hudson Bay
Prince Albert
Lake Winnipeg
Winnipeg
Lake of the Woods
L. Nipigon
Limit of trees
Approximate boundary of the Northlands
Miles
0
500

Structure and Physical Features

Almost every major structural region of Canada is represented in the Northlands. One, however, is dominant – this is the Laurentian Shield.

Basically the Laurentian Shield is composed of Pre-Cambrian rocks, in places sedimentary in origin, but often metamorphosed and crystalline. In many places there are igneous intrusions, and it is here that conditions are favourable for the concentration of minerals. To the south-west of Hudson bay the Pre-Cambrian rocks are masked by Ordovician, Silurian, and Devonian strata, with even small areas of Cretaceous material.

The Pre-Cambrian rocks show signs of violent mountain-building movements; but subsequent erosion has reduced the former mountain systems into a monotonous peneplain. The whole area was covered by the Quaternary ice sheets, which removed the loose material, exposed much bare rock, and obliterated the pre-glacial river systems. The resulting scatter of lakes and swamps interconnected by rivers and interrupted by falls and rapids can only be described as chaotic.

Broadly speaking, the outer edge of the Shield is marked by the line of major lakes comprising Great Bear and Great Slave lakes, Athabasca and Reindeer lakes, Lake Winnipeg, the Lake of the Woods, and the Great Lakes. While the land generally slopes down towards Hudson bay, the Great Lakes drain southward and then eastward to the Atlantic, while Great Bear, Great Slave, and Athabasca lakes drain westward to the Mackenzie, and so to the Beaufort Sea.

The second main structural region comprises the continuation of the Great Plains, on which, farther south, the prairies are developed. The strata, which are horizontal or only gently disturbed, are of various ages, from Ordovician to Tertiary. The lead and zinc minerals bordering Great Slave lake occur in the Middle Devonian, while the Upper Devonian contains the oil which is tapped at Norman Wells, on the Mackenzie river, about 100 miles south of the Arctic Circle.

Towards the north, in the Mackenzie lowland, are soft shales and sandstones of Cretaceous age; these are coal-bearing, and are mined in quite small quantities at Moose River, in order to supply the Arctic town of Aklavik. In the middle and lower districts of the Mackenzie system there are soft Tertiary sands and clays. The Mackenzie is navigable, and in the absence of rail and road transport it forms the main artery for the carriage of freight in the Mackenzie district of the North-west Territories.

West of the Mackenzie river the land rises to a plateau whose general level is above 3000 feet; and from its surface rises a series of parallel mountain chains arranged north-west and south-east, whose summits attain 8000 to 9000 feet. This, the Yukon Plateau, is essentially a platform of old metamorphic rocks, but in its basins there are Palæozoic and Mesozoic strata.

The 141st meridian forms part of the international boundary between the Yukon Territory and Alaska, and corresponds broadly with a physical boundary. To the east is the lofty and unbroken Yukon Plateau; to the west is a series of parallel mountain ranges separated by deep valleys, plains, and basins. There is nevertheless a common unifying element in that both are traversed by the Yukon river; across this border, unlike the main international boundary, communications and economic activity flow freely, and both the Yukon and Alaska share many of the problems of the Northlands.

In Alaska the general trend of the mountain ranges is east and west, or a little north of east and south of west. This is reflected in the irregular, indented coastline, which runs transverse to the structure, and in the long Alaska peninsula and its thousand-mile extension in the Aleutian Islands.

Moving from north to south, we see first a low-lying coastal plain bordering the Arctic Ocean, treeless and frozen for most of the year, and about 100 miles wide at its greatest extent. It is overlooked from the south by the lofty Brooks Range, whose bare summits rise to over 7000 feet. Farther south are plains and basins, each with its scatter of small settlements. They include the plains of the upper and lower Yukon river, that of the Koyukuk river, and the basin west of Fairbanks. The basins are separated by plateaux and mountains, the most prominent being the Kuskokwim mountains, with summits at about 5000 feet.

In the south and south-east is the continuous curve formed by the Alaska mountains, the Alaskan peninsula, and the Aleutian Islands. The Alaska mountains rise to summits of 11,000, 12,000, and 13,000 feet, and nourish many glaciers. The peninsula extends for 500 miles in the form of a narrow mountainous ridge, and its smooth curve continues in the 50 or so Aleutian islands, which extend for a further 1100 miles.

The whole belt forms one of the most striking manifestations of volcanic activity in the world, for in a strip of country only 25 miles wide are about 80 volcanoes, 32 of them active. Here is one of the largest craters known – that of Aniakchak – with a mean diameter of more than six miles. Katmai, near the head of the peninsula, is notorious for the eruption of 1912, whose three colossal explosions were heard 750 miles away. The ash from this outburst blotted out the sun for three days, and devastated hundreds of square miles of wooded country. The summit of the cone, which formerly reached 7500 feet, was blown off, leaving a crater 2½ miles in diameter, whose jagged rim now reaches only 4500 feet.

Parallel with and to the south of the great volcanic arc lies one of the deepest oceanic trenches, whose greatest depths surpass 24,000 feet. Here is clearly one of the zones of instability in the earth's surface; and the volcanic belt corresponds with an earthquake zone. At Easter, 1964, 118 Alaskans died in one of the fiercest earthquakes ever recorded. Violent earth tremors passed through Anchorage, the largest city in the state, and its main street dropped ten feet.

In a 'panhandle' over 500 miles long the Alaskan boundary marches with those of the Yukon and British Columbia, and encloses valuable forest-land, many islands, and sheltered waterways. The few roads and the single railway cross the frontier without interruption.

Climate and the Possibilities of Agriculture

With the exception of the districts bordering the Pacific Ocean, this is a region of long and intensely cold winters and short but surprisingly warm summers (Fig. 122). It is generally agreed, however, that the winters are less severe than one might expect, and that, given appropriate clothing and equipment, open-air work and play can be carried on throughout the year. The shortness of the summer is offset to a large extent by the increased hours of daylight, so that in favourable localities cultivation can take place, sometimes with surprising success.

The Federal (Canadian) Department of Agriculture maintains experimental stations at Fort Simpson, on the Mackenzie river, and at Whitehorse, on the upper Yukon, while the University of Alaska does similar work at Fairbanks. Wheat, barley, oats, and fodder crops grow successfully, together with tomatoes, potatoes, cabbages, and other vegetables, and tree and berry fruits.

In the Northwest Territories there are estimated to be 500,000 acres of potential ranching land in the Slave river basin and between 100,000 and 200,000 acres of mixed farming country in the valley of the Liard. In the Yukon the valleys are estimated to contain potentially 250,000 to 500,000 acres of farm-land, though at present agriculture is limited to about a thousand acres of vegetable gardens in the neighbourhoods of Whitehorse, Dawson, and Mayo.

Within the Northlands the most significant boundary is the tree-line; this rarely corresponds with the Arctic Circle, yet it marks in a real sense the southern limit of the geographical 'Arctic'. The tree-line corresponds broadly with the course of the mean July isotherm 50°F. It includes all the northern islands, a coastal belt along the northern and western fringes of Alaska, the whole of Keewatin, and the Ungava peninsula of Quebec. Within this zone the mean annual precipitation is less than ten inches. There are no important mining ventures within this region, though there are many small and scattered Aleut and Eskimo villages, as well as modern outposts linked with defence.

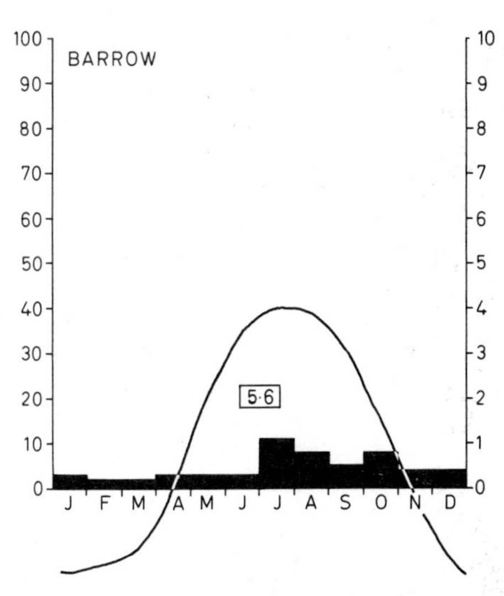

Fig. 122. BARROW: TEMPERATURE AND PRECIPITATION
For key see Fig. 46 (p. 117).

The winter temperatures in parts of the Northlands are little different from those in such centres as Saskatoon, Edmonton, and Winnipeg. At Whitehorse, in the Yukon, the average temperature during the five coldest months is 10°F. – one degree higher than at Winnipeg. Yellowknife in winter is colder, at −8°, but its summers are surprisingly warm, and the average for the three summer months, at 57°, is only three degrees below that of Edmonton.

Surprising too are the high temperatures reached during the short summer. Fort Yukon, in north-east Alaska, lies on the Arctic Circle, and it holds the official records for both the highest and the lowest temperatures in the state: the lowest was −78°F.; the highest was 100°! Most of Alaska is similar in climate to the regions farther east. Precipitation at Fairbanks amounts to only 11 inches annually, and there is a very great range of temperature: during midwinter nights at Fairbanks the temperature falls to the −50's and occasionally reaches −70°; but in June the air is pleasantly warm and the long hours of sunshine may send the temperature into the 90's.

Long summer days bring some compensation to the dweller in the Northlands. The Arctic Circle marks the limit of the summer midnight sun, and correspondingly the absence of daylight in midwinter. Yellowknife is 300 miles south of the Arctic Circle, but even here sunrise and sunset blend for a fortnight each side of midsummer. One can read a newspaper out of doors, and the local golf club begins its tournament at midnight on midsummer's day.

The defect of the climate of the north lies not so much in its low temperatures as in the length of its winters. This is reflected in its growing season – that is, the number of days in the year that are free from killing frost. At Saskatoon in the prairies the growing season lasts 112 days; at Whitehorse in the Yukon the growing season is 78 days; at Mayo, 200 miles farther north, it is reduced to 64 days.

The severity of the winter may also be estimated by the length of time during which the temperature is below comfort level (which we may conventionally accept as being 65°F.) and qualified by the extent to which it is below that level. This may be measured in 'degree days': for every day whose average temperature is below the comfort line one totals the number of degrees between the average daily temperature and 65°F. On this basis in an average year Winnipeg has about 11,000 degree days, Saskatoon 10,800, and Edmonton 10,300. The corresponding figure for Yellowknife is 15,600. The figures give some indication of the amount of heating required to maintain comfortable temperatures indoors; they suggest that heating costs are likely to be about 50 per cent. higher at Yellowknife than in the prairies. It represents an additional cost burden on all economic activity in the Northlands, but not necessarily a crippling burden.

Very different from these conditions are the districts to the south and west of the Alaska and Coast Ranges, for these mountains act as almost complete climatic barriers. The Aleutian Islands and the Pacific shores are bathed in the warm waters of the Japan Stream. Their harbours are open throughout the year, in striking contrast to all the other harbours of the Northlands, with only the possible exception of one or two on the lower St Lawrence river.

The climate of the Pacific coasts is mild and equable, but damp and misty. Juneau, in the Alaskan 'panhandle', has a mean January temperature of 28°F. and a July temperature of 58°. The intense cold of the interior is missing, but so is its summer sunshine and warmth. In exposed situations the rainfall is very high. Juneau receives 91 inches in the year; in the Aleutians, Unalaska Island receives 80 inches – shared among 250 of the 365 days.

In these conditions trees grow quickly, and there are valuable reserves of Sitka spruce, western hemlock, and Alaska cedar. Almost the whole of south-eastern Alaska is a forest reserve. There is scope too for dairy farming and vegetable cultivation; oats will yield well, but there is insufficient sunshine for wheat.

We illustrate from the Matanuska valley, whose river is fed by glacier sources and flows west to reach the sea near Anchorage. Settlement here dates from 1935, when the United States Government helped to move farmers from the derelict Great Plains (p. 156). It is now a prosperous farming district, producing oats, potatoes, dairy produce, and poultry. In this sheltered valley the growing season is as long as 108 days; well-drained river terraces offer ideal sites for farms. One dairy farm here comprises 560 acres, of which 100 acres have been so far cleared; its cattle browse on rich pastures overlooked by the Talkeetna mountains and glaciers. The farmer grows her own silage (peas, oats, and vetch) but is not yet self-sufficient in hay; her modern dairy is the equal of any in the country. The market for this farming district is the small town of Palmer.

The Eskimos

The interest aroused by the culture and welfare of the Eskimos is out of all proportion to their numbers. In Alaska there are about 20,000 Eskimos and 1500 Aleuts, of related stock; there are a further 12,000 in Canada. In total they represent only a minute fraction of the population of North America. The Eskimos are scattered in small family groups along the shores of the Bering and Beaufort seas, and around the gulfs and bays of the Canadian Arctic regions. They inhabit the south and east coasts of Baffin Island, the north-western and north-eastern shores of Hudson bay, the coasts in the neighbourhood of King William island and as far west as the Mackenzie delta. They and the Aleuts occupy about 45 settlements in Alaska, along the coast and inland bordering the major rivers.

The Arctic seas are rich in fish and mammals, and it is this fact which has attracted the Eskimo to the coast and kept him there. In the water are walrus and whales, and on land fox, bear, and caribou; but it was the seal in particular which formed the basis of the Eskimo culture. In winter, when the ice froze over the bays, the Eskimos moved on to it and hunted the seal through its breathing-holes in the ice. In spring, as the shelf ice broke up, they retreated to the land and harpooned the seals as they came out to bask in the sun; in summer they chased the seals by means of light, skin-covered kayaks. The seal provided meat and clothing, oil for lamps, and bone for tools. The Eskimo supplemented his diet in summer by berries, roots, and edible fungi, by caribou flesh, and by fish trapped in the rivers. In hunting and transport the dog was an indispensable ally.

This close association between the Eskimo and his environment was broken by the appearance of the European. The nineteenth-century whalers came to the Arctic; they slaughtered the walrus and they almost exterminated the whale. In addition they introduced diseases against which the natives had no resistance. Then came the fur-traders: they offered tempting articles at the store – kettles, nails, cooking-pots, and tea – in exchange for fox-skins. But fur-trapping involved longer journeys and increased gear, so that the dog team had to be expanded from two or three to ten or eleven. In its turn this meant that to feed his family and his dogs a trapper needed to kill five or six caribou each week; and so the caribou herds, which are believed to have numbered 4 million head in 1900, were reduced to their present remnant of about 400,000 head.

For some years furs commanded a high price, and for a fox-skin the trapper received 35 dollars. But a drastic decline followed, and in the mid 40's the price fell to $3\frac{1}{2}$ dollars. The Eskimo was now in a sorry plight: his food resources were depleted, and trapping brought little return. Many went ill-clad and undernourished.

Since 1954 the Government has intensified its efforts to ease the hardships of the Eskimo. The immediate relief took the form of family allowances and other money payments, to which the Eskimos in common with other Canadian citizens were fully entitled. But more permanent help was needed, and this has taken several forms.

New caribou herds have been established near the Mackenzie river, and Eskimos have been placed in charge of them. Some families have been transferred from areas with meagre resources to those better supplied with the means of subsistence. A recent experiment has been with the marketing of Arctic char: a trial shipment was made in 1959, and the response was so encouraging that Eskimo fishermen of the Frobisher Bay district in 1960 sent a consignment of 50,000 lb.

The Eskimo is by nature intelligent and resourceful, and quite ready to adopt new ideas where these can be shown to work. Normal and vocational schools are being established, and permanent hostels built. Eskimos have proved themselves successful as carpenters, as members of oil-drilling teams, and as Government employees. At Frobisher they run a cinema, a laundry, and a coffee bar. Above all, many of them are skilled artists and sculptors.

Traditional Eskimo carvings are in the soft local soapstone, fashioned into the likenesses of men, walruses, seals, polar bears, whales, and birds; in addition their artistic ability has been adapted to the production of prints from sealskin and stone. The first display of Eskimo art took place in 1959, and was an immediate success. Exhibitions have now been held in 23 countries; there are art and craft centres at Cape Dorset and Frobisher Bay in the eastern Arctic, and a sculptors' society at Povungnituk.

It seems that the days of self-sufficiency are over. But the future for the Eskimos appears to be hopeful. Their community is young and vigorous: 65 per cent. of them are under 25 years of age and their numbers are quickly increasing. Rapid developments are taking place in the Northlands, and a wise administration will make good use of the extending range of opportunities for the Eskimo population.

ECONOMIC DEVELOPMENT

Almost the entire modern development of the Northlands has been related to its mineral wealth. Many minerals are present, but exploitation so far as been limited to gold, uranium, silver, lead, zinc, copper, iron, and nickel. We examine in turn the districts associated with these minerals: the Labrador and North Shore of Quebec district, the Quebec–Ontario and Steep Rock districts, the Mackenzie Basin, the Yukon Territory, and Alaska. We continue by noticing the salmon fisheries of the Pacific shores, and in conclusion examine the forest and fur industries and the strategic value of the Arctic.

The Quebec–Labrador Region

Sailing up the St Lawrence river in 1534, Jacques Cartier wrote, 'It is appalling and rugged rock and stone, for along the whole of the North Shore I saw not even a cart-load of soil. It seems most likely to me that here is the land God gave to Cain.'

Yet today men are tapping the minerals of the region, railways stretch far inland and deliver the wealth of the orefields to bustling new ports on the North Shore. Even the farming which Cartier thought impossible has made a beginning with 8000 acres of cultivation near Baie Comeau.

Much of the mineral wealth of the region is concentrated in a downwarp of the Laurentian Shield – the Labrador Trough – which extends for over 500 miles from Ungava bay in the north approximately as far as the Hudson bay–St Lawrence water parting in the south. During late Pre-Cambrian times this trough was submerged and filled with sediments in which iron accumulated. The trough is fabulously rich in iron: about 2000 million tons of ore are believed to be contained in it; and of this, it has been shown that about 400 million tons are of high grade, averaging 55 per cent. iron, and available for open-cast working. When the men were constructing a road at Schefferville they found iron ore only two feet below the surface; while digging holes for telephone posts they found an ore body of 15 million tons; and they discovered that by accident they had placed their base camp on another body of 11 million tons.

It is a land of bitterly cold winters, where snow lies even in July (Fig. 123) – a land of lakes and rivers, muskeg swamp, dwarf spruce, caribou moss, and bare rock. In 1950 the Iron Ore Company of Canada began to build a 357-mile railway from the orefield at Schefferville to the shore at Seven Islands. This, the first major railway to be built in North America for 50 years, was begun from several points simultaneously with the aid of helicopters. A new town was laid out on the orefield and a new port constructed at Seven Islands (Fig. 124).

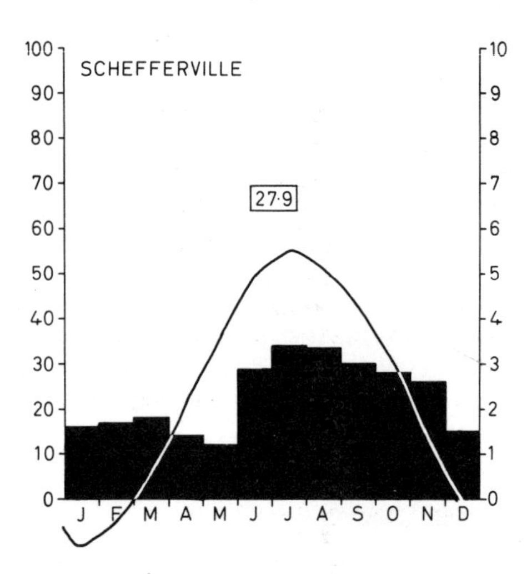

Fig. 123. SCHEFFERVILLE: TEMPERATURE AND PRECIPITATION
For key see Fig. 46 (p. 117).

Schefferville, named after Bishop Lionel Scheffer, has a summer population of over 5000, though when mining ceases in winter it drops to half that size. The town spreads eastward from a nucleus on an esker between two lakes. In the town centre are community buildings, schools, stores, churches, and the Catholic cathedral; gathered around are the pastel-coloured homes, built of asbestos and timber. The hydro-electric plants which supply light and power to the town and the quarries and mills are situated at nearby Menihek and at Clarke City, 360 miles to the south.

Everywhere is the red dust of the iron ore. It is won by huge electric shovels in open pits and loaded into trains of 100 trucks which clatter downhill to Seven Islands. This is a well-equipped ore port, designed to accommodate large ore-carriers. Two 30,000-ton vessels were specially built for the project, but ore from Seven Islands is shipped in a variety of vessels, and large quantities feed the steel-works of the United Kingdom.

By the end of the first shipping season in 1954, 600,000 tons of ore had reached the port; output is now at the rate of about 13 million tons annually, and this is by far the chief iron-producing district of Canada, accounting for about 40 per cent. of the entire Canadian output.

The project did not end with the completion of the railway to Schefferville. A spur has been built from mile 224 westward to Wabush lake, where there are large deposits of low-grade ore. A new town, Labrador City, has been constructed there, and mining began in 1965 with an initial output of 6 million tons a year. A future extension of the

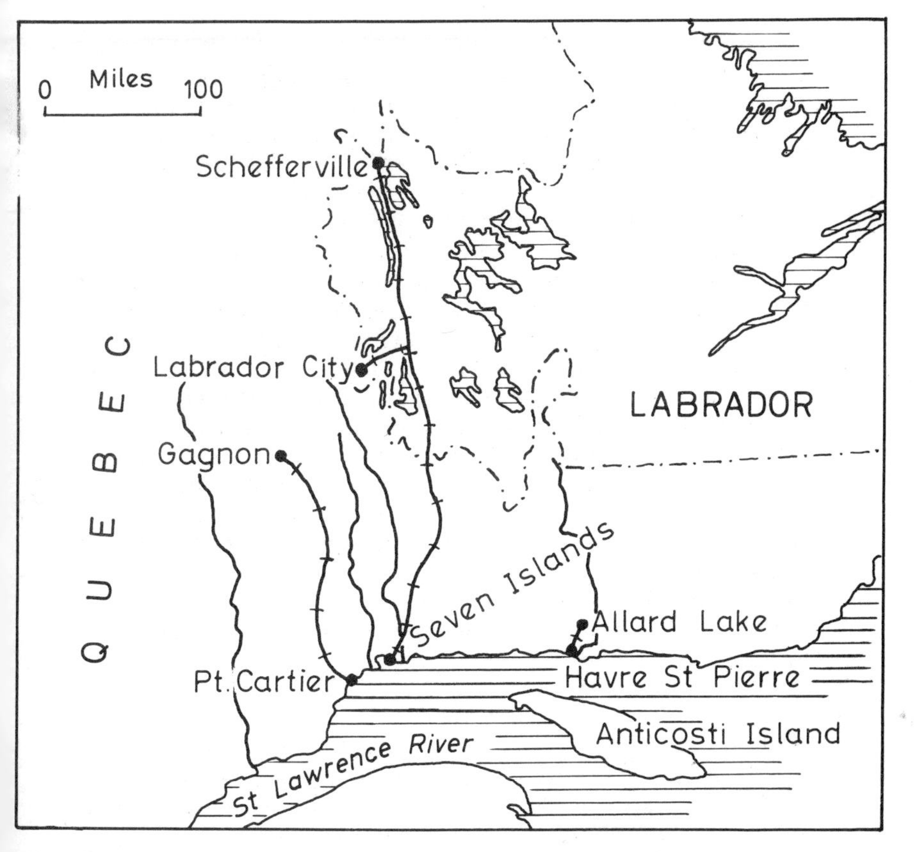

Fig. 124. MINING IN THE QUEBEC–NORTH SHORE REGION

Development in all these districts has taken place only since 1952. Schefferville is the largest Canadian producer of iron; Labrador City and Gagnon are also iron-producers; Allard Lake is one of the world's major sources of titanium.

railway north-west from Schefferville is likely, for the ore bodies are known to extend in that direction.

This same pattern – new port, railway, orefield – is repeated twice more, though on a lesser scale (Fig. 124). About 20 miles west of Seven Islands is Port Cartier. A few years ago this site was occupied by a family of Red Indians; now a fine new harbour has been excavated from the solid rock, providing a minimum depth of 50 feet of water – sufficient to accommodate the world's largest ore-carriers. A railway nearly 200 miles long was completed in 1961, and a new town named Gagnon was built on the orefield.

As at Wabush lake, these are low-grade iron ores, and they are concentrated on the spot. The area has an important advantage over

Schefferville in that with only a low water content the concentrate can be transported by rail without any danger of its freezing to the trucks; it is believed also that shipment out of the St Lawrence will be possible throughout the year. In 1962 this district, with 18 per cent. of the Canadian output, was second only to Schefferville.

The third mining district of the North Shore lies about 120 miles east of Seven Islands, and is served by the port of Havre St Pierre. The ore-field is at Allard Lake, about 40 miles inland, and the mineral is not iron ore but ilmenite, which contains 30 per cent. iron oxide and 32 per cent. titanium dioxide. Development here was earlier than in the other two districts. Production began in 1952, and the output is at the rate of nearly a million tons of ilmenite a year. The ore is processed at a new smelting plant at Sorel, on the St Lawrence river about 100 miles up-stream of Quebec. This is one of the world's major sources of titanium – a metal which combines lightness with remarkable strength and resistance to corrosion. It has many uses in aircraft and other industries, and the product finds a ready market in the United States, the U.S.S.R., Germany, and the United Kingdom.

The North Shore will perhaps never become a densely peopled region, but it is clear that in favoured districts economic advance will be rapid.

The Quebec–Ontario Mineral Region

About 600 miles to the west of Seven Islands is the second productive mineral region. The Quebec–Ontario provincial boundary passes across a shallow depression whose floor is occupied partly by lakes Abitibi, Timiskaming, and Nipissing. During the retreat phase of the ice sheets a great marginal lake occupied much of this low land – 'Lake Ojibway' – whose remnants form the existing lakes. Around them are the silts and clays of the former lake, which, when not unduly peat-covered, form useful farm-land, particularly for potato-growing. This is the Clay Belt, an oasis of agriculture amid lake, swamp, and forest (Plate 14). In it and around its margins lie some of the most valuable mineral deposits in the whole continent (Fig. 125).

Unlike the North Shore region of Quebec, here the railways came

---

Plate 14. LAKE ABITIBI AND THE CLAY BELT, QUEBEC PROVINCE

The photograph includes the eastern end of Lake Abitibi, which lies astride the provincial boundary between Ontario and Quebec. The district forms part of the Clay Belt, where the Pre-Cambrian rocks of the Laurentian Shield are masked by the silts and clays of the former glacial Lake Ojibway. The growing season is rather short (140–160 days), and in this remote region farming is directed towards supplying the local communities and mining centres. Dairy products provide the main source of income; in addition the farm will perhaps support some pigs and poultry and a vegetable garden. The land farthest from the road has been left in forest.

Photo Royal Canadian Air Force. Crown copyright reserved

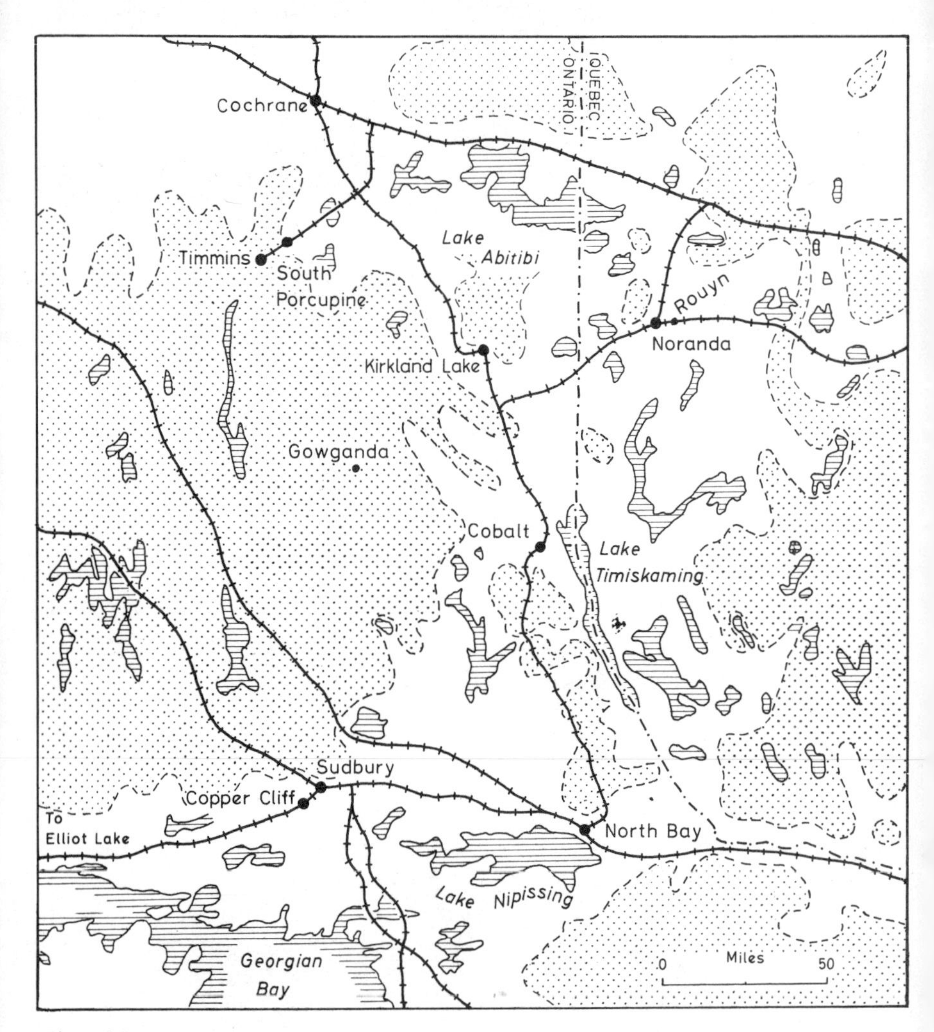

Fig. 125. THE QUEBEC–ONTARIO MINERAL REGION

Lakes Abitibi, Timiskaming, and Nipissing are remnants of former glacial lake 'Ojibway'. Silver deposits at Cobalt and gold at Porcupine, Kirkland Lake, and Noranda were discovered when the region was opened up by the railways.

first, and it was during their construction that many of the orefields were revealed. This was not entirely accidental, for the railway engineer sought out the higher and better-drained land for the line of his route; often this was occasioned by granite intrusions, which provided conditions favourable for the accumulation of minerals.

During the 1880's the main line of the Canadian Pacific Railway was thrusting westward from Ottawa through North Bay and towards

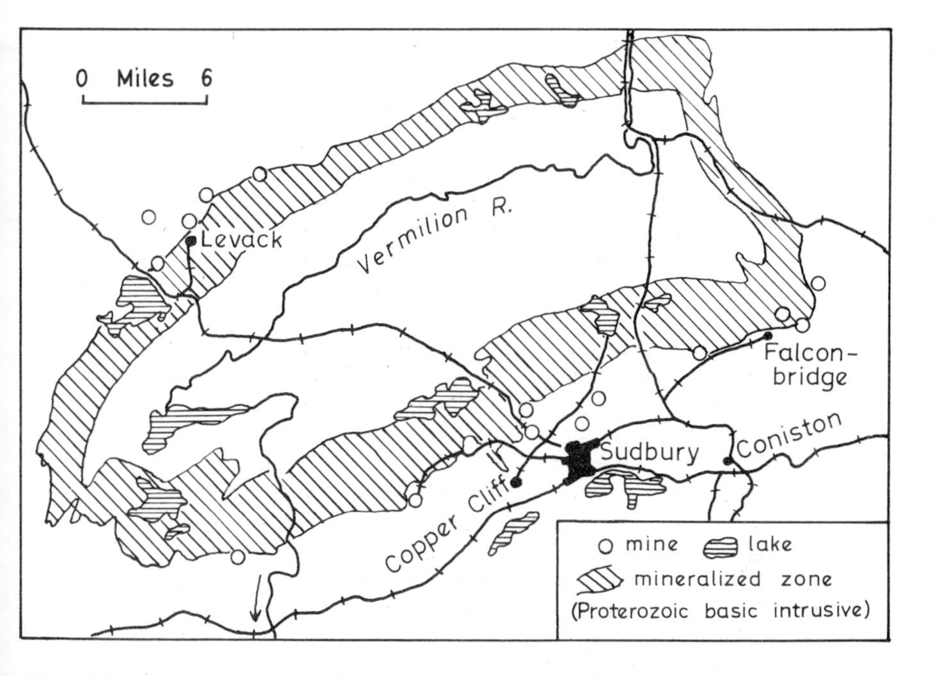

Fig. 126. THE SUDBURY DISTRICT

The shaded area represents basic intrusive material, and forms the rim of a basin in the Archæan rocks. This district produces nearly three-quarters of the world's nickel. There are smelters at Copper Cliff and Coniston.

Fort William. On the way the engineers discovered the copper-nickel ores of Sudbury and Copper Cliff. Between 1902 and 1908 the Ontario Government was building the line which strikes northward to Cochrane from North Bay; again the engineers found minerals – this time the silver deposits of Cobalt. Soon, too, prospectors had located the gold ores of Porcupine and Kirkland Lake, farther north – now the richest goldfields of North America. In 1913 a second westward railway was being built, parallel to but farther north than the Canadian Pacific: it struck westward from Quebec, passed through Cochrane, and skirted Lake Nipigon on its way to Winnipeg. A short loop led to the rich Quebec goldfields of Rouyn and Noranda, and the railway in addition passed through the gold-bearing district of north Ontario.

Sudbury was named by a railway official in honour of his wife, who was born in the East Anglian town of that name. To the north-west of the town is an elongated basin in the Pre-Cambrian rocks, filled with sedimentary material and rimmed by basic intrusive rocks (Fig. 126). In the latter are found the nickel–copper ores that have made the district famous. The ore was discovered in 1883, exposed in the railway cutting.

Today 12 mines in this small area raise nearly three-quarters of the world's nickel, and Sudbury has become the nickel capital of the world.

There are some open-cast workings, but for the most part these are deep mines: the galleries total about 500 miles in length and some of them are more than a mile from the surface. Two main firms engage in nickel production: the headquarters of the International Nickel Company are at Copper Cliff, 4 miles west of Sudbury, while those of the Falconbridge Nickel Mines are at the town of that name, 14 miles north-east of Sudbury.

The ores are essentially blends of copper and nickel, and, in addition to the nickel, yield about 40 per cent. of the Canadian output of copper; they also contain iron, and since 1956 this has been recovered too. These remarkable ores contain in addition small proportions of the platinum group of metals, which include platinum itself, together with rhodium, palladium, iridium, osmium, and ruthenium. Each has its special uses. Finally, the Sudbury ores also contain gold, silver, and lead.

Smelting takes place at Copper Cliff and at Coniston, both places being in the district; further refining is carried out at Port Colborne, on Lake Erie, but some of the concentrates are shipped to South Wales for smelting at Clydach, near Swansea. From here the residues receive their final treatment at the Mond precious metals refinery in west London.

The Sudbury district contains a total population of nearly 150,000, half of whom are in Sudbury itself. This is a young, vigorous, and growing town, with a newly established university and a large sports arena. Thirty different racial groups live and work there in harmony. In comparison with the towns of southern Ontario, Sudbury has much of the pioneer spirit about it, and boasts the lowest average age of any town in Canada – 22 years.

The mining industry at Cobalt dates back to 1903, when the railway was being pushed northward from North Bay. The object was to open up potential farming land and timber country in the Clay Belt. At mile 103 two railway employees noticed the glint of metal in the cutting and sent away some samples for assay: they were found to contain 4000 ounces of silver to the ton – among the richest concentrations ever known. Claims were staked, and the McKinley–Darragh mine was born, named after its two discoverers. At its peak the town of Cobalt numbered 7000 inhabitants. For long the cobalt element in the ore was regarded as unsaleable waste material; but when the price of silver fell new uses were discovered for cobalt, such as in ceramics, in steel alloys, jet engines, animal foods, and nylon hosiery. Canada is one of the leading producers of silver in the world, and 15 per cent. of the output is still obtained from Ontario mines at Cobalt and Gowganda, 50 miles to the west.

After South Africa and the U.S.S.R., Canada is the biggest gold-producer in the world, and 80 per cent. of the output is derived from 29 mines in Ontario and 14 in Quebec. The greatest producing district is Porcupine, in the north-westerly part of the gold-bearing region.

After the rich discoveries of silver in the Cobalt district prospectors became interested in the land to the north, and so found the Porcupine field. In 1909 a prospector slipped on a steep hillside and revealed below the moss a ledge of quartz. He followed it, and it led him to a dome-shaped hill where he could see the gleam of gold: so began the famous Dome mine. A few miles to the west are the Hollinger and McIntyre mines, named after their discoverers. To provide labour for the great Hollinger mine the town of Timmins was laid out on the terraces of the Mattagami river to the west of the mine. Planned in the usual grid manner, its business centre is overlooked by the well-to-do residential district on the highest terrace; later expansion has taken place northward on the damper clay and peat land. Its population amounts to about 27,000.

Fourteen gold-mines are concentrated in an area about 12 miles from east to west and 6 from north to south, threaded by the Ontario Northland railway and a trunk highway. Shaft-heads, water-tanks, tailing heaps, and crushing plants are the elements in this untidy landscape. Both town and mines are supplied by hydro-electric power from the Wawaitin and Sandy falls.

Second only to the Porcupine goldfield in output is the Rouyn field, about 60 miles to the south-east. Here a prospector first found gold in 1912, a few miles east of the railway station of Swastika. Two mines were opened, the town of Kirkland Lake was established, and quickly grew to 20,000 people. The district now has five mines, and includes the Kerr–Addison, the most productive gold-mine in Canada.

On the south-western outskirts of the Quebec–Ontario mineral region lies Elliot lake, and here in 1952 uranium was discovered. A single enterprising company secretly flew in prospectors who staked 1400 claims in the space of a few days. As soon as the news was released another 8000 claims were staked in a mineralized zone 85 miles long and shaped like a great Z. During the following two or three years 11 integrated mines and mills were established, and what was probably the most productive uranium district in the world had come into existence. To serve it a planned community was built, extending along the wooded shores of the lake. About the same time uranium was discovered in the east of Ontario at Bancroft (about 125 miles north-east of Toronto), and four mines were opened there.

The future of the industry, however, is uncertain, for by far the greater part of its product had been exported to the United States. The existing contracts expired in 1966, and so a great industry is gradually running down. At its peak in 1959 there were 23 mines in production, including those in north Saskatchewan and the Northwest Territories; by 1962 the number had shrunk to eight, of which four were at Elliot lake and two at Bancroft. This forced reorganization of the industry may ultimately prove beneficial, if indeed it can survive the loss of its chief market. It is to be hoped that within a few years the demand for uranium for peaceful uses will have risen sufficiently to require a substantial contribution from Canada.

Steep Rock

Steep Rock lies 142 miles west of Port Arthur and only 30 miles north of the United States border; it forms in fact a continuation into Canada of the orefield of Mesabi Range. Today this area is the next producer of iron ore in Canada, after the Quebec–Labrador districts, and accounts for about 12 per cent. of the total output.

A boulder of haematite was discovered here as early as 1890, and its origin was traced back to a body of ore in the bottom of Steep Rock lake. The lake covered seven square miles, and was unusually deep. It proved impracticable to tunnel below it, and a bold plan was evolved – namely, to drain the lake. First the Seine river had to be diverted to cut off the flow of water into the lake; then, in 1943, 14 huge pumps were set working to drain the lake. After five months the bottom was exposed, revealing a thick accumulation of silt. This was scooped out by means of dredgers, and in 1944 the first iron ore was quarried.

There are four ore bodies in the district, and reserves are sufficient to maintain a rate of 8½ million tons per annum for a century. Current production is at the rate of nearly 3½ million tons. Fortunately, the deposits already lay on the main railway line linking Winnipeg with Port Arthur; but that town was traditionally a grain port, and possessed no facilities for iron-ore traffic. Concurrently with the development of the mine, therefore, the Canadian National Railway Company was busy constructing an ore dock at Port Arthur. With a length of 1200 feet, this can accommodate eight ore-carriers simultaneously. Finally a new highway was constructed to link the mine with the port and it was formally opened in 1954. So another district of the Laurentian Shield yields its mineral wealth for the use of man.

The Mackenzie Basin

At present economic development of the great expanse of Canada north of the prairies is confined mainly to the Mackenzie river basin. This wide area, twice the size of the United Kingdom, has good stands of timber in the south and productive fisheries in its streams and lakes. Nevertheless, it is its mineral wealth which has attracted attention, and almost all improvements in transport have been directed to the exploitation of metals.

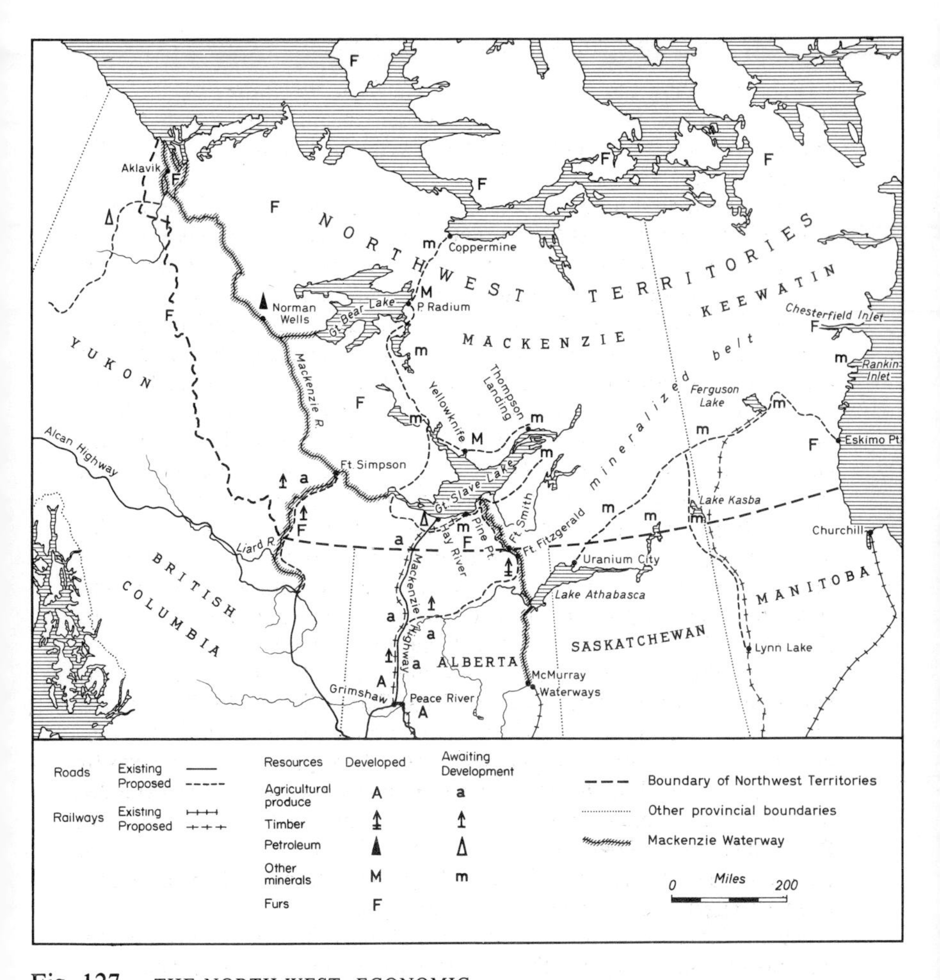

Fig. 127. THE NORTH-WEST: ECONOMIC

This region consists essentially of the Mackenzie basin. The map indicates communications and economic aspects of this central part of the Northlands, together with places named in the text.

Much of the region has been geologically surveyed only recently, so there has been little scientific information to guide the prospector. Maps of the Great Slave Lake district were prepared during the 1930's; but Keewatin was not surveyed geologically until the 1950's, and the survey of the northern islands in the district of Franklin was not begun until 1955.

The earliest mineral production was of petroleum at Norman Wells (Fig. 127), where commercial exploitation began in 1920. The reserves here are estimated to total between 36 and 60 million barrels; but production and refining are limited to the quantities needed locally, by the settlements along the Mackenzie river and on the shores of the Great Bear and Great Slave lakes, and by defence installations in the far north. The current output is from 64 wells, and totals about 350,000 barrels a year.

The region has long been known to possess stores of radioactive minerals: these were first discovered in 1930 on Great Bear lake, and the locality was named Port Radium. Three years later mining began, at first for the production of radium, later for uranium. Until 1956 this was the chief producing area for uranium in Canada, and one of the greatest in the world. With the discovery of more accessible deposits of uranium ore farther south, in Saskatchewan and Ontario, the Port Radium district lost is pre-eminence, though it maintained a constant and important output, valued at 8–9 million dollars annually. Production ceased here, however, in 1960 as a result of the reorganization of the industry in anticipation of the expiry of the American contracts.

In 1933 gold was discovered at Yellowknife, on Great Slave lake. The ore is exceedingly rich – its average gold content is three times as high as that in the Kerr–Addison mine of north Ontario; and it is only this which allows production to continue in so remote a region, where the cost of labour and the cost of living are so high.

The original settlement of Yellowknife was built on a peninsula and two islands on the north shore of Great Slave lake. In 1947–48 a new town was laid out by the Government, and the population has now grown to 3500. Until a few years ago the only access to the town was by water or by air; but the Mackenzie Highway has now been extended for about 200 miles, skirting to the west of the lake, through Fort Providence and Rae, to reach Yellowknife (Fig. 128). The town depends on three gold-mines, one of them 100 miles distant, and together they produce nearly 10 per cent. of Canada's gold.

Further improvements in communications will undoubtedly encourage prospecting, prolong the life of existing mines, and stimulate the opening of new ones; it is therefore most encouraging that the Federal Government has built a new 430-mile railway to span the gap between Grimshaw (the former rail-head) and the Great Slave lake. Farming and forestry will be encouraged along the first 150 miles or so of the line. The new route runs as far as Pine Point, on the south shore of the lake, where attractive deposits of lead–zinc ore are known to be present.

Within the region several other ore deposits are known. There are deposits of lithium and lead-zinc around McLeod bay, in the far north-east of Great Slave lake; and near the northern arm of the lake (now traversed by the new road) are additional resources of lithium and of radioactive minerals. Yet more mineral wealth is known in districts which at present are too remote from transport for economic exploitation.

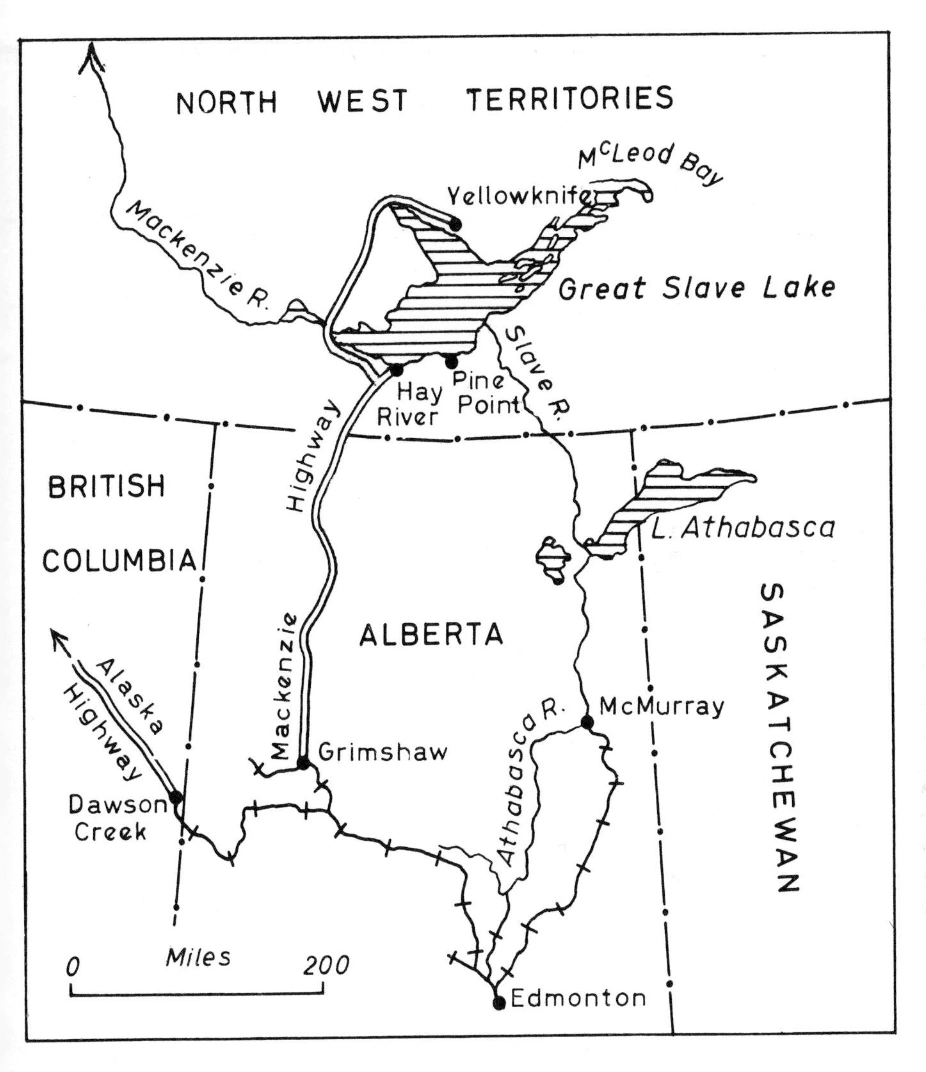

Fig. 128. THE GREAT SLAVE MINERAL DISTRICT
Improved communications are encouraging the exploitation of known mineral resources in this formerly remote region.

During the last few years there has been considerable exploring activity in search of oil in the Northwest Territories. Geological conditions in the western parts of Mackenzie district are considered to be hopeful, for there are thick deposits of sedimentary strata which have been gently folded, so that stratigraphical traps may be expected. Natural gas has been found west of Hay lake, and oil-saturated sand has been discovered in the north-west of Melville Island. No important discovery has yet been reported, but interest in oil possibilities remains active.

Soon the traditional tug and barge services on the Athabasca, Slave, and Mackenzie rivers will be supplemented by new roads and railways. Faster than all is transport by air, and the prospector makes good use of aircraft fitted with floats in summer and skis in winter, for there are innumerable natural landing-points for such vehicles. One can charter aircraft for Fort Smith, Yellowknife, Hay River, and Aklavik.

The Yukon and Alaska

The boundary between the Northwest Territories and the Yukon for the most part follows a major water parting, and is one of the few Canadian political boundaries to correspond with a physical frontier. Most of the Yukon Territory is drained towards the river of that name, which after entering Alaska becomes the main drainage artery of the state. Yukon and Alaska share this common navigable waterway, and to a large extent they share roads and railways; it is therefore appropriate to group them together. The political status of Yukon is not always fully appreciated by the man in the street; thus an American lad newly arrived to take part in the construction of the Alaska Highway wrote home: 'You know, Mom, the British have got this country now, but don't worry, we'll soon get it back.'

Minerals

In both territories the early settlement and economic advance were a result of the discovery of gold. Alaska was purchased by the United States from Russia in 1867, the price being less than two million pounds. Thirteen years later gold was discovered by one Joe Juneau in the Alaskan 'panhandle', and the city which bears his name was soon established. Soon there were many mines in the district; the biggest and last of them closed as recently as 1944, and its deserted buildings still stand on the coastal hillside.

In 1896 it was the turn of the Yukon: gold was found in the gravels of the Indian and Klondike rivers, which join the Yukon river from the east in the neighbourhood of Dawson. In contrast to Juneau, this is a very remote region; yet during the next few years 30,000 people flocked in, and at its peak Dawson boasted 10,000 people. The gateway to the Klondike goldfields was the Alaskan port of Skagway. From here the prospectors struggled overland along the 111 miles of the Chilkoot trail, over the White Pass to join the Yukon river at Whitehorse (Fig. 129) The river was navigable to Dawson, but involved a boat journey of about 200 miles to the goldfields. Later Skagway and Whitehorse were joined by rail, and this single-track, narrow-gauge line is still in use.

The Klondike yielded 100 million dollars' worth of gold during the first seven years of its life; later, production declined, and though the precious metal is still produced in small quantities it has been surpassed in value by other minerals. The population of Dawson has accordingly fallen to about 800 inhabitants: it is a 'ghost' town.

In 1899, at Nome in the Seward peninsula of north-west Alaska, soldiers discovered nuggets of gold among the beach shingle. A town was quickly built there, and at its peak numbered 12,500 people. The production of gold has fallen off, and Nome has shrunk to 1900 people; but two dredgers have remained at work, sifting the gravels in search of gold. The local newspaper is the *Nome Nugget*, and the bank will still assay samples of gold.

In 1902 gold was found at Fairbanks, in east-central Alaska, about 300 miles west of Dawson, in Yukon. People began to move from Dawson to Fairbanks. Fairbanks is almost as remote as Dawson, but prospectors had a choice of three routes to the interior. They could cross the coastal mountains from the ice-free port of Valdez in the south; they could enter from Seward, farther west; but both these routes involved long overland journeys. These could be avoided by entering from the north-west: they could transfer from ocean vessel to Yukon steamer at St Michael, north-east of the Yukon delta; but the journey up the Yukon river and its tributary the Tanana to Fairbanks totalled at least 800 miles. In 1915 the Fairbanks district was made more accessible by the construction of the Alaska railway, from Seward, across the Kenai peninsula, past Anchorage, up the Susitna valley, across the Alaska range, and so into the Fairbanks Basin – 470 miles in all (Fig. 129).

Fairbanks remains the chief gold-producing district of Alaska, and yields nearly half the total supply of the state. Eight huge dredgers are at work there, floating in artificial ponds, sifting the gravels and recovering the gold. Output, however, is falling sharply, and it is in other directions that the future of Alaska must be sought.

At present there appear to be no important deposits of base metals in Alaska, but the Yukon is actively mining lead, zinc, and silver. All are mined in the Mayo district, near the centre of the Territory, about 130 miles east of Dawson. Here about 10 million dollars' worth of the three metals are produced annually, with silver well in the lead: this district in fact is the greatest producer of primary silver in Canada (that is, from silver ores as distinct from by-product recovery). It is a remote, wooded, and mountainous district, connected by road both westward to Dawson and southward to Whitehorse. The ores are treated locally at the small settlement of Elsa.

Other lead–zinc ore bodies have been discovered in five distinct areas near Whitehorse, and copper–nickel ores near Kluane lake, 115 miles

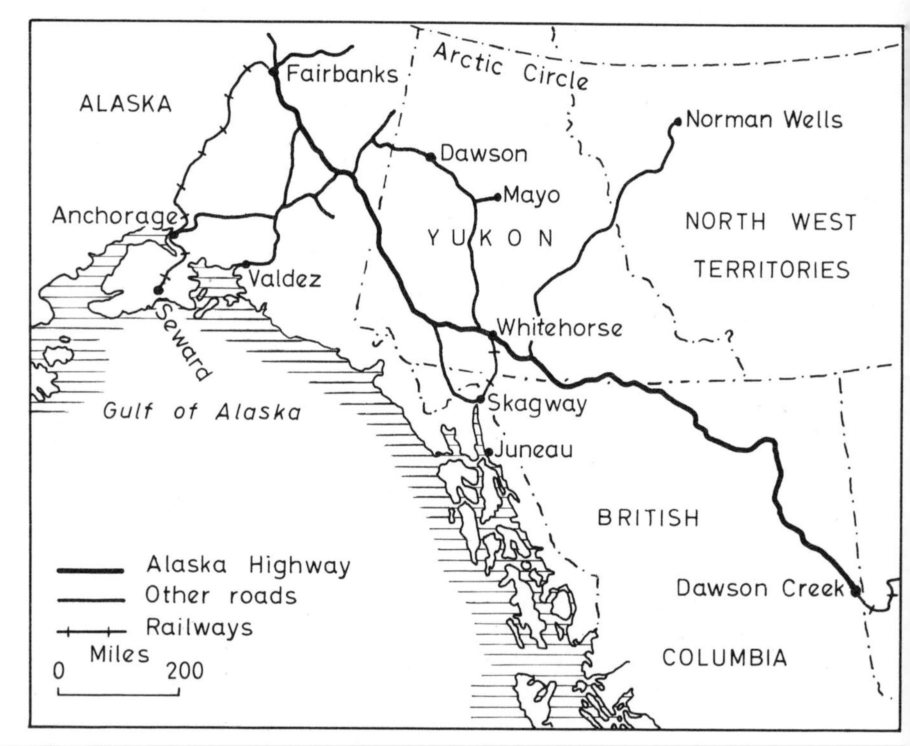

Fig. 129. THE ALASKA HIGHWAY

Officially this is the Alaskan–Canadian Highway, and more than two-thirds of its length is in Canada. It is 1671 miles long, and was built in little more than six months.

to the west. There are many other prospects of these metals, together with silver, and asbestos is known to be present 40 miles north-west of Dawson. Improvements in communications should result in the development of some of these deposits and the location of others. An asset in the exploitation of the region is the abundance of potential hydro-electric power sites. There are estimated to be about $4\frac{1}{2}$ million horse-power available in the headstreams of the Yukon river system. Dawson, Whitehorse, and the Mayo district are all supplied by power-plants, and there are ample resources to supply not only local needs but also those of northern British Columbia.

Communications

Recent transport developments in Alaska and the Yukon have taken the form of the construction of trunk roads. Foremost among them is the Alaskan–Canadian Military Highway. Its popular name, the Alaska Highway, is misleading, for of its 1523 miles more than two-thirds are in Canada – in British Columbia and Yukon Territory (Fig. 129). Its

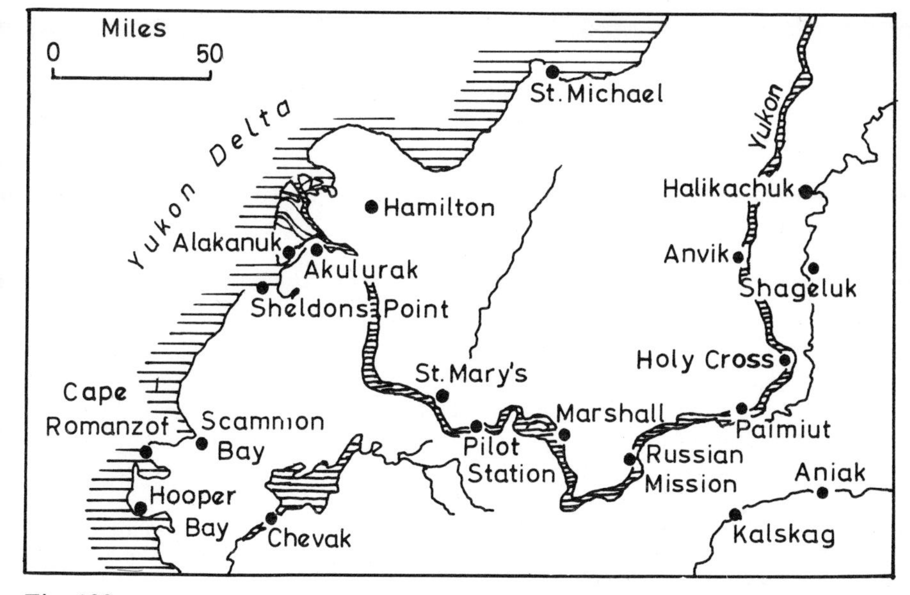

Fig. 130. ALASKA: PART OF THE LOWER YUKON

All the places named are airports, and in the whole of Alaska there are 235 of them. After the discovery of gold at Fairbanks in 1902, steamers sailed up the Yukon river for 800 miles to convey prospectors to the goldfields.

construction during the Second World War was a triumph of skill, energy, and determination, and of organization. It ran through virtually uninhabited and unknown country, through mountainous, forested, and swamp land. Ten thousand American soldiers and 6000 civilians combined on the venture, and they completed the task in a little over six months – an average rate of construction of eight miles a day! The Alaska Highway joins the three railway termini of Dawson Creek (British Columbia), Whitehorse (Yukon), and Fairbanks (Alaska), and passes through a chain of air bases. In addition it has road links to the coast at Valdez and Anchorage; the latter, known as the Glenn Highway, is new.

Only south-eastern Alaska and the southern Yukon enjoy the essentials of a system of land transport: the rest of this vast area relies either on aircraft or on coastal shipping (Fig. 130). In Alaska there are 235 scattered airports, each with its scheduled service; but even this does not give a complete picture, for prospectors and other travellers visit the most remote districts with craft fitted with floats or skis. To illustrate the use of aircraft for pleasure we notice that on Lake Hood, near Anchorage, in central-south Alaska, there are moorings for 166 planes.

For bulky commodities the remote coastal settlements await the arrival of the annual Native Service Ship. This vessel, based on Sitka, visits 45 native villages scattered along 2000 miles of coastline, carrying such articles as drums of oil, tractors, and boats – perhaps 3000 consignments each year.

Fishing

In Alaska the resources of the land are outweighed by those of the sea, and it is the salmon fisheries which provide the major sources of wealth.

'Salmon capital of the world' is Ketchikan – the most southerly and the largest of a whole chain of fishing-ports. Salmon are caught both by seiners, which fling huge nets round the schools of fish, and by smaller boats which trail baited hooks from long poles. There are 12 canneries at Ketchikan, and their combined output is in the neighbourhood of 24 million cans a year. To escape the 20-foot tidal range in the port the docks and warehouses are built on stilts, and this is characteristic of the Pacific ports of Alaska.

A few miles south of Ketchikan is Annette Island, with an Indian reserve: even this operates its own fishing-fleet and has its own cannery, at Metlakatla.

Nearly 200 miles north-west of Ketchikan is Sitka: this was the Russian capital of the territory. Attached to the port is a fleet of 650 fishing-boats, and the salmon and halibut catch is worth about a million United States dollars annually.

At the head of Cook Inlet is Anchorage, which began as the site of workshops during the construction of the Alaska railway. Later its advantageous position in relation to the fertile Matanuska valley, together with its railway communication with the interior, led to a rapid increase in population. Anchorage, with a city population of 44,237 (1960), is by far the largest settlement in Alaska, though the capital remains at Juneau. With hotels and night clubs, four theatres, and a 14-storey block of flats, Anchorage is the only real city in the state.

The fishing-fleet attached to the port brings in the salmon within a range of 100 miles for canning. The tidal range is up to 40 feet, so that warehouses and jetties again are built on stilts. Unlike the ports farther south-east, Anchorage suffers from the disadvantage that its harbour is interrupted by ice in winter. The fishing industry here and elsewhere in the state suffered a severe setback owing to the destruction of harbours and canning plants during the earthquake of 1964 (see p. 326).

Kodiak, to the south-west, on the island of the same name, has its canneries too, which in a good year may fill over half a million cases of tinned salmon. On the north side of the Alaska peninsula the Bristol Bay district is another fishing and canning area. Commercial salmon-fishing does not extend much farther north, but dried salmon is the normal food of man and dog in the coastal districts of Alaska. The total salmon catch of Alaska earns about 60 million dollars annually – more than eight times the nominal purchase price of the territory in 1867.

In recent years the salmon catch has been failing and the fishing-fleets are coming to rely more on halibut and cod, while an experiment is taking place at Homer, on the Kenai peninsula, in the canning of king 'crabs'. A single 'crab' can weigh up to 20 lb, and can fill 12 cans.

The Fur Industry

It was the attraction of the fur-trade which led the Hudson's Bay Company to explore the Northlands and to set up trading-posts there. Furs were the only northern commodity which had a ready sale in Europe, and until the nineteenth century the whole economy of Canada was geared to their production. The fur industry remains important to Canada, but its character has changed. Nearly two-thirds of the furs (by value) are now produced not from wild animals but from creatures reared on farms especially for their pelts. Fur farms are widely distributed through Canada, but are especially numerous in Ontario, British Columbia, Alberta, and Quebec.

With the advance of settlement the wild fur-bearing animals retreated into the north. Their numbers have declined. At the same time fashions in furs have changed, so that the demand for fox-skins has fallen. Prices have declined, so that the trapper's income has been drastically reduced, and many have left the industry to find alternative employment.

Nevertheless, the Government is encouraging the revival of the natural-fur industry by limiting the catch, establishing close seasons, setting up protected areas, and providing for the education of trappers.

Ranch mink are now four times as valuable in total as their nearest rival, beaver; there follow in order wild mink, muskrat, squirrel, white fox, lynx, otter, marten, and ermine (stoat). More than two-thirds of the output is consigned to the United States; of the remainder, more than half is shipped to the United Kingdom. Fur auctions take place at Montreal, North Bay, Winnipeg, Edmonton, and Regina.

Lumbering

Nearly half the entire area of Canada is forested; forest products form the greatest element in the Canadian economy and account for nearly one-third of her exports. During the twentieth century a remarkable change has taken place in the location of the industry: in the first decade of the century 80 per cent. of the timber was cut in the eastern provinces; but since that time the total output has doubled, and the west coast has become by far the leading contributor. As we have seen, British Columbia in fact now furnishes about two-thirds of the total timber output of Canada.

We discuss the forest industries of Newfoundland in Chapter Nine, and those of southern British Columbia in Chapter Eleven. There are also extensive lumbering and pulp industries in Quebec and Ontario. Here we merely draw attention to the important resources of timber in the Northlands. Much of this will remain untapped until communications are improved, and some perhaps will always be too remote from the market for exploitation.

The proportion of mainland Canada and Alaska that is too cold for trees is quite limited (see Fig. 121, p. 323). In Alaska only the western fringe, the Arctic slope, and the plain north of Brooks Range are unforested; in the Yukon, only the coastal strip in the north and the highest mountain ranges. In the Northwest Territories the northern limit of forest passes south-east from the Mackenzie delta to Hudson bay at the Manitoba border. In Quebec and Labrador the forest stretches as far north as parallel 55 and beyond. Clearly not all of this is of merchantable quality. But a beginning has been made in the exploitation of the forest-land in Wood Buffalo Park, astride the boundary of Alberta and the Northwest Territories; and sawmills are operating on the Slave river and on the upper reaches of the Mackenzie.

In the Yukon forest resources are estimated at 45,000 square miles, of which about one-tenth is merchantable. The greatest possibilities, however, lie in the coastal districts of British Columbia, and the 'panhandle' of Alaska, where the moist and equable climate provides ideal conditions for tree growth, and where the deep and sheltered fiords provide access for shipping.

Alaska has made a striking beginning by the establishment of a large modern pulp-mill at Ketchikan. This was opened in 1956, and cost 52 million United States dollars. It is fed from part of the Tongass National Forest, which covers 16 million acres. The Ketchikan mill produces 500 tons of pulp a day; but regeneration is so rapid that the natural growth outpaces the depletion by the mill. A second mill was opened at Sitka in 1959: it was financed largely by Japanese capital, and the pulp is utilized mainly by the Japanese rayon and paper industries.

The Strategic Value of the Northland

During the last few years the far north has witnessed a spectacular – almost an impertinent – challenge to nature in the joint construction by the United States and Canada of the Distant Early Warning Line – the DEW line (Fig. 131).

It consists of a string of about 50 radar stations which extend in a 3000-mile arc from Point Barrow, in western Alaska, to the east of Baffin Island. All are in radio contact one with another. To build and maintain them airstrips were constructed, and men and materials were ferried in, both by plane and by 120 ships in convoy. Construction took

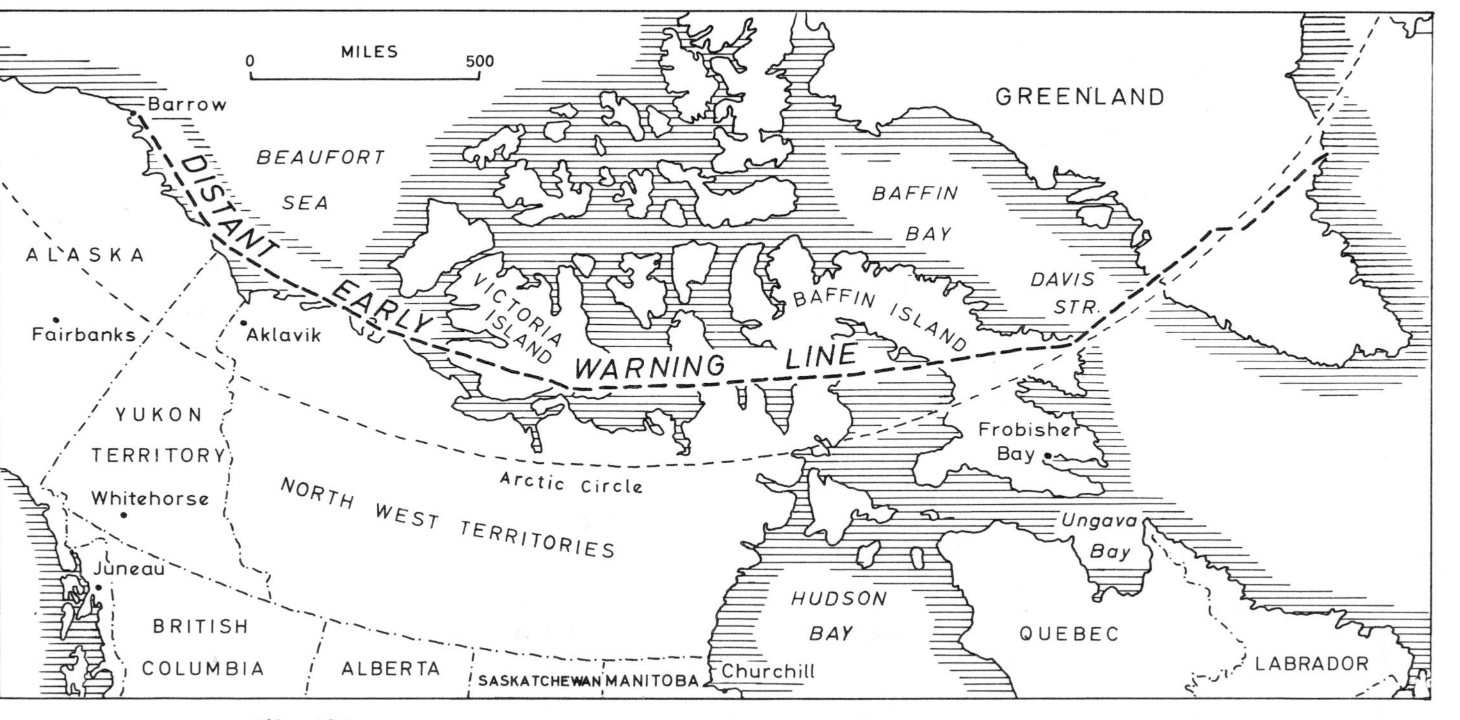

Fig. 131. THE DEW LINE

The purpose of the Distant Early Warning line is to discover any attempt of enemy aircraft to penetrate Canada or the United States by way of the Arctic. It consists of a string of about 50 radar stations stretching in a 3000-mile arc, and is manned by 700 men. Apart from its strategic value, the DEW line has demonstrated that man can live and work successfully in the Arctic.

place during the four years 1954–57, and involved the labours of 23,000 men.

The purpose of the DEW line was to discover any attempt by enemy aircraft to approach Canada or the United States by way of the Arctic. It has, however, accomplished a great deal more: it has demonstrated that man can live and work successfully in the Arctic. The DEW line is manned by 700 men. Aircraft link the sites together, and at most of them they land several times each week. At Point Barrow oil and natural gas have been tapped, and a new outlet has been opened for the oil of Norman Wells.

Far to the east, in Baffin Island, Frobisher Bay has developed as the administrative centre for the eastern Arctic. It stands close to the site where the Elizabethan Sir Martin Frobisher saw the glint of gold. Its first airstrip and small hospital date from 1942. With the construction of the DEW line the settlement experienced a frenzy of activity – with 2500 take-offs a month. Frobisher now has a 9000-foot runway and a modern jetty for use during the short eight-week ice-free season. It also boasts a cinema and a bowling alley, a laundry, barber shops, and coffee bars. Some of these are operated by Eskimos.

The Northlands are believed to contain 33,000 million barrels of oil and 200,000 million cubic feet of natural gas, so that here is potentially a major producer of oil and gas; and exploration permits have been requested over nearly 100 million acres. Atomic-powered submarines have successfully navigated below the polar ice-cap, and for surface transport the 'muskox' is being developed: this is a tracked vehicle, 48 feet long, which can negotiate muskeg, snow, and almost any type of roadless surface. It is possible that we are witnessing the beginning of a new era in the Northlands.

BIBLIOGRAPHY

We have thought it unnecessary to compile a complete bibliography: this would require many pages and the references would be available only in specialist libraries. The student who wishes to read at greater depth will find much of the material he needs in the files of the three American periodicals *Economic Geography, Geographical Review,* and the *National Geographic Magazine,* together with the *Canadian Geographical Magazine.* We confine ourselves here to a list of important general works (many of which contain full bibliographies) and of articles that have appeared during the last ten years or so in the English periodical *Geography.*

GENERAL WORKS

ALEXANDERSSON, GUNNAR and NORSTRÖM, GÖRAN: *World Shipping* (1963)

CHEVRIER, LIONEL: *The St Lawrence Seaway* (New York, 1959)

ESTALL, R. C.: *New England* (1966)

GOTTMAN, JEAN: *Megalopolis* (1961)

GRIFFIN, PAUL, YOUNG, ROBERT and CHATHAM, RONALD: *Anglo–America* (Methuen, 1963)

HATCHER, HARLAN: *The Great Lakes* (Oxford University Press, 1945)

HAYSTEAD, LADD and FITE, GILBERT C.: *The Agricultural Regions of the United States* (Oklahoma, 1955)

HIGBEE, EDWARD: *American Agriculture* (New York, 1958)

HUDSON, F. S.: *North America* (Macdonald and Evans, 1962)

JACKS, G. V. and WHYTE, R. O.: *The Rape of the Earth* (Faber, 1939)

LOBECK, A. K.: *Atlas of American Geology* (New York, 1932)

MEAD, W. R. and BROWN, E. H.: *The United States and Canada: A Regional Geography* (Hutchinson, 1962)

PARKER, W. H.: *Anglo-America* (University of London Press, 1962)

PATERSON, J. H.: *North America: A Regional Geography* (Oxford University Press, 1960)

POUNDS, N. J. G.: *North America* (Murray, 1955)

PUTNAM, DONALD F. and KERR, DONALD: *A Regional Geography of Canada* (Toronto, 1956)

TAYLOR, GRIFFITH: *Canada* (Methuen, 1947)

WATSON, J. WREFORD-: *North America, its Countries and Regions* (Longmans, 1963)

WHITE, C. LANGDON and FOSCUE, EDWIN J.: *Regional Geography of Anglo-America* (New York, 1943)
United States Year Book of Agriculture: Climate and Man (1941)
Year Book of Canada (annually)

ARTICLES IN *GEOGRAPHY*

BAILEY, P. J. M.: 'The Geography of Settlement in Stanstead Township, Province of Quebec' (January 1956)
BIRCH, B. P.: 'Locational Trends in the American Car Industry' (November 1966)
BIRCH, J. W.: 'The Expansion of the Canadian Aluminium Industry' (January 1955)
CANTOR, L. M.: 'Irrigated Agriculture in the Columbia Basin Project' (January 1967)
CURTI, G. PHILIP: 'The Colorado River. Its Utilisation in Southern California' (November 1957)
DAY, E. E. D. and PEARSON, R. E.: 'Closure of the Bell Island Iron Ore Mines' (July 1967)
ESTALL, R. C.: 'Changing Industrial Patterns of New England' (January 1961)
ESTALL, R. C.: 'Appalachian State: West Virginia as a Case Study in the Appalachian Regional Development Problem' (January 1968)
FULLER, G. J.: 'Communications in the Port of New York' (April 1959)
HART, JOHN FRASER: 'Cotton Goes West in the American South' (January 1959)
HOBSON, PEGGIE M.: 'The Alaska Ferry System' (April 1967)
HUMPHREYS, G.: 'The Railway Stimulus in Labrador–Ungava' (April 1957)
MANNERS, G.: 'Decentralization in Metropolitan Boston' (November 1960)
MARCUS, ROBERT B. and MOOKHERJEE, DEBNATH: 'Problems of Florida's Water Resources' (November 1962)
PATERSON, J. H.: 'The 1960 Census of the U.S.A.' (November 1962)
THOMAS, T. M.: 'The Exploitation of the Athabasca Tar Sands, Alberta' (July 1963)
THOMAS, T. M.: 'Potash Mining in Saskatchewan' (July 1965)

INDEX